THE SOURCES OF SCIENCE

THE SOURCES OF SCIENCE

Editor-in-Chief: HARRY WOOLF

WILLIS K. SHEPARD PROFESSOR OF THE HISTORY OF SCIENCE
THE JOHNS HOPKINS UNIVERSITY

1. WALLER: Essayes of Natural Experiments

   WITH A NEW INTRODUCTION BY A. RUPERT HALL

2. BOYLE: Experiments and Considerations Touching Colours

   WITH A NEW INTRODUCTION BY MARIE BOAS HALL

3. NEWTON: The Mathematical Works of Isaac Newton, Vols. 1 and 2

   EACH WITH A NEW INTRODUCTION BY DEREK T. WHITESIDE

4. LIEBIG: Animal Chemistry

   WITH A NEW INTRODUCTION BY FREDERIC L. HOLMES

5. KEPLER: Kepler's Conversation with Galileo's Sidereal Messenger

   TRANSLATED AND EDITED BY EDWARD ROSEN

7. TAYLOR: Scientific Memoirs Selected from the Transactions of Foreign Academies of Science and Learned Societies, and from Foreign Journals, 7 vols.

   WITH A NEW PREFACE BY HARRY WOOLF

10. BULLETTINO DI BIBLIOGRAFIA E DI STORIA DELLE SCIENZE MATEMATICHE E FISICHE, 20 vols.

    EDITED BY B. BONCOMPAGNI

11. GREW: The Anatomy of Plants

    WITH A NEW INTRODUCTION BY CONWAY ZIRKLE

13. THE WORKS OF WILLIAM HARVEY, M. D.

    TRANSLATED FROM THE LATIN WITH A LIFE OF THE AUTHOR BY ROBERT WILLIS, M. D.

14. BREWSTER: Memoirs of the Life, Writings, and Discoveries of Sir Isaac Newton

    WITH A NEW INTRODUCTION BY RICHARD S. WESTFALL

19. SEMMELWEIS: Die Aetiologie, der Begriff, und die Prophylaxis des Kindbettfiebers

    WITH A NEW INTRODUCTION BY ALAN F. GUTTMACHER, M. D.

23. DELAMBRE: Histoire de l'Astronomie Ancienne, 2 vols.

WITH A NEW PREFACE BY OTTO NEUGEBAUER

24. DELAMBRE: Histoire de l'Astronomie du Moyen Age

25. DELAMBRE: Histoire de l'Astronomie Moderne

WITH A NEW INTRODUCTION BY I. BERNARD COHEN

26. DARMSTAEDTER: Naturforscher und Erfinder. Biographische Miniaturen

30. WILSON: The Cell in Development and Inheritance

WITH A NEW INTRODUCTION BY HERMANN J. MULLER

The Mathematical Works of Isaac Newton

VOLUME 2

THE MATHEMATICAL WORKS OF ISAAC NEWTON

VOLUME 2

Assembled with an Introduction by
DR. DEREK T. WHITESIDE,
RESEARCH ASSISTANT,
WHIPPLE SCIENCE MUSEUM,
CAMBRIDGE, ENGLAND

THE SOURCES OF SCIENCE

1967

JOHNSON REPRINT CORPORATION
New York and London

Library of Congress Catalog Card Number: 64-17026

Printed in the United States of America

INTRODUCTION

In this second volume we assemble appropriate English versions of Newton's published mathematical work other than in calculus, that is, in the fields of algebra, finite differences, and geometry. As before, we restrict our choice to those tracts which have been influential historically,[1] namely to the "Arithmetica Universalis" (1684), the "Enumeratio Linearum Tertii Ordinis" (1695), and the "Methodus Differentialis" (1710?). Corresponding Latin texts of each of these may be found in the first volume of Samuel Horsley's "Isaaci Newtoni Opera Omnia."[2] Those portions of the "Principia" (notably Book 1, Sections 4 and 5, and Book 3, Lemma 5) where Newton introduces certain otherwise unpublished researches in pure geometry and finite differences may now easily be consulted in Cajori's revised version of Motte's 1729 English rendering,[3] and these we will not reproduce out of context. Of our chosen works, the "Universal Arithmetick" is, as its origin in a course of undergraduate lectures would suggest, tolerably easy to understand: only on a few knotty points will the reader's comprehension be stretched to the breaking point. The other two short tracts are of a different order of difficulty: both are severely technical, highly condensed, and on many important points of argument lacking proof, but they will reward the patient student. For the detailed commentary on particular sections which is at times needed in all three texts we have no room here, but dare once more to refer to our planned edition in eight volumes of all Newton's known

[1] We in fact exclude only a few unfinished papers which have appeared in the last three quarters of a century, notably fragments of Newton's early work on cubics which were inadequately reproduced in appendix (pp. 132–143) to W. W. Rouse Ball's "On Newton's Classification of Cubic Curves," *Proceedings of the London Mathematical Society* **22,** 104–143, 1891 and the finite difference manuscripts (ULC.Add 3964.5) which were printed by D. C. Fraser in his "An unpublished Manuscript by Sir Isaac Newton," *Journal of the Institute of Actuaries* **58,** 75–84, 1927. In the current revival of interest in Newton's scientific output, several of his short early dynamical papers have been published since 1959 by H. W. Turnbull and J. W. Herivel: for details consult the bibliography to my "Expanding World of Newtonian Research," *History of Science* **1,** 27–29, 1962.

[2] London, 1779. See Vol. 1, Introduction, p. viii, footnote 4.

[3] "Sir Isaac Newton's Mathematical Principles of Natural Philosophy . . . Translated into English by Andrew Motte in 1729. The translations revised, and supplied with an historical and explanatory appendix, by Florian Cajori," California, 1934. The work has been reissued several times, most recently (1962) in a two-volume paperbound edition. As a check on Cajori's idiosyncrasies the wary reader should look at I. B. Cohen's "Pemberton's Translation of Newton's Principia, With Notes on Motte's Translation," *Isis* **54,** 319–351; especially 341–351, 1963.

mathematical papers and to the inadequate existing commentaries.[4] It is in our view much more important that we set his published tracts firmly in the general context of the flow of his mathematical thought from childhood to senility. Only then will we be able to see at what stage they solidified Newton's thinking on a particular topic and so judge their influence in the wider field of his exact scientific thought.

In our earlier introduction we rapidly sketched Newton's growth to mathematical maturity through his grammar-bound schooldays in a Lincolnshire market town and the scholastic discipline of his early undergraduate years in Cambridge until, about the summer of 1664, he first began to pursue his own researches.[5] These in the first instance developed from his extensive, apparently unaided reading in the more valuable of the available mathematical source-works. As he noted later, "in ye year 1664 a little before Christmas I being then senior Sophister [undergraduate] I bought Schooten's Miscellanies & Cartes's Geometry (having read this Geometry & Oughtred's Clavis above half a year before) & borrowed Wallis's works."[6] Indeed, Frans van Schooten's "Exercitationes Mathematicæ" (Leiden, 1657) (whose fifth book is entitled "Sectiones Miscellaneæ" and which had Huygens' "De Ratiociniis in Ludo Aleæ" in appendix), William Oughtred's "Clavis Mathematicæ" (read by Newton in its expanded third edition of 1652), and the two weighty volumes of John Wallis' "Opera Mathematica" (Oxford, 1657/1656, perhaps bound with his "Commercium Epistolicum," 1658, and "De Cycloide," 1659), together with Schooten's modernised edition of François Viète's "Opera Omnia Mathematica" (Leiden, 1646) and on a more elementary level Isaac Barrow's compact edition of Euclid's "Elements" and "Data" were at this time minutely digested and stored for future regurgitation.[7] From Viète, Oughtred, Schooten, Wallis, and the third book of Descartes' "Geometrie" above all, he drew a knowledge of contemporary algebra, particularly of the theory of equations, which was to be a cornerstone of his own mathematical advances; while from the "Geometrie," helped by some rich examples

[4] See Vol. 1, Introduction, p. vii, footnote 3, and the concluding bibliographical portion of the present essay.

[5] I have examined the conditioning factors in Newton's mathematical growth in greater detail in "Isaac Newton: birth of a mathematician," *Notes and Records of the Royal Society* **19**, 53–62, 1964.

[6] ULC.Add 4000,14v. The passage is dated 4 July 1699.

[7] Newton's annotations of all these works are extant. A small pocket book (ULC.Add 4000), devoted to mathematics and the mathematical theory of music, contains algebraical and geometrical notes on Schooten, Oughtred, Viète, and Wallis, while a second (now in the Fitzwilliam Museum, Cambridge) has lengthy annotations of the geometrical portions of Schooten's "Exercitationes" and his two-volume edition of Descartes' Latin "Geometria." Newton's own copy of the "Exercitationes" (Trinity College. NQ.16.184) has inserted a hitherto unrecorded autograph fragment, while the margins of his copy of Barrow's 1655 Euclid (Trinity College. NQ.16.201) are in many places crowded with his corrections and additions. Further evidence of the overriding influence of Descartes is to be found in the early part of Newton's "Waste Book" (ULC.Add 4004), many of whose pages are virtually commentaries on specified sections of the "Geometrie" and its appendices in Schooten's second Latin edition.

to be found in Schooten's "Exercitationes" and possibly parts of Wallis' "Opera," he absorbed a thorough understanding of existing techniques in analytical geometry. Of less ultimate interest, perhaps, were the insights into contemporary number theory which he had from Huygens and Wallis, and into higher pure geometry from Viète, Schooten, and appendices to the "Geometria." In each field Newton acquired through hard reading the necessary prerequisites for carrying out original research: an adequate notation in which to express the mathematical structures under examination, an excellent grasp of the hard core of contemporary knowledge, and a keen sense of fruitful directions in which each field might be developed. And at all times Newton was quick to put his fertile mind to work, generalising existing theories and creating new approaches.

As with his researches in calculus, it is not difficult to isolate Descartes and Wallis as the great formative influences on Newton in the areas of analytical geometry and algebra. Indeed his first true mathematical advances in the autumn and winter of 1664/1665 depend narrowly on both. In Book 2 of the "Geometrie," Descartes' especial problem had been to show that the 3/4 line locus of the ancients was a general conic: using his system of oblique coordinates he had easily been able to resolve the locus problem analytically as a second-degree equation tying two variable Cartesian coordinate lengths, and had then introduced, awkwardly and implicitly, a transformation of his coordinate axes which reduced the general second-degree equation in two variables to one of three standard forms, so showing the (nondegenerate) locus to be an ellipse, parabola, or hyperbola. Descartes had then gone on to give a brief analytical discussion of some particular higher algebraic curves (notably his trident and oval and the conchoid), but his attempted classification of the general algebraic curve by paired degrees was a failure. Newton saw immediately that the idea of invariance under coordinate transformation, nervously introduced by Descartes in a single case, was basic to any satisfactory analytical treatment of algebraic geometry, and in particular that the concept of degree (invariant under a linear coordinate transform) was essential to any general classification of curves. In a series of unpublished researches pursued during the autumn of 1664[8] he therefore began with an exhaustive consideration of possible linear transformations of oblique Cartesian coordinate systems, one into another. Satisfied at last on that point, he passed on to other questions. The Greeks had given a well-nigh complete discussion of the straight line, circle, and conics, and Descartes had outlined how their synthetic approach could be represented analytically as a general theory of algebraic curves of first and second degree, but how to list typical properties of, say, a cubic and use these to identify particular characteristics of a third-degree curve from its defining equation? This problem, attacked repeatedly over the rest

[8] These researches, the first of which is dated September 1664, were entered by Newton in his Waste Book (ULC.Add 4004,15v ff.).

of Newton's creative life, was finally to be given a full solution, the bare skeleton of which he set down in the "Enumeratio." For the moment, not knowing quite where to start, he tried both to generalise such conic properties as diameters and asymptotes to higher curves, formulating corresponding conditions on the analytical representing equation, and to sketch particular cubics and quartics, such as the Cartesian folium, from given equations and in given coordinate systems (usually Cartesian but sometimes polar, bipolar, and others of his own invention). In neither was he completely successful. On the one hand he soon found, for example, that not all cubics have conic-type diameters and that such antisymmetric nondiametral cubics as the Wallisian parabola may have a centre; and on the other, that exact tracing of all but a few simple cubics was extremely tricky—indeed, several of the curve shapes which at that time passed his own careful inspection are wrongly drawn, having incorrect infinite branches or inflexions.

Possibly deterred by his lack of success, Newton went on, in December 1664, to a second reading of Wallis' "Opera." We have already discussed[9] how his discovery of the general binomial theorem was a corollary to his study of Wallis' "Arithmetica Infinitorum." Less well known is his indebtedness to Wallis' work for several of his notational innovations, such as his use of fractional indices, and such techniques as his preferred algebraic resolution of the reduced cubic equation.[10] About the same time, moreover, he began in his Waste Book and elsewhere to note down stray thoughts on the root-properties of equations, to plan an elementary systematisation of plane and spherical trigonometry, and to improve on Viète's advances in the theory of angular sections.[11] His first comprehensive researches into the theory and construction of equations[12] were started towards the middle of 1665, and he quickly formulated the general relationship between the roots of an equation and its coefficients, applying this property to several problems and inducing from an examination of squares, cubes, fourth powers, and so on successively up to eighth powers, the "Newton" rule which expresses the sum of the nth powers of the roots of an equation in terms of the corresponding coefficients. Soon he was worrying at the fundamental problem of how to isolate and determine the quality of the roots of a given equation. Correcting Descartes' rather ambiguous statement of his

[9] Volume 1, Introduction, pp. xi–xii.

[10] This resolution, noted by him (ULC.Add 4000,23r) from pp. 17–26 of Wallis' dedication to his tract "Adversus Marci Meibomii de Proportionibus Dialogum Tractatus Elencticus" (printed in his "Operum Mathematicorum Pars Prima," Oxford, 1657) was to reappear in the "Arithmetica" ("Universal Arithmetick," 2nd ed., pp. 220–222, London, 1728).

[11] As set forth in Alexander Anderson's commentary "Ad Angularium Sectionum Analyticen Theoremata ΚΑΘΟΛΙΚΩΤΕΡΑ," edited by Schooten in his "Francisci Vietæ Opera Mathematica," pp. 287–304, Leiden, 1646.

[12] See especially ULC.Add 4004,55r–56r ("Concerning Equations when the ratio of their rootes is considered," dated May 1665); 67v–69r ("Of the construction of Problems," dated 30 May 1665); and 83r–89r (loose researches on root operations, in particular the delimitation of the roots of given equations).

sign rule in Book 3 of "Geometria," Newton carefully remarked that the rule gave only an upper bound to the number of real roots and "Hence it appears y^t to know ye particular constitution of any Equation it is cheifely necessary to understand w^t imaginary roots it hath."[13] In succeeding pages he came to grips with the isolation of complex root-pairs and brilliantly opened up several new avenues of approach, suggesting tests for determining the absence of complex pairs and modifying Descartes' simple sign rule in diverse ingenious ways in the attempt to arrive at a satisfactory algorithm for locating imaginary pairs. Of the latter (few of which he could begin to justify rigorously), one later printed in the "Arithmetica" especially caught the attention of such eighteenth-century mathematicians as Maclaurin and Euler by its difficulty and was indeed formally proved only two centuries later by Sylvester.[14] Passing on to the evaluation of real roots, Newton evolved new methods, based on an elementary finite-difference technique, for the factorisation of polynomials and, in the case of surd factors, the technique of representing the polynomial as the difference of two squares which later appeared in his "Arithmetica" as the "Reduction of Equations by surd Divisors."[15] Finally, in those cases where exact analytical methods failed, he greatly improved the geometrical construction of the real roots of equations expounded by Descartes in the third book of "Geometrie": in particular, where Descartes had constructed the real roots of the general sextic as the meet of a circle and his trident, Newton convincingly urged the practical advantage of replacing the trident by the Wallisian parabola, and proceeded to give a beautifully simple construction of the equation $y^3 + 3by^2 - 2bc^2 = 0$ which determines the inflexion points in a conchoid by the meet of a circle and the conchoid itself.

Thereafter for a while Newton's interest in geometry and algebra seems to have lagged. Towards the end of 1667, however, for some reason we can probably no longer know, his interest in both pure and analytical geometry was again excited. Following up his earlier researches in the field of higher plane curves, he attacked the problem of the analytical classification of cubics head on. Taking[16] the most general form of the third-degree equation in two variables z and v (that is, supposing

$$av^3 + bzv^2 + cz^2v + dz^3 + ev^2 + fzv + gz^2 + hv + kz + l = 0)$$

or in corresponding geometrical terms, the most general cubic relationship between oblique Cartesian coordinate lengths z and v, Newton transformed by his pre-

[13] ULC.Add 4004,85r. Compare Descartes' "Geometria," Vol. 1, p. 70, 1659.

[14] See Newton's "Universal Arithmetick," 2nd ed., pp. 195–198, 1728; and J. J. Sylvester's "On an elementary proof and generalisation of . . . Newton's hitherto undemonstrated rule for the discovery of imaginary roots," *Proceedings of the London Mathematical Society* **1,** 1–16, 1865, reproduced in his "Collected Mathematical Papers," Vol. 2, pp. 498–513, Cambridge, 1904. Compare also H. W. Turnbull, "The Mathematical Discoveries of Newton," pp. 49–51, London, 1945.

[15] "Universal Arithmetick," 2nd ed., pp. 38–44 and 208–220 respectively.

[16] ULC.Add 3961.1,2r ff.

viously discovered formulas to new oblique axes x and y, deriving an equation of eighty-four terms. This he showed, with a marvelous grasp of mathematical essentials, could without loss of generality be reduced to the basic canonical form of the cubic

$$Axy^2 + Bx^3 + Cx^2 + Dy + Ex + F = 0$$

Moreover, by considering various possibilities of degeneracy in this basic form, he isolated the three further possible canonical forms of the cubic, which are represented geometrically by the set of five divergent parabolas, the Cartesian trident, and the Wallisian parabola. Even more brilliantly he then[17] went deeply into the technical details of subdividing the general cubic into its component genera and these into species, introducing the diametral hyperbola (which shares one asymptote with the cubic and bisects all "chords" of the cubic parallel to that asymptote) for the purpose: the highlight of the discussion is his full-scale investigation of the shape, inflexions, and infinite branches of that most difficult case of all, the tridiametral cubic without particularity. Elsewhere, in papers now in private possession, Newton took the experience he had gained to heart and in some "Generall Theorems" on plane curves discussed properties (tangents, diameters, centres, asymptotes, and the like) of the general algebraic curve, inducing them where necessary—one paper is headed "Conick propertys to bee examined in other curves"—from his prior knowledge of conics and cubics. Here, in particular, for the first time was formulated the concept of a general diameter as the (linear) locus of the arithmetic mean of the intercepts made by a set of parallels, but more generally all of Newton's new ideas laid the groundwork necessary for future advance in the study of higher curves.

No less startling in their own way were the researches he carried through in pure geometry at about the same period; researches, unfortunately, whose manuscript evidence is also in private possession. Newton had in the winter of 1664/1665 in his reading of Schooten's "Exercitationes" carefully studied the content of its fourth book.[18] There Schooten had given a variety of moving-rod constructions for each of the conics, ellipse, parabola, and hyperbola, but had failed in his higher aim of finding a uniform description applicable to each indiscriminately. The "organic" construction which Newton elaborated in his present sequence of researches was clearly invented in the first instance as just such a uniform method: in essence, two points or "poles" are supposed fixed in a plane and round each of these rotate the "legs" of a "ruler" inclined to each other at a given angle, so that when the meet of one pair of "legs" is made to trace out a given curve, the meet of the second pair

[17] ULC.Add 3961.1,6r–16r.

[18] "De Organica Conicarum Sectionum in Plano Descriptione Tractatus. Geometris, Opticis: praesertim verò Gnomonicis & Mechanicis Utilis" ("Exercitationes Mathematicæ," pp. 369–516, Leiden, 1657), Newton's notes on which are in the Fitzwilliam Museum pocket book. In his Book 4, in effect, Schooten reproduced his "Organica Descriptio," Leiden, 1646.

"organically" constructs a companion curve as its locus. In general, when the first curve is a straight line the companion curve will be a conic and in a dazzling extension of this Newton explained how to construct a conic passing through given points and touching given lines; more generally he went on to explore the 1,1 geometrical correspondence which ties pairs of points in the given and organically constructed curves, showing how higher curves of known multiplicities of points generate like curves of calculable multiplicity, evolving a general method of tangents at an arbitrary point of the described curve, and even attempting an analytical investigation by an appropriate coordinate system specially designed for the purpose. These researches, finally, were gathered by him in a carefully written tract, "De Modo describendi Conicas sectiones et curvas trium Dimensionum quando sint primi gradûs. &c," which remains unpublished.

From 1669, with his elevation to the Lucasian Professorship at Cambridge and widespread dissemination of the content of his "De Analysi," Newton became and remained a public figure to whom others felt they could turn for help, and many of his Cambridge researches became henceforth a topic of outside gossip. Some time in late 1669 especially, John Collins, having learnt something of his mathematical and optical work through Isaac Barrow, wrote to him the first of a long series of letters which passed between the two during the next few years and enclosed a manuscript Latin version, made by the German expatriate mathematician Nicolaus Mercator, of a recently published Dutch introduction to algebra. Of this work, Gerard Kinckhuysen's "Algebra ofte Stelkonst,"[19] Newton was apparently requested both to assess the mathematical quality and to suggest possible improvements which might be incorporated in a Latin printing. Newton wrote back[20] that "Your Kinck-Huysens Algebra I have made some notes upon. I suppose you are not much in hast of it, wch makes me doe y^t^ only at my leisure," and indeed over the next half year he continued making notes on the "Algebra." Inevitably he could not long remain satisfied with either its content or presentation: "I sometimes thought to have set upon writing a compleate introduction to Algebra, being cheifely moved to it by this that some things I had inserted into Kinck-Huysen were not so congruous as I could have wished to his manner of writing. Thus having composed something pretty largely about reducing problems to an æquation when I came to consider his examples . . . I found most of them solved not by any generall Analyticall method

[19] Haerlem, 1661. Mercator's still unpublished Latin version, interleaved with the sheets of a copy of the Dutch printing and with a few notes in Newton's hand, is now in the Bodleian at Oxford (Savile G.20): having vanished for almost three centuries, it was rediscovered there in 1963 by Christoph Scriba. (See C. J. Scriba, "Mercator's Kinckhuysen translation in the Bodleian Library at Oxford," *British Journal for the History of Science* **2**(1), 45–58, 1964). Kinckhuysen's book is a competent attempt to introduce the algebraic novice to advanced texts, especially Book 3 of Descartes' "Geometrie," but at times rejects the general approach in favour of an automatic presentation of computational procedures.

[20] Newton to Collins, (19?) January 1669/1670 ("Correspondence of Isaac Newton," Vol. 1, p. 20, Cambridge, 1959).

but by particular & contingent inventions."[21] Two years later the intention had become fact, for "The additions to Kinckhuysens Algebra I have long since augmented with what I intended, & particularly with a discourse concerning invention or the way of bringing Problems to an Æquation."[22] When we look at Newton's still unpublished "In Algebram Gerardi Kinckhuysen Observationes,"[23] we can appreciate just how extensive were Newton's revisions of several portions of the work. The section on root-extraction is wholly rewritten, a new introduction is set to Part 2, "De Æquationibus," and many of its sections clarified and enlarged, while Part 3, "Quomodo quæstio aliqua ad æquationem redigatur," is greatly recast, and to Kinckhuysen's algebraic examples are "subjoyned" eight stimulating geometrical ones of Newton's own choosing. More importantly, perhaps, these "Observationes" were the basis in terms both of content and layout on which Newton built the course of mathematical lectures which he began in the autumn of 1673: except for trivial rearrangement, whole sequences of pages were to be re-presented word for word in the copy of those lectures which he deposited in the university archives and which would pass into print as his "Arithmetica Universalis." When therefore we realise how narrowly their earlier passages reproduced Kinckhuysen's "Algebra" we may well understand Newton's reluctance in later years to have these lectures published.

Collins came to be on terms of great friendship with Newton during the early 1670's and it would appear that at least once the former stayed with him in Cambridge, for at some time during that period Collins was permitted to take copies (now in private possession) of a wide variety of Newton's early mathematical and optical manuscripts.[24] One of these[25] reproduces an unfinished work of Newton's on the geometrical construction of quadratic, cubic, and quartic equations,[26] whose writing suggests that it was composed at about the time he wrote his notes on Kinckhuysen. In the main the piece is an elaboration and extension of his 1665 investigations of the same topic, but now, for example, the ellipse generated by a

[21] Newton to Collins, 27 September 1670 ("Correspondence," Vol. 1, pp. 43–44, 1959).

[22] Newton to Collins, 25 May 1672 ("Correspondence," Vol. 1, p. 161, 1959).

[23] ULC.Add 3959.1,2r–21r. Newton and Collins tried many times over the years 1670–1676 to have Kinckhuysen's "Algebra" and Newton's "Observationes" on it published (mostly together with Newton's 1671 tract on fluxions) but, due largely to the booksellers' unwillingness to incur the large financial risks involved, their efforts ultimately came to nothing. See the article by C. J. Scriba quoted in footnote 19, especially § III.

[24] Collins' letter to Wallis (late 1677?) ("Correspondence of Isaac Newton," Vol. 2, pp. 242–243, 1960) gives interesting independent proof of the extent of his knowledge of Newton's unpublished work.

[25] "Constructiones Geometricæ Æquationum per D. Isaac Newtonum," described by James Wilson a century later in his edition of the "Mathematical Tracts of the late Benjamin Robins," Vol. 2, Appendix, pp. 346–347.

[26] ULC.Add 3963.9. In large part (and with additions), the piece is reproduced verbatim in the appendix to the "Arithmetica" ("Universal Arithmetick," 2nd ed., pp. 225–257, 1728).

trammel construction is preferred to the parabola in the geometrical construction of the quartic by the meets of a circle and conic.

More generally in his growing correspondence with Collins and others Newton was asked to resolve a variety of elementary mathematical problems and this he did with considerable success, untangling annuity questions, approximately summing harmonic progressions, and gauging the content of volumes of revolution with equal facility. One query, in particular, was to open up a rich field of future investigation. Some time late in April 1675, a certain J. Smith wrote to Newton inquiring how best to compile a table of the square, cube, and fourth roots of the natural numbers. In his reply[27] Newton suggested that the easiest way to compute such a table was by an equal-interval finite difference scheme in which between every known root nine further roots might be subtabulated and the operation repeated as many times as necessary. From the primitive form of his difference scheme it is clear that Newton was still a novice in such matters.[28] Over the next two years his ideas slowly developed, and when in October 1676 he came to acquaint Leibniz with his new methods for preparing logarithmical and trigonometrical tables in a first draft[29] of a covering letter to his mediary, Henry Oldenburg, he wrote: "To fill in the gaps in the terms of any table when first differences are sufficient . . . is an obvious and well-known operation. But when second, third, and higher differences intervene, there would seem to be needed a general rule for eliciting these differences and for compounding them in the best way. I have a formula which pleases me exceedingly though hardly suitable to be set down here and in no way worthy to be sent on to Leibniz; however, since it may be applied to the calculation of any kind of table, I will not hesitate to describe it at some length for the use of computers, and so if you know any and you think these matters sufficiently important you may pass them on." The six following "Regulæ" which he sketches (without giving any proof) may all be deduced as corollaries of particular applications of a general

[27] Newton to Smith, 8 May 1675. The original, once in the possession of William Jones, is now lost, but a transcript of an inaccurate copy made by Jones for Cotes in 1711 was first published in J. Edleston's "Correspondence of Sir Isaac Newton and Professor Cotes," pp. 216–219, Cambridge, 1850, and is the version printed in Newton's "Correspondence," Vol. 1, pp. 342–344, 1959. An hitherto unacknowledged, slightly variant second copy in the hand of John Keill is now in Cambridge University Library (ULC.Res 1894, Packet No. 9(3)).

[28] The source of Newton's inspiration is not easy to determine with accuracy. There is nothing to justify—and a lot to condemn—the widespread belief that he was familiar with the work of Henry Briggs ("Arithmetica Logarithmica," 1624; "Trigonometria Britannica," 1633). He had certainly glanced at the equal-interval scheme laid out by Nicolaus Mercator in his "Logarithmotechnia," pp. 11 ff., London, 1668, and perhaps also at Gabriel Mouton's "Observationes Diametrorum Solis et Lunæ Apparentium," Lib. III, Caput Tertium "De nonnullis numerorum proprietatibus," pp. 368–396, Lyons, 1670.

[29] First printed (but wrongly identified as part of the "Regula Differentiarum") by D. C. Fraser in the *Journal of the Institute of Actuaries* **58**, 75–77, 1927.

central-difference formula for interpolating a function tabulated at equal intervals of argument. The more general interpolation formulas for unequal intervals were expounded by him in an unfinished manuscript, "Regula Differentiarum,"[30] of about the same date, and not long after he revised his researches in an unpublished entry in his Waste Book[31] which, with some addition and rearrangement, forms the major part (all but Propositions V, VI, and the concluding scholium) of the "Methodus Differentialis" printed in 1711.

We may pass over the relatively unimportant unpublished research in number theory and trigonometry[32] which Newton was pursuing in the late 1670's. It is more consequential to notice at this period his renewed interest in pure geometry, inspired perhaps by background reading required in the composition of his Lucasian lectures. If we rightly interpret the order of the numerous jottings which he made about this time, Newton began by constructing improved proofs of a miscellany of elementary theorems and by noting down his thoughts on the structure of elementary geometry, but soon came to consider more difficult special problems: the Apollonian one of drawing a circle to touch three given circles (or lines or points in degeneracy), for example, but supremely that of establishing the identity of the Greek 3/4 line locus with the "locus solidus" or general conic. Descartes had shown this identity by analytical means and he himself, in his work on the organic construction, had invented a general method of describing conics subject to given conditions: why then, since the 3/4 line locus implicitly demanded the construction of a conic through five given points, should he not synthetically reduce the locus condition to an organic construction? Having planned out a preliminary attack in a short paper, "Veterum Loca solida restituta," Newton carried through his program brilliantly in his "Solutio Problematis Veterum de Loco solido."[33] In the first five propositions of the latter, the reduction of the 3/4 line locus to the general conic is developed step by step on rigidly classical lines, and in Propositions 6 and 7 full reduction to the organic method is made. But Newton, his mind dancing on, could not leave it there and in the latter part of the tract posed himself the complementary problem: "It remains to show how to know whether some proposed locus be solid or not." In its resolution he introduced the notion of a theorem's proof being

[30] ULC.Add 3964.5,1r–2r, rather inadequately transcribed by D. C. Fraser in *Journal of the Institute of Actuaries* **58,** 78–84, 1927. In his added commentary and in his essay on "Newton and Interpolation" ("Isaac Newton, 1642–1727," ed. W. J. Greenstreet, pp. 45–69; especially 54–61, London, 1927), Fraser makes much of the fact that the work is composed in terms of adjusted differences: these would, in fact, seem merely an early form which Newton later completely abandoned for the simpler divided difference scheme which appears in all his published work.

[31] ULC Add 4004,82r–84r.

[32] ULC.Add 3964.1 and 3959.4,5 respectively.

[33] ULC.Add 4004,89v–90v and 3963.12 respectively. Compare my "Patterns of Mathematical Thought in the Later Seventeenth Century," *Archive for History of Exact Sciences* **1,** 179–388; especially 275–279, 307–311. 1961.

"geometrically simple," that is, constructible (though not necessarily constructed) by the intersection of straight lines: in modern language, two geometrical curves are "simply" related to each other if their points may be set in 1,1 correspondence with each other—indeed in his "Prop 11" Newton derives the most general analytical relationship ($\alpha = bx + cy + [d/e]xy$) which holds between two biunivocal parameters x and y. Thus armed, in the following theorem he proved the criterion, remarkable for its day, that a locus is solid (a conic) if and only if it is contructible as the meet of two pencils in 1,1 correspondence (which we now know as "Chasles'" theorem). Equally brilliantly in the sequel he passed on to split the general conic into its three nondegenerate species by considering the existence and quality of its infinite branches alone and applied his general theory to resolve a locus problem of Fermat's. Nor was he yet finished. Almost in the same breath of inspiration he seized on this last method of discriminating species by infinite branches, quickly applying it in a series of unpublished drafts[34] to the discrimination of the genera and species of the general cubic without, as in his previous researches, reducing it to its basic canonical form. In these pages, far in advance of contemporary thought, the true quality of Newton's mathematical intelligence (a subtle mixture of controlled excitement, fundamental insight, and technical facility) may be seen in its full vigour.

In the meantime Newton was steadily year by year carrying out his professorial duties, making himself available to the few Cambridge undergraduates who chose to profit by mathematical conversation with him, but more especially devoting himself to the preparation and delivery of his Lucasian lectures. In 1683 he was among other things[35] in the eleventh year of an introductory course on algebra. Contrary to statute, he had not made yearly deposit of these lectures and apparently some pressure was now put upon him to do so. Thereupon he somewhat hurriedly summarised a decade of lectures, writing them up in a thick bound volume which he deposited in the University Library soon after and which was to be printed by Whiston in 1707 as his "Arithmetica Universalis."[36] Having discussed its prehistory

[34] Now in ULC.Add 3961.1,18r–19(bis)v and in private possession. Compare pp. 140–143 of Rouse Ball's "On Newton's Classification of Cubic Curves" (footnote 1).

[35] Bound by statute if not in reality to give ten lectures a term, Newton does in fact seem to have lectured on other mathematical topics. In particular, among undergraduate notes made by Henry Wharton at Cambridge in 1683, "Theoremata et Problemata quædam Anno 1683 a me conscripta Mensibus Julio, Augusto, Septembri Horis Subsecivis" [Lambeth Palace Library, London. Codex H. Wharton 592: compare Edleston's "Correspondence" (footnote 27), p. xcv, note†] there is a piece, "Trigo(no)metriæ Fundamenta a Viro Cl. Isäaco Newtono, Matheseos Professore, anno 1683 data," which may have been delivered as a lecture. (It is in fact an improved version of ULC.Add 3959.5,47r ff.)

[36] From examination of the handwriting (which shows the volume to have been written in a single period of time), from certain inconsistencies between his proposed datings of the lectures (particularly in 1679) and the dates of his known absences from Cambridge, but especially from comparison of the lecture fragment given by Newton to Flamsteed in midsummer 1674 [Herstmonceaux Library. Flamsteed Papers Vol. 42, frontispiece, reproduced by Edleston in his "Correspondence" (footnote 27), pp. 252–253]

we need say little about its structure before directing the reader to the English version reproduced below: its first pages are little altered repeats of corresponding portions of his revision of Kinckhuysen's "Algebra," its central section incorporates a wide variety of particular problems modified from those given by others or invented anew, and the concluding pages reproduce his early researches into equations, while the final appendix repeats with few additions the latter half of his tract on the geometrical construction of equations of a decade earlier. Compact, fundamental, comprehensive, and yet at times highly original, it was easy to understand and in later years was deservedly to become the most widely read of all Newton's mathematical pieces.

In the middle 1680's Newton became absorbed in the composition of his "Philosophiæ Naturalis Principia Mathematica." For the most part, unfortunately, this greatest of all his works lies outside the limits of the present essay. However, Newton did include, particularly in Book 1 (largely given over to the technical study of planetary dynamics), several passages which have only tenuous reference to his main theme and which he perhaps inserted in the first instance more to pad out an intendedly brief work than because of their pressing relevance—indeed in his first revisions of the "Principia" a few years later he intended to throw many of them out of the main body of the work into an added mathematical appendix. These passages, moreover, contain important theorems which, though revised from earlier known drafts, do not occur elsewhere in Newton's papers in quite the same form or generality. In Book 1 we may, neglecting, for example, Lemma 28 on the inadequately proved and refutable conjecture that no closed algebraic curve is quadrable, isolate the propositions on geometrical conics in Sections 4 and 5: at least half do not begin to claim relevance to the "Motion of bodies" while the first theorems of Section 5 repeat much of the unpublished tract "Solutio Problematis Veterum de Loco solido" of a few years earlier, but Lemma 22 on linear projection and the following projective theorems are wholly new as well as being of the highest importance in the history of geometry.[37] Later in Book 3 we may likewise single out Lemma 5 as the last and most sophisticated presentation of his "master theorem" in finite-difference interpolation.[38] The further mathematical richnesses of the "Principia" we must leave the reader to discover for himself.

---

with the relevant portion of the deposited copy (ULC.Dd.9.68), it is clear that the latter is not a word for word transcript of his lectures. Indeed, Newton's dissatisfaction with the form of the deposited volume is evidenced by the unfinished revised version, "Arithmeticæ Universalis Liber Primus" (ULC.Add 3993), which he began a little later. A correlation of the deposited copy with the 1707 printed work is given by Edleston in his "Correspondence," pp. xcii–xcv.

[37] I have discussed the significance of these projective theorems, with suitable bibliographical references, in Chapter 6 of my "Patterns of Mathematical Thought in the Later Seventeenth Century" (footnote 33).

[38] Discussed by D. C. Fraser in relation to his previous results on pp. 52–54 of his "Newton and Interpolation" (footnote 30).

With the publication of the "Principia" the conventional account of Newton's mathematical achievement ends. We have seen in our previous introduction how false this is to his further calculus researches, and in the other areas, too, of his mathematical genius we must not neglect one final sustained creative burst in the early 1690's. Tired, it would seem, with the analytical investigations developed in the "Principia" and in the still more recent researches for his "De Quadratura Curvarum," and also having freshly read Commandino's Latin version of Pappus' "Mathematical Collections,"[39] Newton's interest in pure geometry revived and he acquired a still greater respect for the quality and technical achievement of Greek geometrical thought. Like so many other mathematicians of his and other centuries, he was attracted inevitably to attempted restoration of Euclid's three books of porisms on the basis of Pappus' uniquely surviving account, one rendered virtually unintelligible in Commandino's garbled Latin version of the original lacuna-filled Greek manuscript.[40] Relying extensively on the richnesses of his own geometrical knowledge, Newton came roughly to the same conclusion as that later propounded by Michel Chasles in his "Les trois livres de porismes d'Euclide" (Paris, 1860): Euclid's porisms were essentially various types of projectivity restricted to the straight line and circle and developed implicitly in terms of the invariance of cross-ratio by such metric theorems as Menelaus' (on the unit-product of the ratios cut off by a general transversal on the sides of a plane triangle). These ideas he thought of writing up towards the end of 1692 in a comprehensive "Liber Geometriæ,"[41] but as draft succeeded draft his original intention became somewhat modified and later versions of the "Liber," more analytical in character, were intended to be added to a revised second edition of the "Principia" as a comprehensive mathematical compendium.[42] Of mathematical by-products of the researches which underlay these succeeding versions perhaps the most notable was his projective discussion of cubics based on Lemma 22 of Book 1 of the "Principia": relying on the invariance of convexity and the passing of the horizontal into the line at infinity he established that all of the seventy-two species of cubic he isolated could be generated as the projection of some one of the five divergent parabolas.[43] With this still fresh in his mind, Newton in the autumn of 1695 began his last group of creative researches, intending

[39] Probably in Manolessi's inferior second edition (Bologna, 1660) of the *editio princeps* of 1588.

[40] Thus in commentary on his own improved Latin rendering (given in preface to his edition of Apollonius' "De Sectione Rationis," Oxford, 1706) Edmond Halley could write: "This account of porisms I neither understand nor see how it will profit the reader: what Pappus means here I am not given to conjecture."

[41] Drafts of this exist *passim* in ULC.Add 3963.

[42] In a memorandum (University Library, Edinburgh. David Gregory MS C42) compiled about July 1694, of which an English translation is printed in the "Correspondence of Isaac Newton," Vol. 3, pp. 384–386, David Gregory has preserved the most elaborate known account of what Newton intended to publish in his "Liber Geometriæ" at this time.

[43] ULC.Add 3961.3, revised as 4004,153r–159r. Independently half a century later Patrick Murdoch broadly repeated Newton's synthetic arguments in his "Neutoni Genesis Curvarum," London, 1746.

to generalise and reorder all his previous essays in analytical geometry. In a series of drafts he systematised his knowledge of general Cartesian coordinate transformations and simplified his analytical reduction of the cubic to its four canonical representing equations: then inverting the logical sequence of his earlier drafts of the "Enumeratio" of thirty years before, he wrote up a new approach to the classification of cubics, one which subdivides them into the same subordinate species as before, but in which the diametral hyperbola assumes a fundamental role and analytical considerations become mere corollaries, while reduction of the general cubic by coordinate transformation is wholly omitted.[44] This version is substantially the one added by him as the first Latin appendix to his "Opticks" in 1704.

With Newton's departure from Cambridge in the beginning of 1696 for the public life of London, his geometrical and algebraic researches ended in any real sense, though the continuing agility of his mind is fully attested, for example, by his quick and adequate reply to two challenge problems set by Johann Bernoulli the following year.[45] Indeed, the last years of his life were confined mathematically to the revision of already existing works for publication and in elaborately furthering his own ends in the fluxion priority dispute. Typical of the former are the tract on finite differences, the "Methodus Differentialis," which we reproduce in this volume in translation, and his editing of the second edition of the "Arithmetica Universalis" in 1722.[46] The latter is not relevant to our theme and we may leave Newton quietly resting in old age from a crowded mathematical life.

As in our earlier introduction we conclude with some bibliographical details.

The "Arithmetica Universalis; sive De Compositione et Resolutione Arithmetica Liber. Cui accessit Halleiana Æquationum Radices Arithmetice inveniendi methodus. In Usum Juventutis Academicæ" was first published at Cambridge in 1707 under the supervision of William Whiston, Newton's successor in the Lucasian Professorship, from the copy deposited in the University Library in the middle 1680's of Newton's Lucasian lectures on arithmetic and algebra during the years 1673–1683[47]

[44] See ULC.Add 3961.2,15r–21(bis)r and 3961.1,38r–50v.

[45] Bernoulli's challenges, combining two separate problems (What curve is the brachistochrone? and, What curve is met by a line revolving round a fixed pole in two intercepts such that the sum of their *n*th powers is given?) set in the *Acta Eruditorum* the previous year, were communicated privately to Newton in January 1696/1697 in a 1-page printed flysheet (the "Programma"). His reply, typically blunt and fundamental, was published anonymously in *Philosophical Transactions* **19**, 384–389, 1697: an autograph draft of this together with his copy of the "Programma" is preserved in the archives of the Royal Society (Letter Book N.1.61b). (The printed version is repeated in Castillione's "Opuscula," Vol. 1, pp. 293–294, 1744 and in Horsley's "Opera Omnia," Vol. 4, 411–416, 1782.)

[46] For details see the following bibliographical section.

[47] The publication was apparently against Newton's wishes. The professorial statutes (printed in Whiston's "An Account of Mr. Whiston's Prosecution at, and Banishment from, the University of Cambridge . . . now Reprinted . . . With an Appendix: Containing Mr. Whiston's farther Account," pp. 42–46, "A Copy of Mr. Lucas's Statutes. Confirmed by the Royal Authority," London, 1718) laid down

Newton was never satisfied either with the content or typographical layout of this edition, or indeed with having Halley's tract on equations tagged on to it in appendix.[48] However he seems to have been stirred finally to action only by the publication in 1720 of a first English translation of the "Arithmetica" ("Universal Arithmetick: or, a Treatise of Arithmetical Composition and Resolution, to which is added, Dr. Halley's method of finding the roots of the Æquations arithmetically. Translated from the Latin by the late Mr. Ralphson, and revised and corrected by Mr. Cunn," London, 1720). Without delay he issued a second Latin edition, "Arithmetica Universalis; sive De Compositione et Resolutione Arithemetica Liber. Editio Secunda, In quo multa immutantur & emendantur, nonnulla adduntur" (London, 1722), in which the Halley tract is banished, running heads altered, the order of the

---

that a minimum of ten lectures per year were to be deposited in the University archives and to be freely open to public inspection. [However, the deposited copy (ULC.Dd.9.68) at times fails to meet this minimum and, in particular, only six lectures are entered under the heading "Octob. 1678."] By implication the copyright over the deposited lectures was retained by Cambridge University and it seems clear that Newton himself had no legal power to prevent their publication. In his "Ad Lectorem" Whiston wrote ("Arithmetica Universalis," a3r ff., 1707) that "I have taken pains that this little book, imperfect though it be and by reason of the demands of [its author's] position composed at speed and in no way intended for the press, shall however now be published for the use of undergraduates." Behind the scenes Newton had fought—and lost—a battle some of whose finer points came to light only recently when W. G. Hiscock edited extracts from David Gregory's memoranda in the library of Christ Church, Oxford ("David Gregory, Isaac Newton and their Circle," Oxford, 1937). On July 21, 1706, Gregory noted (Hiscock, p. 36) that Newton "was forced seemingly to allow of [its printing], about 14 months agoe, when he stood for Parliament-man at [Cambridge] University. He has not seen a sheet of it, nor knows he what volume it is in, nor how many sheets it will make, nor does he well remember the contents of it. He intends to goe down to Cambridge this summer and see it, & if it doe not please him, to buy up the Coppyes." Gregory later added to the same note that "The Title is at last agreed to be this. Arithmetica Universalis, sive Tractatus de Resolutione et Compositione Arithmetica." On September 1 following, Gregory noted that "I saw Sr. Isaac Newton's Algebra. There are just 20 sheets or 320 pages in 8vo printed. The Title is, Arithmetica Universalis sive Algebræ Elementa. The running title is, Algebræ Elementa. He is not pleased with the Titles, as not agreeing with the Introduction. . . . He intends a Preface himself, in which he is to tell all he would have changed (which chiefly consists in putting out) and that against the next edition." Finally, about the beginning of January 1707, Gregory wrote that "There is to be subjoyned to the end of Sir Isaac Newton's Algebra the Construction of Solid Problemes by an Ellipsis & a Circle: but no other alterations." In the sequel Newton had none of his way: the printed version has no author's introduction and the unsatisfactory title is retained for all but the first sheet, while a short tract of Edmond Halley's, "Methodus Nova Accurata & facilis inveniendi Radices Æquationum quarumcumque generaliter" (significantly omitted by Newton from his own revised edition of 1722) was added in appendix from the *Philosophical Transactions,* **18,** 136–148, 1694. The first part of the final title, "Arithmetica Universalis" (which repeats that of his later unfinished redraft, ULC.Add 3993), is probably Newton's choice but the later phrase has a distinctly non-Newtonian ring to it.

[48] The full extent of Newton's dissatisfaction can be gauged only from a study of his personal copy of the work (now in private possession). Apart from the major changes—complete rewriting of the running heads, widespread rearrangement of the sixty-one geometrical problems which form the heart of the book, and omission of Halley's appended tract—which he was to introduce into his own Latin revision, Newton intended still further alterations, and in particular the cancellation of almost all his own appendix on the geometrical construction of equations.

problems changed, and a certain number of minor corrections to the text incorporated, but which lacks the author's promised preface and whose only essential addition is a small clarifying footnote on page 97.[49] This edition has since been adopted (rightly so) by all subsequent editors and translators as their working text. A revised English version—the one here reproduced—which incorporates the changes in the new Latin edition but retains (against Newton's implicit wish) the appendage of Halley's tract was issued six years later ("Universal Arithmetick: Or, A Treatise of Arithmetical Composition and Resolution. To which is added, Dr. Halley's Method of finding the Roots of Equations Arithmetically. Written in Latin by Sir Isaac Newton, and Translated by the late Mr. Ralphson and Revised and Corrected by Mr. Cunn. The Second Edition, very much Corrected," London, 1728). Four years later two continental editions of the Latin text appeared: G. J. 's Gravesande's "Arithmetica Universalis; sive de Compositione et Resolutione Arithmetica Liber. Auctore Is. Newton, Eq. Aur." (Leiden, 1732), rather sparely edited but in its preface rightly identifying the editor of the second edition as Newton himself and adding to Halley's appended tract two more by the same author together with a further five by John Colson, Demoivre, Maclaurin, and George Campbell: and "Arithmetica Universalis. Perpetuis Commentariis illustrata et aucta a J. A. Lecchi" (Milan, 1732), three volumes. The fullest edition which has so far appeared are the two volumes, rather pompously overstuffed but in many instances excellently commented, of G. Castillione ("Arithmetica Universalis: sive de Compositione et Resolutione Arithmetica. Auctore Is. Newton, Eq. Aur. Cum Commentario Johannis Castillionei," Amsterdam, 1761): based on 's Gravesande's Leiden edition, this includes all the many texts there appended, together with a valuable original essay by R. Boscovich on a cometary proposition (Prop. 52 of the first edition, Prop. 56 of the second). Of less importance is an abridgment of the same year ("Arithmetica Universalis summi Newtoni, contracta, illustrata, et locupletata; præeunte logica analitica a Godef. Ant. Décoré," Leiden, 1761). A virtually plain Latin text of the "Arithmetica" was incorporated by Horsley, apparently from 's Gravesande's edition, in the first volume of his "Opera" ("Isaaci Newtoni Opera quæ exstant Omnia. Commentariis illustrabat Samuel Horsley," Vol. 1, pp. 1–229, London, 1779). A mediocre revision of Raphson's English version had appeared a few years earlier ("Universal Arithmetick: or, a Treatise of Arithmetical Composition and Resolution. Written in Latin by Sir Isaac Newton. Translated by The late Mr. Ralphson; and Revised and Corrected by Mr. Cunn. To which is added, a Treatise upon the Measures of Ratios. By James Maguire. . . . The whole illustrated and explained In a Series of Notes By the Rev. Theaker Wilder . . . ," London, 1769) and at the

[49] The original autograph draft of this note (ULC.Add 3960.7,95r) still exists. In all copies of the second edition which I have seen, page 315/316 is a cancel: clearly the bad mathematical mistake on the original leaf, allowed by Whiston to pass into print in 1707, was noticed by Newton himself only at the last moment in 1722.

turn of the century there was published an uninspired French translation ["Arithmétique universelle de Newton, traduite avec des notes explicatives par N. Beaudeux," Paris, An X(= 1802), 2 vols.]. Since that date the only edition, in Latin original or translation, has been A. P. Juŝkeviĉ's recent first Russian version, with excellent notes and commentary ("Isaak N'juton: Vseobŝĉaja arifmetika ili kniga ob arifmetiĉeskikh sinteze i analize. Perevod, stat'ja i kommentarii A. P. Juŝkeviĉa," Moscow, 1948). We here have no space to detail the numerous partial commentaries which the "Arithmetica" has inspired over the past two and a half centuries.

The "Enumeratio Linearum tertii Ordinis," drafted in its final form by Newton in 1695 (ULC.Add 3961.1,38r–50v), was first published by him as the former of two mathematical appendices ("Two Treatises of the Species and Magnitudes of Curvilinear Figures") added to his "Opticks," pp. 138–169, London, 1704: the marked copy used by the printers (ULC.Add 3961.2,1r–14r), slightly altered from the preceding draft, still exists. Somewhat corrected and with a few additions the work was reprinted two years later in the Latin edition of the "Opticks" ("Optice," Appendix, pp. 1–24, London, 1706): the diagram sheets are printed from the same blocks as in the first edition. This is the standard Latin text reproduced by all subsequent editors.[50] Later reprints of the Latin text were made by William Jones in his "Analysis per Quantitatum Series, Fluxiones ac Differentias: cum Enumeratione Linearum Tertii Ordinis" (pp. 67–92, London, 1711; reissued at Amsterdam in 1723 in appendix to a reprint of the second edition of Newton's "Principia"), by Castillione ("Opuscula Mathematica," Vol. 1, pp. 245–270, Lausanne and Geneva, 1744), by Horsley ("Isaaci Newtoni Opera Omnia," Vol. 1, pp. 529–560, 1779) and by J. B. M. Duprat ("Isaaci Newtoni Enumeratio Linearum Tertii Ordinis," Paris, 1791). A hitherto unrecognised first English version of the work, perhaps authorised by Newton himself, was printed by John Harris in his "Lexicon Technicum. Or, an Universal Dictionary of Arts and Sciences" (Volume 2, Article: "CURVES. The incomparable Sir Isaac Newton gives this following Enumeration of Geometrical Lines of the Third or Cubick Order," London, 1710) and is reproduced below. Much better known is the later rendering by C. R. M. Talbot in his excellent commented edition "Sir Isaac Newton's Enumeration of Lines of the Third Order, Generation of Curves by Shadows, Organic Description of Curves, and Construction of Equations by Curves" (London, 1860). Other excellent early commentaries are James Stirling's "Lineæ Tertii Ordinis Neutonianæ, sive Illustratio Tractatus D. Newtoni De Enumeratione Linearum Tertii Ordinis" (Oxford, 1718; reissued by Duprat in appendix to his edition of the "Enumeratio," Paris, 1797[51] and Patrick Murdoch's

[50] However, Newton's own copy of "Optice" (ULC.Adv.b.39.4) contains corrections which have never been incorporated in any published edition: notably (cf. ULC.Add 3964.8,16r), he radically revised p. 5, ll. 3–9.

[51] See H. Wieleitner, "Zwei Bemerkungen zu Stirlings 'Lineæ Tertii Ordinis Neutonianæ,'" *Bibliotheca Mathematica* (3) **14,** 55–62, 1913–1914.

"Neutoni Genesis Curvarum per Umbras, seu Perspectivæ Universalis Elementa; Exemplis Coni Sectionum et Linearum Tertii Ordinis illustrata" (London, 1746),[52] while W. W. Rouse Ball's "On Newton's Classification of Cubic Curves" (footnote 1) is fundamental. Recently Maximilian Miller has contributed a brief survey, "Newton, Aufzählung der Linien dritter Ordnung" (*Wissenschaftliche Zeitschrift der Hochschule für Verkehrswesen Dresden* **1,** 5–32, 1953).

The "Methodus Differentialis," lastly, has apparently a curiously ambiguous printing history. Newton's draft ULC.Add 4004,82r–84r, composed perhaps in late 1676, is clearly the basis for the piece with this title with which William Jones closed his "Analysis per Quantitatum Series . . ." (pages 93–101) in 1711. In his prefatory remarks ("Præfatio," (c^v)) Jones noted that "As a crowning piece there is subjoined a short tract, entitled Methodus Differentialis, which with the author's permission I have transcribed from his autograph." I have not been able to locate Newton's original of this tract—and am not convinced that one existed[53]—but the transcript that Jones made (now in private possession) is indeed identical with the printed version. Jones's edition, repeated in the 1723 reissue of his "Analysis," is the source for all subsequent versions and commentaries. The "Methodus" duly appeared in the eighteenth-century compendia of Castillione ("Opuscula Mathematica," Vol. 1, pp. 271–282, 1744) and of Horsley ("Opera Omnia," Vol. 1, pp. 519–528, 1779) but since that time only (in photocopy of Jones's printing) in D. C. Fraser's "Newton's Interpolation Formulas," *Journal of the Institute of Actuaries* **51,** 85–93, 1918 (reissued in his bound volume of the same title, pp. 9–17, London, 1927).

In this volume we reproduce the English translation appended by Fraser to his reprint of the Latin text (*Journal of the Institute of Actuaries* **51,** 94–101, 1918 = "Newton's Interpolation Formulas," pp. 18–25, London, 1927), the only one known to us in any language. Roger Cotes' "De Methodo Differentiali Newtoniana" (pp. 23–33 of the "Opera Miscellanea Rogeri Cotes" appended by R. Smith to his edition of Cotes' "Harmonia Mensurarum," Cambridge, 1722) and James Stirling's "De Interpolatione Serierum" (Pars II, pp. 85–153 of his "Methodus Differentialis: sive Tractatus de Summatione et Interpolatione Serierum Infinitarum," London, 1730) remain invaluable contemporary amplifications of Newton's tract. For more modern

[52] Compare H. Wieleitner, "Die Behandlung der Perspektive durch Murdoch," *Bibliotheca Mathematica* (3) **14,** 320–335, 1913–1914.

[53] I find it difficult to see why the original autograph of the "Methodus" should, alone of all Newton's significant pieces, no longer apparently be preserved. From examination of an autograph draft of Prop. V and part of the concluding scholium (ULC.Add 3965.12,236v, whose writing we may date as little before 1711) it is clear that when it was written Newton had still not decided on inserting Prop. VI and that the final form of the work had not been fixed. It is possible that Jones made his copy of Props. I–IV directly from Newton's original draft (suitably transposed according to his direction) and that the two concluding propositions and final scholium were alone separately drafted in 1710. The title is presumably Newton's.

commentary consult the articles of D. C. Fraser already quoted (especially footnote 30) and Maximilian Miller's "Newtons Differenzmethode," *Wissenschaftliche Zeitschrift für Verkehrswesen Dresden* **2**, 1–13, 1954 (in Russian with German summary).

CONTENTS

"Universal Arithmetick: or, a Treatise of Arithmetical Composition and Resolution. Written in Latin by Sir Isaac Newton, and Translated by the late Mr. Ralphson, and Revised and Corrected by Mr. Cunn." (London 1728). Pages i-iv, 1-257.

Universal Arithmetick:

OR, A

TREATISE

OF

ARITHMETICAL

COMPOSITION and RESOLUTION.

UNIVERSAL

ARITHMETICK:

OR, A

TREATISE

OF

ARITHMETICAL

COMPOSITION and RESOLUTION.

To which is added,

Dr. HALLEY's Method of finding the Roots of EQUATIONS Arithmetically.

Written in LATIN by Sir ISAAC NEWTON, *and Tranſlated by the late Mr.* RALPHSON, *and Reviſed and Corrected by Mr.* CUNN.

The Second Edition, very much Corrected.

LONDON:

Printed for J. SENEX, in *Fleet-ſtreet*, W. and J. INNYS, near S. *Paul's*, J. OSBORNE and T. LONGMAN in *Pater-noſter-row*.

M. DCC. XXVIII.

TO THE

READER.

TO ſay any thing in Praiſe of the enſuing Treatiſe, were an Attempt as needleſs and impertinent, as to write a Panegyrick on its Author. It is enough that the Subject is ALGEBRA; *and that it was written by Sir* Iſaac Newton: *Thoſe who know any thing of the Sciences, need not be told the Value of the former; nor thoſe who have heard any thing of Philoſophy and Mathematicks, to be inſtructed in the Praiſes of the latter. If any thing could add to the Eſteem every Body has for the* Analytick *Art, it muſt be, that Sir* Iſaac *has condeſcended to handle it; nor could any thing add to the Opinion the World has of that illuſtrious Author's Merit, but that he has written with ſo much Succeſs on that wonderful Subject.*

It is true, we have already a great many Books of Algebra, *and one might even furniſh a mo-*

a moderate Library purely with Authors on that Subject: But as no Body will imagine that Sir Isaac *would have taken the Pains to compose a new one, had he not found all the old ones defective; so, it will be easily allowed, that none was more able than he, either to discover the Errors and Defects in other Books, or to supply and rectify them in his own.*

The Book was originally writ for the private Use of the Gentlemen of Cambridge, *and was delivered in Lectures, at the publick Schools, by the Author, then* Lucasian *Professor in that University. Thus, not being immediately intended for the Press, the Author had not prosecuted his Subject so far as might otherwise have been expected; nor indeed did he ever find Leisure to bring his Work to a Conclusion: So that it must be observed, that all the Constructions, both Geometrical and Mechanical, which occur towards the End of the Book, do only serve for finding the first two or three Figures of Roots; the Author having here only given us the Construction of Cubick Equations, though he had a Design to have added, a general Method of constructing Biquadratick, and other higher Powers, and to have particularly shewn in what Manner the other Figures of Roots were to be extracted. In this unfinished State it continued till the Year* 1707, *when Mr.* Whiston, *the Author's Successor in the* Lucasian *Chair, considering that it was but small in Bulk, and yet ample in Matter, not too much crowded with Rules and Precepts, and yet well furnished with choice Examples, (serving not only as* Praxes *on the Rules, but as Instances of the great Usefulness of the Art it self; and, in short, every Way qualified to conduct the young Student from his first setting out on this Study) thought it Pity so noble and useful a Work should be doomed to a College-Confinement, and obtained Leave to make it Publick. And in order to supply what the Author had left undone, subjoyned the General and truly Noble Method of extracting the Roots of Equations, published by Dr.* Halley *in the* Philosophical Transactions, *having first procured both those Gentlemen's Leave for his so doing.*

As to the publishing a Translation of this Book, the Editor is of Opinion, that it is enough to excuse his Undertaking, that such Great Men were concerned in the Original; and is perswaded, that the same Reason which engaged Sir Isaac *to write, and Mr.* Whiston *to publish the* Latin *Edition, will bear him out in publishing this* English *one: Nor will the Reader require any farther Evidence, that the Translator has done Justice to the Original, after I have assured him, that Mr.* Ralphson *and Mr.* Cunn *were both concerned in this Translation.*

A D-

ADVERTISEMENT.

THIS New Edition, in *Engliſh*, of Sir ISAAC NEWTON's ALGEBRA, has been very carefully compared with the correct Edition of the Original, that was publiſhed in 1722; and ſuitable Emendations have been every where made accordingly. What was there wanting, is a general Method of finding, in Numbers, the Roots of Equations; and the Doctrine of the *Loci* and by their Means the Geometrical Conſtruction of Equations. The firſt is ſupplied by Dr. HALLEY's Method, which is here annexed. The other the Reader may find delivered with great Perſpicuity and Elegance, by the *Marquiſs de l'Hoſpital*, in his *Analytical Treatiſe* of the *Conick Sections:* Where, beſides, he will meet with great Variety of very difficult Problems, which are ſolved after ſo excellent a Manner, as not to be given over, until they are at length brought to the moſt elegant Conſtruction they are capable of. As this Part of *Algebra* is the moſt difficult, ſo it is the moſt neceſſary; and has never, I believe, been handled to any good Purpoſe, by any Writer whatever, beſides that illuſtrious Author. What *Schoten* has pretended to do on this Head, in general, at the End of *Cartes*'s *Geometry*, is the moſt clumſy Performance imaginable.

Uni-

Univerſal Arithmetick:

OR, A

TREATISE

OF

Arithmetical COMPOSITION and RESOLUTION.

COMPUTATION is either perform'd by *Numbers*, as in Vulgar Arithmetick, or by *Species*, as uſual among Algebraiſts. They are both built on the ſame Foundations, and aim at the ſame End, *viz.* *Arithmetick* Definitely and Particularly, *Algebra* Indefinitely and Univerſally; ſo that almoſt all Expreſſions that are found out by this Computation, and particularly Concluſions, may be called *Theorems*. But Algebra is particularly excellent in this, that whereas in Arithmetick Queſtions are only reſolv'd by proceeding from given Quantities to the Quantities ſought, Algebra proceeds in a retrograde Order, from the Quantities ſought, as if they were given, to the Quantities given, as if they were ſought, to the end that we may ſome way or other come to a Concluſion or Equation, from which one may bring out the Quantity ſought. And after this Way the moſt difficult Problems are reſolv'd, the Reſolutions whereof would be ſought in vain from only common Arithmetick. Yet Arith-

B metick

metick in all its Operations is so subservient to Algebra, as that they seem both but to make one perfect *Science of Computing*; and therefore I will explain them both together.

Whoever goes upon this Science, must first understand the Signification of the Terms and Notes, and learn the fundamental Operations, *viz.* Addition, Subtraction, Multiplication, and Division; Extraction of Roots, Reduction of Fractions, and of Radical Quantities, and the Methods of ordering the Terms of Equations, and *exterminating the unknown Quantities* (where they are more than one). Then let [the Learner] proceed to exercise himself in these Operations, by bringing Problems to Equations; and, lastly, let him consider the Nature and Resolution of Equations.

Of the Signification of some Words and Notes.

By *Number* we understand not so much a Multitude of Unities, as the abstracted Ratio of any Quantity, to another Quantity of the same Kind, which we take for Unity. And this is threefold; integer, fracted, and surd: An *Integer* is what is measured by Unity, a *Fraction*, that which a submultiple Part of Unity measures, and a *Surd*, to which Unity is incommensurable.

Every one understands the Notes of *whole Numbers*, (0, 1, 2, 3, 4, 5, 6, 7, 8, 9) and the Values of those Notes when more than one are set together. But as Numbers plac'd on the left Hand, next before Unity, denote Tens of Units, in the second Place Hundreds, in the third Place Thousands, &c. so Numbers set in the first Place after Unity, denote tenth Parts of an Unit, in the second Place hundredth Parts, in the third Place thousandth Parts, &c. and these are call'd *Decimal Fractions*, because they always decrease in a Decimal Ratio; and to distinguish the Integers from the Decimals, we place a Comma, or a Point, or a separating Line. Thus the Number 732 ∠ 569 denotes seven hundred thirty-two Units, together with five tenth Parts, six centesimal, or hundredth Parts, and nine millesimal, or thousandth Parts of Unity; which are also written thus, 732, ∠ 569; or thus, 732.569; or also thus, 732 ∠ 569, and so the Number 57104,2083 fifty-seven thousand one hundred and four Units, together with two tenth Parts, eight thousandth Parts, and three ten thousandth Parts of Unity; and the Number 0,064 denotes six centesimals and four millesimal Parts. The Notes of Surds and fracted Numbers are set down in the following Pages.

When the Quantity of any Thing is unknown, or look'd upon as indeterminate, so that we cannot express it in Numbers, we denote it by some Species, *or by some Letter.* And if we consider known Quantities as indeterminate, we denote them, for distinction sake, with the initial Letters of the Alphabet, as a, b, c, d, and the unknown ones by the final ones, z, y, x, &c. Some substitute Consonants or great Letters for known Quantities, and Vowels or little Letters for the unknown ones.

Quantities are either Affirmative, *or greater than nothing*; *or* Negative, *or less than nothing.* Thus in humane Affairs, Possessions or Stock may be call'd affirmative Goods, and Debts negative ones. And so in local Motion, Progression may be call'd affirmative Motion, and Regression negative Motion; because the first augments, and the other diminishes the Length of the Way made. And after the same manner in Geometry, if a Line drawn any certain Way be reckon'd for Affirmative, then a Line drawn the contrary Way may be taken for Negative. As if AB [*See Fig.* 1.] be drawn to the right, and BC to the left; and AB be reckon'd Affirmative, then BC will be Negative; because in the drawing it diminishes AB, and reduces it either to a shorter, as AC, or to none, if C chances to fall upon the Point A, or to less than none, if BC be longer than AB from which it is taken. A *negative* Quantity is denoted by the Sign $-$; the Sign $+$ is prefix'd to an *affirmative* one; and $\mp$ denotes an uncertain Sign, and $\pm$ a contrary uncertain one.

In an Aggregate of Quantities the Note $+$ *signifies, that the Quantity it is prefix'd to, is* to be added, *and the Note* $-$, *that it is* to be subtracted. And we usually express these Notes by the Words *Plus* (or *more*) and *Minus* (or *less*). Thus $2+3$, or 2 more 3, denotes the Sum of the Numbers 2 and 3, that is 5. And $5-3$, or 5 less 3, denotes the Difference which arises by subducting 3 from 5, that is 2: And $-5+3$ signifies the Difference which arises from subducting 5 from 3, that is -2; and $6-1+3$ makes 8. Also $a+b$ denotes the Sum of the Quantities a and b, and $a-b$ the Difference which arises by subducting b from a; and $a-b+c$ signifies the Sum of that Difference, and of the Quantity c. Suppose if a be 5, b 2, and c 8, then $a+b$ will be 7, and $a-b$ 3, and $a-b+c$ will be 11. Also $2a+3a$ is $5a$, and $3b-2a-b+3a$ is $2b+a$; for $3b-b$ makes $2b$, and $-2a+3a$ makes a, whose Aggregate, or Sum, is $2b+a$, and so in others. These Notes $+$ and $-$ are called *Signs*. And when neither is prefix'd, the Sign $+$ is always to be understood.

B 2

Multiplication, properly ſo call'd, is that which is made by Integers, as ſeeking a new Quantity, ſo many times greater than the Multiplicand, as the Multiplier is greater than Unity. But for want of a better Word, that is alſo called *Multiplication*, which is made uſe of in Fractions and Surds, to find a new Quantity in the ſame *Ratio* (whatever it be) to the Multiplicand, as the Multiplier has to Unity. Nor is Multiplication made only by abſtract Numbers, but alſo by concrete Quantities, as by Lines, Surfaces, Local Motion, Weights, *&c.* as far as theſe being related to ſome known Quantity of their kind, as to Unity, may expreſs the Ratios of Numbers, and ſupply their Place. As is if the Quantity A be to be multiply'd by a Line of 12 Foot, ſuppoſing a Line of 2 Foot to be Unity, there will be produc'd by that Multiplication 6 A, or ſix times A, in the ſame manner as if A were to be multiply'd by the abſtract Number 6; for 6 A is in the ſame Ratio to A, as a Line of 12 Foot has to a Line of 2 Foot. And ſo if you were to multiply any two Lines, A C [*See Fig.* 2.] and A D by one another, take A B for Unity, and draw B C, and parallel to it D E, and A E will be the Product of this Multiplication; becauſe it is to A D as A C to the Unity A B. Moreover, Cuſtom has obtain'd, that the Geneſis or Deſcription of a Surface, by a Line moving at right Angles upon another Line, ſhould be called the Multiplication of thoſe two Lines. For tho' a Line, however multiply'd, cannot become a Surface, and conſequently this Generation of a Surface by Lines is very different from Multiplication, yet they agree in this, that the Number of Unities in either Line, multiply'd by the Number of Unities in the other, produces an abſtracted Number of Unities in the Surface comprehended under thoſe Lines, if the ſuperficial Unity be defin'd as it is uſed to be, *viz.* a Square whoſe Sides are linear Unities. As if the right Line [*Fig.* 3.] A B conſiſt of four Unities, and A C of three, then the Rectangle A D will conſiſt of four times three, or 12 ſquare Unities, as from the Scheme will appear. And there is the like Analogy of a Solid and a Product made by the continual Multiplication of three Quantities. And hence it is, that the Words to *multiply into*, the *Content*, a *Rectangle*, a *Square*, a *Cube*, a *Dimenſion*, a *Side*, and the like, which are Geometrical Terms, are applied to Arithmetical Operations. For by a *Square*, or *Rectangle*, or a *Quantity of two Dimenſions*, we do not always underſtand a Surface, but moſt commonly a Quantity of ſome other kind, which is produc'd by the Multiplication of two other Quantities, and very often a Line which is produc'd by the Multiplication of two other Lines. And ſo we call a *Cube*, or a *Parallelopiped*, or a *Quantity of three Dimenſions*, that which is produc'd by two Multiplications. We ſay likewiſe the *Side* for a *Root*, and uſe *Draw* into inſtead of *Multiply*; and ſo in others.

A Number prefix'd immediately before any Species, denotes that Species to be ſo often to be taken. Thus 2 *a* denotes two *a*'s, 3 *b* three *b*'s, 15 *x*, fifteen *x*'s.

Two or more Species immediately connected together denote a Product *or Quantity made by the Multiplication of all the Species together.* Thus *a b* denotes a Quantity made by multiplying *a* by *b*, and *a b x* denotes a Quantity made by multiplying *a* by *b*, and the Product again by *x*. As ſuppoſe, if *a* were 2, and *b* 3 and *x* 5, then *a b* would be 6, and *a b x* 30.

Among Quantities multiplying one another, the Sign ×, or the Word *by* or *into*, is made uſe of to denote the Product ſometimes. Thus 3 × 5, or 3 by or into 5 denotes 15; but the chief Uſe of theſe Notes is, when compound Quantities are multiply'd together. As if $y-2b$ were to multiply $y+b$, the way is to draw a Line over each Quantity, and then write them thus, $\overline{y-2b}$ into $\overline{y+b}$, or $\overline{y-2b}\times\overline{y+b}$.

Diviſion is properly that which is made uſe of for integer or whole Numbers, in finding a new Quantity ſo much leſs than the Dividend, as Unity is than the Diviſor. But by Analogy, the Word may alſo be uſed when a new Quantity is ſought, that ſhall be in any ſuch *Ratio* to the Dividend, as Unity has to the Diviſor; whether that Diviſor be a Fraction or ſurd Number, or other Quantity of any other kind. Thus to divide the Line [*See Fig.* 4.] A E by the Line A C, A B being Unity, you are to draw E D parallel to C B, and A D will be the Quotient. Moreover, it is call'd *Diviſion*, by reaſon of a certain Similitude, when a Rectangle is applied to a given Line as a Baſe, in order thereby to know the Heighth.

One Quantity below another, with a Line interpoſed, denotes a Quotient, *or a Quantity ariſing by the Diviſion of the upper Quantity by the lower.* Thus $\frac{6}{2}$ denotes a Quantity ariſing by dividing 6 by 2, that is 3; and $\frac{5}{8}$ a Quantity ariſing by the Diviſion of 5 by 8, that is one eighth Part of the Number 5. And $\frac{a}{b}$ denotes a Quantity which ariſes by dividing *a* by *b*; as ſuppoſe *a* was 15 and *b* 3, then $\frac{a}{b}$ would denote

denote 5. Likewise thus $\frac{ab-bb}{a+x}$ denotes a Quantity arising by dividing $ab-bb$ by $a+x$. And so in others. These sorts of Quantities are called *Fractions*, and the upper Part is call'd by the Name of the *Numerator*, and the lower is call'd the *Denominator*.

Sometimes the Divisor is set before the divided Quantity, and separated from it by a Mark resembling an Arch of a Circle. Thus to denote the Quantity which arises by the Division of $\frac{axx}{a+b}$ by $a-b$, it may be wrote thus, $\overline{a-b)}\,\frac{axx}{a+b}$.

Although we commonly denote Multiplication by the immediate Conjunction of the Quantities, yet an Integer before a Fraction, denotes the Sum of both. Thus $3\frac{1}{2}$ denotes three and a half,

If a Quantity be multiply'd by itself, the Number of Facts *or Products is, for Shortness sake, set at the Top of the Letter.* Thus for aaa we write a^3, for $aaaa$ a^4, for $aaaaa$ a^5, and for $aaabb$ we write a^3bb, or a^3b^2; as, suppose if a were 5 and b be 2, then a^3 will be $5\times5\times5$ or 125, and a^4 will be $5\times5\times5\times5$ or 625, and a^3b^2 will be $5\times5\times5\times2\times2$ or 500. Where Note, that if a Number be written immediately between two Species, it always belongs to the former; thus the Number 3 in the Quantity a^3bb, does not denote that bb is to be taken thrice, but that a is to be thrice multiply'd by itself. Note, moreover, that these Quantities are said to be of so many *Dimensions*, or of so high a *Power* or *Dignity*, as they consist of Factors or Quantities multiplying one another; and the Number set on forwards at the Top of the Letter is called the Index of those Powers or Dimensions; thus aa is of two Dimensions, or of the 2d Power, and a^3 of three, as the Number 3 at the Top denotes. aa is also called a *Square*, a^3 a *Cube*, a^4 a *Biquadrate* or *squared Square*, a^5 a *Quadrato-Cube*, a^6 a *Cubo-Cube*, a^7 a *Quadrato-Quadrato-Cube* or *Squared-Squared Cube*, and so on: And the Quantity a, by whose Multiplication by itself these Powers are generated, is called their *Root, viz.* it is the Square Root of the Square aa, the Cube Root of the Cube aaa, &c.

But when a Root, multiply'd by itself, produces a Square, and that Square, multiply'd again by the Root, produces a Cube, *&c.* it will be (by the Definition of Multiplication) as Unity to the Root, so that Root to the Square, and that Square to the Cube, *&c.* And consequently *the square Root* of any Quantity will be a mean Proportional between Unity and that Quantity, and *the Cube Root* the first of two mean Proportionals, and *the Biquadratick Root* the first of three, and so on. Wherefore Roots are known by these two Properties or Affections, first, that by multiplying themselves they produce the superiour Powers; 2dly, that they are mean Proportionals between those Powers and Unity. Thus, 8 is the Square Root of the Number 64, and 4 the Cube Root of it, is hence evident, because 8×8, and $4\times4\times4$ make 64, or because as 1 to 8, so is 8 to 64, and 1 is to 4 as 4 to 16, and as 16 to 64. And hence, if the Square Root of any Line, as AB [*See Fig.* 5.] is to be extracted, produce it to C, and let BC be Unity; then upon AC describe a Semicircle, and at B erect a Perpendicular, meeting the Circle in D; then will BD be the Root, because it is a mean Proportional between AB and Unity BC.

To denote the Root of any Quantity, we use to prefix this Note $\surd$ *for a Square Root, and this* $\surd\,3$: *if it be a Cube Root, and this* $\surd\,4$: *for a Biquadratick Root*, &c. Thus $\surd\,64$ denotes 8; and $\surd\,3:64$ denotes 4; and $\surd\,aa$ denotes a; and $\surd\,ax$ denotes the Square Root of ax; and $\surd\,3:4axx$ the Cube Root of $4axx$. As if a be 3, and x 12; then $\surd\,ax$ will be $\surd\,36$, or 6; and $\surd\,3:4axx$ will be $\surd\,3:1728$, or 12. And when these Roots cannot be extracted, the Quantities are called *Surds*, as $\surd\,ax$; or *Surd Numbers*, as $\surd\,12$.

There are some, that to denote the Square or first Power, make use of q, and of c for the Cube, qq for the Biquadrate, and qc for the Quadrato-Cube, *&c.* After this Manner for the Square, Cube, and Biquadrate of A, they write Aq, Ac, Aqq, &c. and for the Cube Root of $abb-x^3$, they write $\surd\,c:abb-x^3$. Others make use of other sorts of Notes, but they are now almost out of Fashion.

The Mark $=$ *signifies, that the Quantities on each Side of it are* equal. Thus $x=b$ denotes x to be equal to b.

The Note :: *signifies that the Quantities on both Sides of it are* proportional. Thus $a.b::c.d$ signifies, that a is to b as c to d; and $a.b.e::c.d.f$ signifies that a, b, and e, are to one another respectively, as c, d, and f, are among themselves; or that a to c, b to d, and e to f, are in the same *Ratio*.

Lastly, the Interpretation of any Marks or Signs that may be compounded out of these, will easily be known by Analogy. Thus $\frac{3}{4}a^3bb$ denotes three quarters of a^3bb, and $3\frac{a}{c}$ signifies thrice

thrice $\frac{a}{c}$, and $7\sqrt{ax}$ ſeven times $\sqrt{ax}$. Alſo $\frac{a}{b}x$ denotes the Product of x by $\frac{a}{b}$; and $\frac{5ee}{4a+9e}z^3$ denotes the Product made by multiplying z^3 by $\frac{5ee}{4a+9e}$, that is the Quotient ariſing by the Diviſion of $5ee$ by $4a+9e$; and $\frac{2a^3}{9c}\sqrt{ax}$, that which is made by multiplying $\sqrt{ax}$ by $\frac{2a^3}{9c}$; and $\frac{7\sqrt{ax}}{c}$ the Quotient ariſing by the Diviſion of $7\sqrt{ax}$ by c; and $\frac{8a\sqrt{cx}}{2a+\sqrt{cx}}$ the Quotient ariſing by the Diviſion of $8a\sqrt{cx}$ by the Sum of the Quantities $2a+\sqrt{cx}$. And thus $\frac{3axx-x^3}{a+x}$ denotes the Quotient ariſing by the Diviſion of the Difference $3axx-x^3$ by the Sum $a+x$, and $\sqrt{\frac{3axx-x^3}{a+x}}$ denotes the Root of that Quotient, and $\overline{2a+3c}\sqrt{\frac{3axx-x^3}{a+x}}$ denotes the Product of the Multiplication of that Root by the Sum $2a+3c$. Thus alſo $\sqrt{\frac{1}{4}aa+bb}$ denotes the Root of the Sum of the Quantities $\frac{1}{4}aa$ and bb, and $\sqrt{\frac{1}{2}a+\sqrt{\frac{1}{4}aa+bb}}$ denotes the Root of the Sum of the Quantities $\frac{1}{2}a$ and $\sqrt{\frac{1}{4}aa+bb}$, and $\frac{2a^3}{aa-zz}\sqrt{\frac{1}{2}a+\sqrt{\frac{1}{4}aa+bb}}$ denotes the Root multiply'd by $\frac{2a^3}{aa-zz}$. And ſo in other Caſes.

But Note, that in complex Quantities of this nature, there is no neceſſity of giving a particular Attention to, or bearing in your Mind the Signification of each Letter; it will ſuffice in general to underſtand, *e. g.* that $\sqrt{\frac{1}{2}a+\sqrt{\frac{1}{4}aa+bb}}$ ſignifies the Root of the Aggregate or Sum of $\frac{1}{2}a+\sqrt{\frac{1}{4}aa+bb}$;

I what-

whatever that Aggregate may chance to be, when Numbers or Lines are ſubſtituted in the room of Letters. And thus it is as ſufficient to underſtand, that $\frac{\sqrt{\frac{1}{2}a+\sqrt{\frac{1}{4}aa+bb}}}{a-\sqrt{ab}}$ ſignifies the Quotient ariſing by the Diviſion of the Quantity $\sqrt{\frac{1}{2}a+\sqrt{\frac{1}{4}aa+bb}}$ by the Quantity $a-\sqrt{ab}$, as much as if thoſe Quantities were ſimple and known, though at preſent one may be ignorant what they are, and not give any particular Attention to the Conſtitution or Signification of each of their Parts; which I thought I ought here to admoniſh, leſt young Beginners ſhould be deterr'd in the very Beginning, by the Complexneſs of the Terms.

Of ADDITION.

THE Addition of Numbers, where *they are not very compounded*, is manifeſt of itſelf. Thus it is at firſt Sight evident, that 7 and 9 or $7+9$ make 16, and that $11+15$ make 26. But in *more compounded Numbers*, the Buſineſs is perform'd *by writing the Numbers in a Row downwards, or one under another, and ſingly collecting the Sums of the Columns.* As if the Numbers 1357 and 172 are to be added, write either of them (ſuppoſe 172) under the other 1357, ſo that the Units of the one, *viz.* 2, may exactly ſtand under the Units of the other, *viz.* 7, and the other Numbers of the one exactly under the correſpondent ones of the other, *viz.* the Place of Tens under Tens, *viz.* 7 under 5, and that of Hundreds, *viz.* 1, under the Place of Hundreds of the other, *viz.* 3. Then beginning at the right hand, ſay 2 and 7 make 9, which write underneath. Alſo 7 and 5 make 12, the laſt of which two Numbers, *viz.* 2, write underneath, and reſerve in your mind the other, *viz.* 1, to be added to the two next Numbers, *viz.* 1 and 3. Then ſay 1 and 1 make 2, which being added to 3 they make 5, which write underneath, and there will remain only 1, the firſt Figure of the upper Row of Numbers, which alſo muſt be writ underneath; and then you have the whole Sum, *viz.* 1529.

$$\begin{array}{r} 1357 \\ 172 \\ \hline 1529 \end{array}$$

Thus, to add the Numbers $87899+13403+885+1920$ into one Sum, write them one under another, ſo that all the Units may make one Column, the Tens another, the Hundreds a third, and the Places of Thouſands a fourth, and ſo

C on.

on. Then say, 5 and 3 make 8, and $8+9$ make 17; then write 7 underneath, and the 1 add to the next Rank, saying 1 and 8 make 9, $9+2$ make 11, and $11+9$ make 20; and having writ the 0 underneath, say again as before, 2 and 8 make 10, and $10+9$ make 19, and $19+4$ make 23, and $23+8$ make 31; then reserving 3 in your Memory, write down 1 as before, and say again, $3+1$ make 4, $4+3$ make 7, and $7+7$ make 14, wherefore write underneath 4, and lastly say $1+1$ make 2, and $2+8$ make 10, which in the last Place write down, and you will have the Sum of them all.

$$\begin{array}{r} 87899 \\ 13403 \\ 1920 \\ 885 \\ \hline 104107 \end{array}$$

After the same manner we also add Decimals, as in the following Example may be seen:

$$\begin{array}{r} 630,953 \\ 51,0807 \\ 305,25 \\ \hline 987,3037 \end{array}$$

Addition *is perform'd in Algebraick Terms or Species, by connecting the Quantities to be added with their proper Signs, and moreover by uniting into one Sum those that can be so united.* Thus a and b make $a+b$; a and $-b$ make $a-b$; $-a$ and $-b$ make $-a-b$; $7a$ and $9a$ make $7a+9a$; $-a\sqrt{ac}$ and $b\sqrt{ac}$ make $-a\sqrt{ac}+b\sqrt{ac}$, or $b\sqrt{ac}-a\sqrt{ac}$; for it is all one, in what Order soever they are written.

Affirmative Quantities, which agree in Species, are united together, by adding the prefix'd Numbers that are multiply'd into those Species. Thus $7a+9a$ make $16a$. And $11bc+15bc$ make $26bc$. Also $3\frac{a}{c}+5\frac{a}{c}$ make $8\frac{a}{c}$, and $2\sqrt{ac}+7\sqrt{ac}$ make $9\sqrt{ac}$, and $6\sqrt{ab-xx}+7\sqrt{ab-xx}$ make $13\sqrt{ab-xx}$. And in like manner, $6\sqrt{3}+7\sqrt{3}$ make $13\sqrt{3}$. Moreover $a\sqrt{ac}+b\sqrt{ac}$ make $\overline{a+b}\sqrt{ac}$, by adding together a and b as Numbers multiplying $\sqrt{ac}$. And so $\overline{2a+3c}\sqrt{\frac{3axx-x^3}{a+x}}+3a\sqrt{\frac{3axx-x^3}{a+x}}$ make $\overline{5a+3c}\sqrt{\frac{3axx-x^3}{a+x}}$ because $2a+3c$ and $3a$ make $5a+3c$.

Affir-

Affirmative Fractions, that have the same Denominator, are united by adding their Numerators. Thus $\frac{1}{5}+\frac{2}{5}$ make $\frac{3}{5}$, and $\frac{2ax}{b}+\frac{3ax}{b}$ make $\frac{5ax}{b}$; and thus $\frac{8a\sqrt{cx}}{2a+\sqrt{cx}}+\frac{17a\sqrt{cx}}{2a+\sqrt{cx}}$ make $\frac{25a\sqrt{cx}}{2a+\sqrt{cx}}$, and $\frac{aa}{c}+\frac{bx}{c}$ make $\frac{aa+bx}{c}$.

Negative Quantities are added after the same way as Affirmative. Thus -2 and -3 make -5; $-\frac{4ax}{b}$ and $-\frac{11ax}{b}$ make $-\frac{15ax}{b}$; $-a\sqrt{ax}$ and $-b\sqrt{ax}$ make $-\overline{a-b}\sqrt{ax}$.

But when a *Negative Quantity is to be added to an Affirmative one,* the Affirmative must be diminish'd by the Negative one. Thus 3 and -2 make 1; $\frac{11ax}{b}$ and $-\frac{4ax}{b}$ make $\frac{7ax}{b}$; $-a\sqrt{ac}$ and $b\sqrt{ac}$ make $\overline{b-a}\sqrt{ac}$. And Note, that when the Negative Quantity is greater than the Affirmative, the Aggregate or Sum will be Negative. Thus 2 and -3 make -1; $-\frac{11ax}{b}$ and $\frac{4ax}{b}$ make $-\frac{7ax}{b}$, and $2\sqrt{ac}$ and $-7\sqrt{ac}$ make $-5\sqrt{ac}$.

In the Addition of a greater Number of Quantities, or more compound ones, it will be convenient to observe the Method or Form of Operation we have laid down above in the Addition of Numbers. As if $17ax-14a+3$, and $4a+2-8ax$, and $7a-9ax$, were to be added together, dispose them so in Columns, that the Terms that contain the same Species may stand in a Row one under another, *viz.* the Numbers 3 and 2 in one Column, the Species $-14a$, and $4a$, and $7a$, in another Column, and the Species $17ax$ and $-8ax$ and $-9ax$ in a third. Then I add the Terms of each Column by themselves, saying 2 and 3 make 5, which I write underneath, then $7a$

$$\begin{array}{rrr} 17ax & -14a & +3 \\ -8ax & +4a & +2 \\ -9ax & +7a & \\ \hline * & -3a & +5 \end{array}$$

C 2

and

and $4a$ make $11a$ and moreover $-14a$ make $-3a$, which I alſo write underneath, laſtly, $-9ax$ and $-8ax$ make $-17ax$, to which $17ax$ added make o. And ſo the Sum comes out $-3a+5$.

After the ſame manner the Buſineſs is done in the following Examples.

$$\begin{array}{r} 12x + 7a \\ 7x + 9a \\ \hline 19x + 16a \end{array} \qquad \begin{array}{r} 11bc - 7\sqrt{ac} \\ 15bc + 2\sqrt{ac} \\ \hline 26bc - 5\sqrt{ac} \end{array} \qquad \begin{array}{r} -\frac{4ax}{b} + 6\sqrt{3} + \frac{1}{5} \\ +\frac{11ax}{b} - 7\sqrt{3} + \frac{2}{5} \\ \hline \frac{7ax}{b} - \sqrt{3} + \frac{3}{5} \end{array}$$

$$\begin{array}{r} -6xx + \frac{3}{7}x \\ 5x^3 + \frac{5}{7}x \\ \hline 5x^3 - 6xx + \frac{8}{7}x \end{array} \qquad \begin{array}{r} aay + 2a^3 - \frac{a^4}{2y} \\ -2ayy - 4aay - a^3 \\ y^3 + 2ayy - \frac{1}{2}aay \\ \hline y^3 \quad * - 3\frac{1}{2}aay + 3a^3 - \frac{a^4}{2y} \end{array}$$

$$\begin{array}{r} 5x^4 + 2ax^3 \\ -3x^4 - 2ax^3 + 8\frac{1}{4}a^3\sqrt{aa+xx} \\ -2x^4 + 5bx^3 - 20a^3\sqrt{aa-xx} \\ -4bx^3 - 7\frac{1}{4}a^3\sqrt{aa+xx} \\ \hline * bx^3 + a^3\sqrt{aa+xx} - 20a^3\sqrt{aa-xx}. \end{array}$$

Of SUBTRACTION.

THE Invention of the Difference of Numbers that are not *too much compounded*, is of itſelf evident; as if you take 9 from 17, there will remain 8. But in *more compounded Numbers*, Subtraction is perform'd *by ſubſcribing* or ſetting underneath *the Subtrahend, and ſubtracting each of the lower Figures from each of the upper ones.* Thus to ſubtract 63543 from 782579, having ſubſcrib'd 63543, ſay, 3 from 9 and there remains 6, which write underneath; and 4 from 7 and there remains 3, which write likewiſe underneath; then 5 from

5 from 5 and there remains nothing, which in like manner ſet underneath; then 3 comes to be taken from 2; but becauſe 3 is greater than 2, you muſt borrow 1 from the next Figure 8, which, together with 2, make 12, from which 3 may be taken and there will remain 9, which write likewiſe underneath; and then when beſides 6 there is alſo 1 to be taken from 8, add the 1 to the 6, and the Sum 7 being taken from 8, there will be left 1, which in like manner write underneath. Laſtly, when in the lower Rank of Numbers there remains nothing to be taken from 7, write underneath the 7, and ſo you have the Difference 719036.

$$\begin{array}{r} 782579 \\ 63543 \\ \hline 719036 \end{array}$$

But eſpecial Care is to be taken, that the Figures of the Subtrahend be placed or ſubſcribed in their proper or homogeneous Places; viz. the Units of the one under the Units of the other, and the Tens under the Tens, and likewiſe the Decimals under the Decimals, &c. as we have ſhewn in Addition. Thus to take the Decimal, 0,63 from the Integer 547, they are not to be diſpoſed thus $\begin{array}{r} 547 \\ 0{,}63 \end{array}$, but thus $\begin{array}{l} 547 \\ \;\;0{,}63 \end{array}$; *viz.* ſo that the 0, which ſupplies the Place of Units in the Decimal, muſt be placed under the Units of the other Number. Then o being underſtood to ſtand in the empty Places of the upper Number, ſay, 3 from 0, which ſince it cannot be, 1 ought to be borrow'd from the foregoing Place, which will make 10, from which 3 is to be taken, and there remains 7, which write underneath. Then that 1 which was borrow'd added to 6 make 7, and this is to be taken from o above it; but ſince that cannot be, you muſt again borrow 1 from the foregoing Place to make 10, then 7 from 10 leaves 3, which in like manner is to be writ underneath; then that 1 being added to 0, makes 1, which 1 being taken from 7 leaves 6, which again write underneath. Laſtly, write the two Figures 54 (ſince nothing remains to be taken from them) underneath, and you'll have the Remainder 546,37.

$$\begin{array}{l} 547 \\ \;\;\;0{,}63 \\ \hline 546{,}37 \end{array}$$

For Exerciſe ſake, we here ſet down ſome more Examples, both in Integers and Decimals.

1673

1673	1673	458074	35,72	46,5003	308,7
1541	1580	9205	14,32	3,078	25,74
132	93	448869	21,4	43,4223	282,96

If a greater Number is to be taken from a less, you must first subtract the less from the greater, and then prefix a negative Sign to the Remainder. As if from 1541 you are to subtract 1673, on the contrary I subtract 1541 from 1673, and to the Remainder 132 I prefix the Sign $-$.

In Algebraick Terms, Subtraction *is perform'd by connecting the Quantities, after having changed all the Signs of the Subtrahend, and by uniting those together which can be united,* as we have done in Addition. Thus $+7a$ from $+9a$ leaves $9a-7a$ or $2a$; $-7a$ from $+9a$ leaves $+9a+7a$, or $16a$; $+7a$ from $-9a$ leaves $-9a-7a$, or $-16a$; and $-7a$ from $-9a$ leaves $-9a+7a$, or $-2a$; so $3\frac{a}{c}$ from $5\frac{a}{c}$ leaves $2\frac{a}{c}$; $7\sqrt{ac}$ from $2\sqrt{ac}$ leaves $-5\sqrt{ac}$; $\frac{2}{9}$ from $\frac{5}{9}$ leaves $\frac{3}{9}$; $-\frac{4}{7}$ from $\frac{3}{7}$ leaves $\frac{7}{7}$; $-\frac{2ax}{b}$ from $\frac{3ax}{b}$ leaves $\frac{5ax}{b}$; $\frac{8a\sqrt{cx}}{2a+\sqrt{cx}}$ from $\frac{-17a\sqrt{cx}}{2a+\sqrt{cx}}$ leaves $\frac{-25a\sqrt{cx}}{2a+\sqrt{cx}}$; $\frac{aa}{c}$ from $\frac{bx}{c}$ leaves $\frac{bx-aa}{c}$; $a-b$ from $2a+b$ leaves $2a+b-a+b$, or $a+2b$; $3az-zz+ac$ from $3az$ leaves $3az-3az+zz-ac$ or $zz-ac$; $\frac{2aa-ab}{c}$ from $\frac{aa+ab}{c}$ leaves $\frac{aa+ab-2aa+ab}{c}$, or $\frac{-aa+2ab}{c}$; and $\overline{a-x}\sqrt{ax}$ from $\overline{a+x}\sqrt{ax}$ leaves $\overline{a+x-a+x}\sqrt{ax}$, or $2x\sqrt{ax}$, and so in others. But where Quantities consist of more Terms, the Operation may be managed as in Numbers, as in the following Examples:

12 x

$$\begin{array}{r}12x+7a\\ 7x+9a\\ \hline 5x-2a\end{array}\qquad \begin{array}{r}15bc+2\sqrt{ac}\\ -11bc+7\sqrt{ac}\\ \hline 26bc-5\sqrt{ac}\end{array}\qquad \begin{array}{l}5x^3+\frac{5}{7}x\\ 6x^2-\frac{3}{7}x\\ \hline 5x^3-6xx+\frac{8}{7}x\end{array}$$

$$\begin{array}{l}\frac{11ax}{b}-7\sqrt{3}+\frac{2}{5}\\ \frac{4ax}{b}-6\sqrt{3}-\frac{1}{5}\\ \hline \frac{7ax}{b}-\sqrt{3}+\frac{3}{5}\end{array}$$

Of MULTIPLICATION.

NUMBERS which arise or are produced by the Multiplication of any two Numbers, not greater than 9, are to be learnt and retain'd in the Memory: As that 5 into 7 makes 35, and that 8 by 9 make 72, &c. and then the Multiplication of greater Numbers is to be perform'd after the Rule of these Examples.

If 795 is to be multiply'd by 4, write 4 underneath, as you see here. Then say, 4 into 5 makes 20, whose last Figure, *viz.* 0, set under the 4, and reserve the former 2 for the next Operation. Say moreover, 4 into 9 makes 36, to which add the former 2, and there is made 38, whose latter Figure 8 write underneath as before, and reserve the former 3. Lastly, say, 4 into 7 makes 28, to which add the former 3 and there is made 31, which being also set underneath, you'll have the Number 3180, which comes out by multiplying the whole 795 by 4.

$$\begin{array}{r}795\\ 4\\ \hline 3180\end{array}$$

Moreover, if 9043 be to be multiply'd by 2305, write either of them, *viz.* 2305 under the other 9043 as before, and multiply the upper 9043 first by 5, after the Manner shewn, and there will come out 45215; then by 0, and there will come out 0000; thirdly, by 3, and there will come out 27129; lastly, by 2, and there will come out 18086. Then dispose these Numbers so coming out in a descending Series, or under one another, so that the last Figure of every lower Row shall stand one Place nearer to the left Hand than the last of the next superiour Row. Then add all these together,

$$\begin{array}{r}9043\\ 2305\\ \hline 45215\\ 0000\\ 27129\\ 18086\\ \hline 20844115\end{array}$$

together, and there will arise 20844115, the Number that is made by multiplying the whole 9043 by the whole 2305.

In the same manner *Decimals* are multiply'd by Integers or other Decimals, or both, as you may see in the following Examples:

72,4	50,18	3,0925
29	2,75	0,0132
6516	25090	78050
1448	35126	117075
2099,6	10036	39025
	137,9950	0,05151300

But Note, *in the Number coming out, or the Product, so many Figures must be cut off to the right Hand for Decimals, as there are Decimal Figures both in the Multiplyer and the Multiplicand.* And if by Chance there are not so many Figures in the Product, the deficient Places must be fill'd up to the left Hand with o's, as here in the third Example.

Simple Algebraick Terms are multiply'd by multiplying the Numbers into the Numbers, and the Species into the Species, and by making the Product Affirmative, *if both the Factors are Affirmative, or both Negative; and* Negative *if otherwise.*

Thus $2a$ into $3b$, or $-2a$ into $-3b$ make $6ab$, or $6ba$: for it is no matter in what order they are placed. Thus also $2a$ by $-3b$, or $-2a$ by $3b$ make $-6ab$. And thus, $2ac$ into $8bcc$ make $16abccc$, or $16abc^3$; and $7axx$ into $-12aaxx$ make $-84a^3x^4$; and $-16cy$ into $31ay^3$ make $-496acy^4$; and $-4z$ into $-3\sqrt{az}$ make $12z\sqrt{az}$. And so 3 into -4 make -12, and -3 into -4 make 12.

Fractions are multiply'd, by multiplying their Numerators by their Numerators, and their Denominators by their Denominators. Thus $\frac{2}{5}$ into $\frac{3}{7}$ make $\frac{6}{35}$; and $\frac{a}{b}$ into $\frac{c}{d}$ make $\frac{ac}{bd}$; and $2\frac{a}{b}$ into $3\frac{c}{d}$ make $6 \times \frac{a}{b} \times \frac{c}{d}$, or $6\frac{ac}{bd}$; and $\frac{3acy}{2bb}$ into $\frac{-7cyy}{4b^3}$ make $\frac{-21accy^3}{8b^5}$; and $\frac{-4z}{c}$ into

into $\frac{-3\sqrt{az}}{c}$ make $\frac{12z\sqrt{az}}{cc}$; and $\frac{a}{b}x$ into $\frac{c}{d}xx$ make $\frac{ac}{bd}x^3$. Also 3 into $\frac{2}{5}$ make $\frac{6}{5}$ as may appear, if 3 be reduced to the Form of a Fraction, *viz.* $\frac{3}{1}$ by making use of Unity for the Denominator. And thus $\frac{15aaz}{cc}$ into $2a$ make $\frac{30a^3z}{cc}$. Whence note by the way, that $\frac{ab}{c}$ and $\frac{a}{c}b$ are the same; as also $\frac{abx}{c}$, $\frac{ab}{c}x$, and $\frac{a}{c}bx$, also $\frac{\overline{a+b}\sqrt{cx}}{c}$ and $\frac{a+b}{a}\sqrt{cx}$; and so in others.

Radical Quantities of the same Denomination (that is, if they are both Square Roots, or both Cube Roots, or both Biquadratick Roots, &c.) are multiply'd by multiplying the Terms together under the same Radical Sign. Thus $\sqrt{3}$ into $\sqrt{5}$ make $\sqrt{15}$; and $\sqrt{ab}$ into $\sqrt{cd}$ make $\sqrt{abcd}$; and $\sqrt[3]{5ayy}$ into $\sqrt[3]{7ayz}$ make $\sqrt[3]{35aay^3z}$; and $\sqrt{\frac{a^3}{c}}$ into $\sqrt{\frac{abb}{c}}$ make $\sqrt{\frac{a^4bb}{cc}}$ that is * $\frac{aab}{c}$. And $2a\sqrt{az}$ into $3b\sqrt{az}$ make $6ab\sqrt{aazz}$, that is $6aabz$; and $\frac{3xx}{\sqrt{ac}}$ into $\frac{-2x}{\sqrt{ac}}$ make $\frac{-6x^3}{\sqrt{aacc}}$, that is $\frac{-6x^3}{ac}$; and $\frac{-4x\sqrt{ab}}{7a}$ into $\frac{-3dd\sqrt{5cx}}{10ee}$ make $\frac{12ddx\sqrt{5abcx}}{70aee}$.

Quantities that consist of several Parts, are multiply'd by multiplying all the Parts of the one into all the Parts of the other, as is shewn in the Multiplication of Numbers. Thus, $c-x$ into a make $ac-ax$, and $aa+2ac-bc$ into $a-b$ make $a^3+2aac-aab-3bac+bbc$. For $aa+2ac-bc$ into $-b$ make $-aab-2acb+bbc$, and into a make $a^3+2aac-abc$, the Sum whereof is

D a^3+

* *See the Chapter of* Notation.

$a^3 + 2aac - aab - 3abc + bbc$. A Specimen of this Sort of Multiplication, together with other like Examples, you have underneath :

$$\begin{array}{r}
aa + 2ac - bc \\
a - b \\
\hline
- aab - 2abc + bbc \\
a^3 + 2aac - abc \quad\quad\quad\; \\
\hline
a^3 + 2aac - aab - 3abc + bbc
\end{array}
\qquad\qquad
\begin{array}{r}
a + b \\
a + b \\
\hline
ab + bb \\
aa + ab \quad\;\; \\
\hline
aa + 2ab + bb
\end{array}$$

$$\begin{array}{r}
a + b \\
a - b \\
\hline
- ab - bb \\
aa + ab \quad\;\; \\
\hline
aa \quad * \; - bb
\end{array}
\qquad
\begin{array}{r}
yy + 2ay - \frac{1}{2}aa \\
yy - 2ay + aa \\
\hline
aayy + 2a^3y - \frac{1}{2}a^4 \\
- 2ay^3 - 4aayy + a^3y \quad\quad \\
y^4 + 2ay^3 - \frac{1}{2}aayy \quad\quad\quad\quad\quad\quad \\
\hline
y^4 \quad * \quad - 3\frac{1}{2}aayy + 3a^3y - \frac{1}{2}a^4
\end{array}$$

$$\begin{array}{c}
\frac{2ax}{c} - \sqrt{\frac{a^3}{c}} \\
3a + \sqrt{\frac{abb}{c}} \\
\hline
\frac{2ax}{c}\sqrt{\frac{abb}{c}} - \frac{aab}{c} \\
\frac{6aax}{c} - 3a\sqrt{\frac{a^3}{c}} \\
\hline
\frac{6aax}{c} - 3a\sqrt{\frac{a^3}{c}} + \frac{2ax}{c}\sqrt{\frac{aab}{c}} - \frac{aab}{c}.
\end{array}$$

Of

Of DIVISION.

DIVISION *is performed in Numbers, by seeking how many times the Divisor is contained in the Dividend, and as often subtracting, and writing so many Units in the Quotient; and by repeating that Operation upon Occasion, as often as the Divisor can be subtracted.*

Thus, to divide 63 by 7, seek how many times 7 is contained in 63, and there will come out precisely 9 for the Quotient; and consequently $\frac{63}{7}$ is equal to 9. Moreover, to divide 371 by 7, prefix the Divisor 7, and beginning at the first Figures of the Dividend, coming as near them as possible, say, how many times 7 is contained in 37, and you will find 5; then writing 5 in the Quotient, subtract 5 × 7, or 35, from 37, and there will remain 2, to which set the last Figure of the Dividend, *viz.* 1; and then 21 will be the remaining Part of the Dividend for the next Operation; say therefore as before, how many times 7 is contained in 21? and the Answer will be 3; wherefore writing 3 in the Quotient, take 3 × 7, or 21, from 21 and there will remain 0. Whence it is manifest, that 53 is precisely the Number, that arises from the Division of 371 by 7.

$$\begin{array}{l}
7)\ 371\ (53 \\
\quad\ \underline{35} \\
\quad\ \ \ 21 \\
\quad\ \ \ \underline{21} \\
\quad\ \ \ \ \ 0
\end{array}$$

And thus to divide 4798 by 23, first beginning with the initial Figures 47, say, how many times is 23 contained in 47? Answer 2; wherefore write 2 in the Quotient, and from 47 subtract 2 × 23, or 46, and there will remain 1, to which join the next Number of the Dividend, *viz.* 9, and you will have 19 to work upon next Say therefore, how many times is 23 contained in 19? Answer 0; wherefore write 0 in the Quotient; and from 19 subtract 0 × 23, or 0, and there remains 19, to which join the last Number 8, and you will have 198 to work upon next:

$$\begin{array}{l}
23)\ 4798\ (208,6086,\ \&c. \\
\quad\ \ \underline{46} \\
\quad\ \ \ 19 \\
\quad\ \ \ \underline{00} \\
\quad\ \ \ 198 \\
\quad\ \ \ \underline{184} \\
\quad\ \ \ \ \ 140 \\
\quad\ \ \ \ \ \underline{138} \\
\quad\ \ \ \ \ \ \ 20 \\
\quad\ \ \ \ \ \ \ \underline{00} \\
\quad\ \ \ \ \ \ \ 200 \\
\quad\ \ \ \ \ \ \ \underline{184} \\
\quad\ \ \ \ \ \ \ \ \ 160
\end{array}$$

D 2 Where-

Wherefore in the laſt Place ſay, how many times is 23 contained in 198 (which may be gueſs'd at from the firſt Figures of each, 2 and 19, by taking notice how many times 2 is contain'd in 19)? I anſwer 8; wherefore write 8 in the Quotient, and from 198 ſubtract 8 × 23, or 184, and there will remain 14 to be farther divided by 23; and ſo the Quotient will be $208\frac{14}{23}$. And if this Fraction is not liked, you may continue the Diviſion in Decimal Fractions as far as you pleaſe, by adding always a Cypher to the remaining Number. Thus to the Remainder 14 add 0, and it becomes 140. Then ſay, how many times 23 in 140? Anſwer 6; write therefore 6 in the Quotient; and from 140 ſubtract 6 × 23, or 138, and there will remain 2; to which ſet a Cypher (or 0) as before. And thus the Work being continued as far as you pleaſe, there will at length come out this Quotient, *viz.* 208,6086, &c.

After the ſame Manner the Decimal Fraction 3,5218 is divided by the Decimal Fraction 46,1, and there comes out 0,07639, &c. *Where note, that there muſt be ſo many Figures cut off in the Quotient, for Decimals, as there are more in the laſt Dividend than in the Diviſor*: As in this Example 5, becauſe there are 6 in the laſt Dividend, *viz.* 0,004370, and 1 in the Diviſor 46,1.

```
46,1) 3,5218 (0,07639
      322,7
      -----
       2948
       2766
       ----
        1820
        1383
        ----
         4370
```

We have here ſubjoin'd more Examples, for Clearneſs ſake, *viz.*

```
9043) 20844115 (2305.          72,4) 2099,6 (29
      18086                          1448
      -----                          ----
       27581                          6516
       27129                          6516
       -----                          ----
         45215                           0
         45215
         -----
             0
```

50,18)


```
50,18) 137,995 (2,75          0,0132) 0,051513 (3,9025.
       10036                            396
       -----                            ---
        37635                           1191
        35126                           1188
        -----                           ----
         25090                             330
         25090                             264
         -----                             ---
             0                             660
                                           660
                                           ---
                                             0
```

In Algebraick Terms Diviſion is performed by the Reſolution of what is compounded by Multiplication. Thus, ab divided by a gives for the Quotient b, $6ab$ divided by $2a$ gives $3b$; and divided by $-2a$ gives $-3b$. $-6ab$ divided by $2a$ gives $-3b$; and divided by $-2a$ gives $3b$. $16abc^3$ divided by $2ac$ gives $8bcc$. $-84a^3x^4$ divided by $-12aaxx$ gives $7axx$. Likewiſe $\frac{6}{35}$ divided by $\frac{2}{5}$ gives $\frac{3}{7}$. $\frac{ac}{bd}$ divided by $\frac{a}{b}$ gives $\frac{c}{d}$. $\frac{-21accy^2}{8b^5}$ divided by $\frac{3acy}{2bb}$ gives $\frac{-7cyy}{4b^3}$. $\frac{6}{5}$ divided by 3 gives $\frac{2}{5}$; and reciprocally $\frac{6}{5}$ divided by $\frac{2}{5}$ gives $\frac{3}{1}$, or 3. $\frac{30a^3z}{cc}$ divided by $2a$ gives $\frac{15aaz}{cc}$; and reciprocally divided by $\frac{15aaz}{cc}$ gives $2a$. Likewiſe $\sqrt{15}$ divided by $\sqrt{3}$ gives $\sqrt{5}$. $\sqrt{abcd}$ divided by $\sqrt{cd}$ gives $\sqrt{ab}$. $\sqrt{a^3c}$ by $\sqrt{ac}$ gives $\sqrt{aa}$, or a. $\sqrt[3]{35aay^3z}$ divided by $\sqrt[3]{5ayy}$ gives $\sqrt[3]{7ayz}$. $\sqrt{\frac{a^4bb}{cc}}$ divided by $\frac{a^3}{c}$ gives $\sqrt{\frac{abb}{c}}$. $\frac{12ddx\sqrt{5abcx}}{70aee}$ divided by $\frac{-3dd\sqrt{5cx}}{10ee}$ gives $\frac{-4x\sqrt{ab}}{7a}$. And ſo $\overline{a+b}\sqrt{ax}$ divided by $a+b$ gives $\sqrt{ax}$; and reciprocally divided by

$\sqrt{ax}$

$\sqrt{ax}$ gives $a+b$. And $\frac{a}{a+b}\sqrt{ax}$ divided by $\frac{1}{a+b}$ gives $a\sqrt{ax}$, or divided by a gives $\frac{1}{a+b}\sqrt{ax}$, or $\frac{\sqrt{ax}}{a+b}$; and reciprocally divided by $\frac{\sqrt{ax}}{a+b}$ gives a. But in Diviſions of this ſort you are to take care, that the Quantities divided by one another be of the ſame kind, *viz.* that Numbers be divided by Numbers, and Species by Species, Radical Quantities by Radical Quantities, Numerators of Fractions by Numerators, and Denominators by Denominators; alſo in Numerators, Denominators, and Radical Quantities, the Quantities of each kind muſt be divided by homogeneous ones, or Quantities of the ſame kind.

Now if the Quantity to be divided cannot be thus reſolved by the Diviſor propoſed, it is ſufficient, when both the Quantities are Integers, to write the Diviſor underneath, with a Line between them. Thus to divide ab by c, write $\frac{ab}{c}$; and to divide $\overline{a+b}\sqrt{cx}$ by a, write $\frac{\overline{a+b}\sqrt{cx}}{a}$, or $\frac{a+b}{a}\sqrt{cx}$. And ſo $\sqrt{ax-xx}$ divided by $\sqrt{cx}$ gives $\frac{\sqrt{ax-xx}}{\sqrt{cx}}$, or $\sqrt{\frac{ax-cx}{cx}}$. And $\overline{aa+ab}\sqrt{aa-2xx}$ divided by $\overline{a-b}\sqrt{aa-xx}$ gives $\frac{aa+ab}{a-b}\sqrt{\frac{ax-2xx}{aa-xx}}$. And $12\sqrt{5}$ divided by $4\sqrt{7}$ gives $3\sqrt{\frac{5}{7}}$.

But when theſe Quantities are Fractions, multiply the Numerator of the Dividend into the Denominator of the Diviſor, and the Denominator into the Numerator, and the *firſt Product* will be the Numerator, and the *latter* the Denominator of the Quotient. Thus to divide $\frac{a}{b}$ by $\frac{c}{d}$ write $\frac{ad}{bc}$, that is, multiply a by d and b by c. In like manner,

$\frac{3}{4}$

$\frac{3}{7}$ by $\frac{5}{4}$ gives $\frac{12}{35}$. And $\frac{3a}{4c}\sqrt{ax}$ divided by $\frac{2c}{5a}$ gives $\frac{15aa}{8cc}\sqrt{ax}$, and divided by $\frac{2c\sqrt{aa-xx}}{5a\sqrt{ax}}$ gives $\frac{15a^3x}{8cc\sqrt{aa-xx}}$. After the ſame manner, $\frac{ad}{b}$ divided by c (or by $\frac{c}{1}$) gives $\frac{ad}{bc}$. And c (or $\frac{c}{1}$) divided by $\frac{ad}{b}$ gives $\frac{bc}{ad}$. And $\frac{3}{7}$ divided by 5 gives $\frac{3}{35}$. And 3 divided by $\frac{5}{4}$ gives $\frac{12}{5}$. And $\frac{a+b}{c}\sqrt{cx}$ divided by a gives $\frac{a+b}{ac}\sqrt{cx}$. And $\overline{a+b}\sqrt{cx}$ divided by $\frac{a}{c}$ gives $\frac{ac+bc}{a}\sqrt{cx}$. And $2\sqrt{\frac{axx}{c}}$ divided by $3\sqrt{od}$ gives $\frac{2}{3}\sqrt{\frac{axx}{ccd}}$; and divided by $3\sqrt{\frac{cd}{x}}$ gives $\frac{2}{3}\sqrt{\frac{ax^3}{ccd}}$. And $\frac{1}{5}\sqrt{\frac{7}{11}}$ divided by $\frac{1}{2}\sqrt{\frac{3}{7}}$ gives $\frac{2}{5}\sqrt{\frac{49}{33}}$, and ſo in others.

A Quantity compounded of ſeveral Terms, is divided by dividing each of its Terms by the Diviſor. Thus $aa+3ax-xx$ divided by a gives $a+3x-\frac{xx}{a}$. But when the Diviſor conſiſts alſo of ſeveral Terms, the Divſion is perform'd as in Numbers. Thus to divide $a^3+2aac-aab-3abc+bbc$ by $a-b$, ſay, how many times is a contained in a^3, *viz.* the firſt Term of the Diviſor in the firſt Term of the Dividend? Anſwer aa. Wherefore write aa in the Quotient; and having ſubtracted $a-b$ multiply'd into aa, or a^3-aab from the Dividend, there will remain $2aac-3abc+bbc$ yet to be divided. Then ſay again, how many times a in $2aac$? Anſwer $2ac$. Wherefore write alſo $2ac$ in the Quotient, and having ſubtracted $a-b$ into $2ac$, or $2aac-2abc$ from the aforeſaid Remainder, there will yet remain $-abbc+bc$. Wherefore ſay again, how many times a in $-abc$? Anſwer $-bc$, and then

4 write

write $-bc$ in the Quotient; and having, in the laſt Place, ſubtracted $+a-b$ into $-bc$, *viz.* $-abc+bbc$ from the laſt Remainder, there will remain nothing; which ſhews that the Diviſion is at an end, and the Quotient coming out $aa+2ac-bc$.

But that theſe Operations may be duly reduced to the Form which we uſe in the Diviſion of Numbers, *the Terms both of the Dividend and the Diviſor muſt be diſpoſed in order, according to the Dimenſions of that Letter which is judged moſt proper for the Operation*; ſo that thoſe Terms may ſtand firſt, in which that Letter is of moſt Dimenſions, and thoſe in the ſecond Place whoſe Dimenſions are next higheſt; and ſo on to thoſe wherein that Letter is not at all involv'd, or into which it is not at all multiply'd, which ought to ſtand in the laſt Place. Thus in the Example we juſt now brought, if the Terms are diſpoſed according to the Dimenſions of the Letter a, the following Diagram will ſhew the Form of the Work, *viz.*

$$\begin{array}{l} a-b)\ a^3 \begin{smallmatrix}+2aac\\-aab\end{smallmatrix} -3abc+bbc\ (aa+2ac-bc \\ \quad\ \underline{a^3-aab} \\ \quad\ 0+2aac-3abc \\ \qquad\ \ \underline{2aac-2abc} \\ \qquad\qquad 0-abc+bbc \\ \qquad\qquad\ \underline{-\ abc+bbc} \\ \qquad\qquad\quad 0 \qquad 0 \end{array}$$

Where may be ſeen, that the Term a^3, or a of three Dimenſions, ſtands in the firſt Place of the Dividend, and the Terms $\begin{smallmatrix}2aac\\-aab\end{smallmatrix}$, in which a is of two Dimenſions, ſtand in the ſecond Place, and ſo on. The Dividend might alſo have been writ thus;

$$a^3 \begin{smallmatrix}+2c\\-b\end{smallmatrix} aa-3bca+bbc.$$

Where the Terms that ſtand in the ſecond Place are united, by collecting together the Factors of the Letter according to which the Order is made. And thus if the Terms were to be diſpoſed according to the Dimenſions of the Letter b, the Buſineſs muſt be performed as in the following Diagram, the Explication whereof we ſhall here ſubjoin.

$-b$

$$\begin{array}{l} -b+a)\ cbb \begin{smallmatrix}-3ac\\-aa\end{smallmatrix} b \begin{smallmatrix}+a^3\\+2aac\end{smallmatrix}\ (-cb \begin{smallmatrix}+2ac\\+aa\end{smallmatrix} \\ \qquad\quad\ \underline{cbb-acb} \\ \qquad\qquad 0 \begin{smallmatrix}-2ac\\-aa\end{smallmatrix} b \begin{smallmatrix}+a^3\\+2aac\end{smallmatrix} \\ \qquad\qquad\ \ \underline{\begin{smallmatrix}-2ac\\-aa\end{smallmatrix} b \begin{smallmatrix}+2aac\\+a^3\end{smallmatrix}} \\ \qquad\qquad\qquad 0 \qquad 0 \end{array}$$

Say, How many times is $-b$ contain'd in cbb? Anſwer $-cb$. Wherefore having writ $-cb$ in the Quotient, ſubtract $\overline{-b+a}\times -cb$, or $bbc-abc$, and there will remain in the ſecond Place $\begin{smallmatrix}-2ac\\-aa\end{smallmatrix} b$. To this Remainder add, if you pleaſe, the Quantities that ſtand in the laſt Place, *viz.* $\begin{smallmatrix}a^3\\2aac\end{smallmatrix}$, and ſay again, how many times is $-b$ contain'd in $\begin{smallmatrix}-2ac\\-aa\end{smallmatrix} b$? Anſwer $\begin{smallmatrix}+2ac\\+aa\end{smallmatrix}$. Theſe therefore being writ in the Quotient, ſubtract $-b+a$ multiply'd by $\begin{smallmatrix}+2ac\\+aa\end{smallmatrix}$ or $\begin{smallmatrix}-2ac\\-aa\end{smallmatrix} b \begin{smallmatrix}+2aac\\+a^3\end{smallmatrix}$, and there will remain nothing. Whence it is manifeſt, that the Diviſion is at an End, the Quotient coming out $-cb+2ac+aa$, as before.

And thus, if you were to divide $aay^4-aac^4+yyc^4+y^6-2y^4cc-a^6-2a^4cc-a^4yy$ by $yy-aa-cc$. I order or place the Quantities according to the Dimenſions of the Letter y, thus:

E $\qquad$ yy

$$yy\begin{matrix}-aa\\-cc\end{matrix}\Big)\,y^6\begin{matrix}+aa\\-2cc\end{matrix}y^4\begin{matrix}-a^4\\+c^4\end{matrix}yy\begin{matrix}-a^6\\-2a^4cc.\\-aac^4\end{matrix}$$

Then I divide as in the following Diagram. Here are added other Examples, in which you are to take Notice, that where the Dimensions of the Letter, which this Method of ordering ranges, don't always proceed in the same Arithmetical Progression, but sometimes interrupted, in the defective Places this Mark * is put.

$$\begin{array}{l}
yy\begin{matrix}-aa\\-cc\end{matrix}\Big)\,y^6\begin{matrix}+aa\\-2cc\end{matrix}y^4\begin{matrix}-a^4\\+c^4\end{matrix}yy\begin{matrix}-a^6\\-2a^4cc.\\-aac^4\end{matrix}\\
\hline
\quad y^6\begin{matrix}-aa\\-cc\end{matrix}y^4 \qquad \left(y^4\begin{matrix}+2aa\\-cc\end{matrix}y^2\begin{matrix}+a^4\\+aacc.\end{matrix}\right.\\
\quad o\begin{matrix}+2aa\\-cc\end{matrix}y^4\begin{matrix}-2a^4\\-aacc\\+c^4\end{matrix}y^2\\
\hline
\quad o \qquad \begin{matrix}+a^4\\+aacc\end{matrix}y^2\\
\qquad\quad \begin{matrix}+a^4\\+aacc\end{matrix}y^2\begin{matrix}-a^6\\-2a^4cc\\-aac^4\end{matrix}\\
\hline
\qquad\quad o \qquad o
\end{array}$$

$$\begin{array}{l}
a+b)\ aa * -bb\ (a-b\\
\quad aa+ab\\
\hline
\quad o-ab\\
\qquad -ab-bb\\
\hline
\qquad o \quad o
\end{array}$$

yy−2ay

$$\begin{array}{l}
yy-2ay+aa)\ y^4 * -3\tfrac{1}{2}aayy+3a^3y-\tfrac{1}{2}a^4\ (yy+2ay-\tfrac{1}{2}aa\\
\quad y^4-2ay^3+aayy\\
\hline
\quad o+2ay^3-4\tfrac{1}{2}aayy\\
\quad\ +2ay^3-4aayy+2a^3y\\
\hline
\qquad o\ -\tfrac{1}{2}aayy+a^3y\\
\qquad\ \ -\tfrac{1}{2}aayy+a^3y-\tfrac{1}{2}a^4\\
\hline
\qquad\quad o \quad o \quad o
\end{array}$$

$$\begin{array}{l}
aa+ab\surd 2+bb)\ a^4 * * * +b^4\ (aa-ab\surd 2+bb\\
\quad a^4+a^3b\surd 2+aabb\\
\hline
\quad -a^3b\surd 2-aabb\\
\quad -a^3b\surd 2-2aabb-ab^3\surd 2\\
\hline
\qquad +aabb+ab^3\surd 2\\
\qquad +aabb+ab^3\surd 1+b^4\\
\hline
\qquad\quad o \quad o \quad o
\end{array}$$

Some begin Division from the last Terms, but it comes to the same Thing, if, inverting the Order of the Terms, you begin from the first. There are also other Methods of dividing, but it is sufficient to know the most easy and commodious.

Of Extraction *of* Roots.

WHEN *the Square Root* of any Number is to be extracted, *it is first to be noted with Points in every other Place, beginning from Unity; then you are to write down such a Figure for the Quotient, or Root, whose Square shall be equal to, or nearest, less than the Figure or Figures to the first Point. And then subtracting that Square, the other Figures of the Root will be found one by one, by dividing the Remainder by the double of the Root as far as extracted, and each Time taking from that Remainder the* E 2 *Square*

Square of the Figure that last came out, and the Decuple of the aforesaid Divisor augmented by that Figure.

Thus to extract the Root out of 99856, first Point it after this Manner, 99856; then seek a Number whose Square shall equal the first Figure 9, *viz.* 3, and write it in the Quotient; and then having subtracted from 9, 3×3, or 9, there will remain 0; to which set down the Figures to the next Point, *viz.* 98 for the following Operation. Then taking no Notice of the last Figure 8, say, How many times is the Double of 3, or 6, contained in the first Figure 9? Answer 1; wherefore having writ 1 in the Quotient, subtract the Product of 1×61, or 61, from 98, and there will remain 37, to which connect the last Figures 56, and you will have the Number 3756, in which the Work is next to be carried on. Wherefore also neglecting the last Figure of this, *viz.* 6, say, How many times is the double of 31, or 62, contained in 375, (which is to be guessed at from the initial Figures 6 and 37, by taking Notice how many times 6 is contained in 37?) Answer 6; and writing 6 in the Quotient, subtract 6×626, or 3756, and there will remain 0; whence it appears that the Business is done; the Root coming out 316.

```
99856 (316
6
098
 61
 3756
 3756
    0
```

Otherwise with the Divisors set down it will stand thus:

```
   99856 (316
   9
 6)98
   61
62)3756
   3756
      0
```

And so in others.

And so if you were to extract the Root out of 22178791, first having pointed it, seek a Number, whose Square (if it cannot be exactly equalled) shall be the next less Square to 22, the Figures to the first Point, and you will find it to be 4. For 5×5, or 25, is greater than 22; and 4×4, or 16, less; wherefore 4 will be the first Figure of the Root. This therefore being writ in the Quotient, from 22 take the Square 4×4, or 16, and to the Remainder 6 adjoin moreover the next Figures 17, and you will have 617, from whose Division by the double of 4 you are to obtain the second Figure of the Root; *viz.* neglecting the last Figure 7, say, how many times is 8 contained in 61? Answer 7; wherefore write 7 in the Quotient, and from 617 take the Product of 7 into 87, or 609, and there will remain 8; to which join the two next Figures 87, and you will have 887, by the Division whereof by the double of 47, or 94, you are to obtain the third Figure; as say, How many times is 94 contain'd in 88? Answer 0; wherefore write 0 in the Quotient, and adjoin the two last Figures 91, and you will have 88791, by whose Division by the double of 470, or 940, you are to obtain the last Figure, *viz.* say, How many times 940 in 8879? Answer 9; wherefore write 9 in the Quotient, and you will have the Root 4709.

```
22178791 (4709,43637 &c.
16
 617
 609
   88791
   84681
    411000
    376736
     3426400
     2825649
      60075100
      56513196
       356190400
       282566169
        73624231
```

But since the Product 9×9409 or 84681 subtracted from 88791, leaves 4110, that is a Sign that the Number 4709 is not the Root of the Number 22178791 precisely, but that it is a little less. And in this Case, and in others like it, if you desire the Root should approach nearer, you must carry on the Operation in Decimals, by adding to the Remainder two Cyphers in each Operation. Thus the Remainder 4110 having two Cyphers added to it, becomes 411000; by the Division whereof by the double of 4709 or 9418, you will have the first Decimal Figure 4. Then having writ 4 in the Quotient, subtract 4×94184, or 376736 from 411000, and there will remain 34264. And so having added two more Cyphers, the Work may be carried

ried on at Pleasure, the Root at length coming out 4709,43637, &c.

But when the Root is carried on half-way, or above, the rest of the Figures may be obtained by Division alone. As in this Example, if you had a mind to extract the Root to nine Figures, after the five former 4709,4 are extracted, the four latter may be had, by dividing the Remainder by the double of 4709,4.

And after this manner, if the Root of 32976 was to be extracted to five Places in Numbers: After the Figures are pointed, write 1 in the Quotient, as being the Figure whose Square 1 × 1, or 1, is the greatest that is contained in 3 the Figure to the first Point; and having taken the Square of 1 from 3, there will remain 2; then having set the two next Figures, *viz*, 29 to it, (*viz.* to 2) seek how many times the double of 1, or 2, is contained in 22, and you will find indeed that it is contained more than ten times; but you are never to take your Divisor ten times, no, nor nine times in this Case; because the Product of 9 × 29, or 261, is greater than 229, from which it would be to be taken. Wherefore say only 8: And then having writ 8 in the Quotient, and subtracted 8 × 28, or 224, there will remain 5; and having set down to this the Figures 76, seek how many times the double of 18, or 36, is contained in 57, and you will find 1, and so write 1 in the Quotient; and having subtracted 1 × 361, or 361 from 576, there will remain 215. Lastly, to obtain the remaining Figures, divide this Number 215 by the Double of 181, or 362, and you will have the Figures 59, which being writ in the Quotient, you will have the Root 181,59.

```
     . . .
     32976 (181,59
     1
  2) 229
     224
 36) 576
     361
362) 215 (59, &c.
```

After the same way Roots are also extracted out of Decimal Numbers. Thus the Root of 329,76 is 18,159; and the Root of 3,2976 is 1,8152; and the Root of 0,032976 is 0,18159, and so on. But the Root of 3297,6 is 57,4247; and the Root of 32,976 is 5,74247. And thus ths Root of 9,9856 is 3,16. But the Root of 0,99856 is 0,999279, *&c.* as will appear from the following Diagrams.

3297,60


```
      3297,60 (57,4247 &c.
      25
  10) 797
      749
 114) 4860
      4576
1148) 284 (247
```

```
    9,9856 (3,16
    9
 6) 98
    61
62) 3756
    3756
    0
```

```
      0,998560 (0,999279 &c.
      81
  18) 1885
      1701
 198) 18460
      17901
1998)   559 (279
```

I will comprehend the Extraction of the Cubick Root, and of all others, under one general Rule, consulting rather the Ease of understanding the Praxis than the Expeditiousness of it, lest I should too much retard the Learner in Things that are of no frequent Use, *viz. every third Figure beginning from Unity is first of all to be pointed, if the Root to be extracted be a* Cubick one; *or every fifth, if it be a* Quadrato-Cubick, *or of the fifth Power,* &c. *and then such a Figure is to be writ in the Quotient, whose greatest Power* (i. e. *whose* Cube, *if it be a* Cubick *Power, or whose* Quadrato-Cube, *if it be the* fifth Power, *&c.*) *shall either be equal to the Figure or Figures before the first Point, or the next less; and then having subtracted that Power, the next Figure will be found by dividing the Remainder augmented by the next Figure of the Resolvend, by the next greatest Power of the Quotient, multiplied by the Index of the Power to be extracted, that is, by the* triple Square *of the Quotient, if the Root be a* Cubic one; *or by the* quintuple Biquadrate, *i. e.* five times the Biquadrate *if the Root be of* the fifth Power, *&c. And having again subtracted the greatest Power of the whole Quotient from the first Resolvend, the third Figure will be found by dividing that Remainder augmented by the next Figure of the Resolvend, by the next greatest Power of the whole Quotient multiplied by the Index of the Power to be extracted*; and so on *in infinitum.*

Thus

Thus to extract the Cube Root of 13312053, the Number is first to be pointed after this manner, *viz.* 13312053. Then you are to write in the Quotient the Figure 2, whose Cube 8 is the next less Cube to the Figures 13, [which is not a perfect Cube Number] or to the first Point; and having subtracted that Cube, there will remain 5; which being augmented by the next Figure of the Resolvend 3, and divided by the triple Square of the Quotient 2, by seeking how many times 3 × 4, or 12, is contained in 53, it gives 4 for the second Figure of the Quotient. But since the Cube of the Quotient 24, *viz.* 13824 would come out too great to be subtracted from the Figures 13312 that preceed the second Point, there must only 3 be writ in the Quotient. Then the Quotient 23 being in a separate Paper or Place multiplied by 23 gives the Square 529, which again multiplied by 23 gives the Cube 12167, and this taken from 13312, will leave 1145; which augmented by the next Figure of the Resolvend 0, and divided by the triple Square of the Quotient 23, *viz.* by seeking how many times 3 × 529, or 1587, is contained in 11450, it gives 7 for the third Figure of the Quotient. Then the Quotient 237, multiplied by 237, gives the Square 56169, which again multiplied by 237 gives the Cube 13312053, and this taken from the Resolvend leaves 0. Whence it is evident that the Root sought is 237.

```
                          13312053 (237
Subtract the Cube         8
                   12) rem. 53 (4 or 3
Subtract Cube      12167
         1587) rem. 11450 (7
Subtract Cube      13312053
                   Remains 0
```

And so to extract the Quadrato-Cubical Root of 36430820, it must be pointed over every fifth Figure, and the Figure 3, whose Quadrato-Cube [or fifth Power] 243 is the next less to 364, *viz.* to the first Point must be writ in the Quotient. Then the Quadrato-Cube 243 being subtracted from 364, there remains 121, which augmented by the next Figure of the Resolvend, *viz.* 3, and divided by five times the Biquadrate of the Quotient, *viz.* by seeking how many times 5 × 81, or 405, is contained in 1213, it gives 2 for the second Figure. That Quotient 32 being thrice multiplied by itself, makes the Biquadrate 1048576; and this again multiplied by 32, makes the Quadrato-Cube 33554432, which being subtracted from the Resolvend leaves 2876388. Therefore 32 is the Integer Part of the Root, but not the exact Root; wherefore, if you have a mind to prosecute the Work in Decimals, the Remainder, augmented by a Cypher, must be divided by five times the aforesaid Biquadrate of the Quotient, by seeking how many times 5 × 1048576, or 5242880, is contained in 2876388,0, and there will come out the third Figure, or the first Decimal 5. And so by subtracting the Quadrato-Cube of the Quotient 32,5 from the Resolvend, and dividing the Remainder by five times its Biquadrate, the fourth Figure may be obtained. And so on *in infinitum*.

```
          36430820 (32,5
          243
    405)  1213 (2
          33554432
5242880)  2876388,0 (5
```


When the Biquadratick Root is to be extracted, you may extract twice the Square Root, because $\sqrt{}^{4}$ is as much as $\sqrt{}^{2\times 2}$. *And when the Cubo-Cubick Root is to be extracted, you may first extract the Cube-Root, and then the Square-Root of that Cube-Root, because* $\sqrt{}^{6}$ is the same as $\sqrt{}^{2\times 3}$; *whence some have called these Roots not Cubo-Cubick ones, but Quadrato-Cubes.* And the same is to be observed in other Roots, whose Indexes are not prime Numbers.

The Extraction of Roots out of simple Algebraick Quantities, is evident, even from the Notation itself; as that $\sqrt{aa}$ is a, and that $\sqrt{aacc}$ is ac, and that $\sqrt{9aacc}$ is $3ac$, and that $\sqrt{49a^4xx}$ is $7aax$. And also that $\sqrt{\frac{a^4}{cc}}$, or $\frac{\sqrt{a^4}}{\sqrt{cc}}$ is $\frac{aa}{c}$, and that $\sqrt{\frac{a^4bb}{cc}}$ is $\frac{aab}{c}$, and that $\sqrt{\frac{9aazz}{25bb}}$ is $\frac{3az}{5b}$, and that $\sqrt{\frac{4}{9}}$ is $\frac{2}{3}$, and that $\sqrt[3]{\frac{8b^6}{27a^3}}$ is $\frac{2bb}{3a}$, and that $\sqrt[4]{aabb}$ is $\sqrt{ab}$. Moreover, that $b\sqrt{aacc}$, or b into $\sqrt{aacc}$, is b into ac or abc. And that $3c\sqrt{\frac{9aazz}{25bb}}$ is $3c \times \frac{3az}{5b}$, or $\frac{9acz}{5b}$. And that $\frac{a+3x}{c}\sqrt{\frac{4bbx^4}{81aa}}$ is $\frac{a+3x}{c} \times \frac{2bxx}{9a}$, or $\frac{2abxx+6bx^3}{9ac}$.

F I say

I say, these are all evident, because it will appear, at first Sight, that the proposed Quantities are produced by multiplying the Roots into themselves (as aa from $a\times a$, $aacc$ from ac into ac, $9aacc$ from $3ac$ into $3ac$, &c.) But when Quantities consist of several Terms, the Business is performed as in Numbers. Thus, to extract the Square Root out of $aa+2ab+bb$, in the first Place, write the Root of the first Term aa, viz. a in the Quotient, and having subtracted its Square $a\times a$, there will remain $2ab+bb$ to find the Remainder of the Root by. Say therefore, How many times is the double of the Quotient, or $2a$, contained in the first Term of the Remainder $2ab$? I answer b; therefore write b in the Quotient, and having subtracted the Product of b into $\overline{2a+b}$, or $2ab+bb$, there will remain nothing. Which shews that the Work is finished, the Root coming out $a+b$.

$$\begin{array}{l} aa+2ab+bb\ (a+b \\ \underline{aa} \\ 0 \\ \quad \underline{+2ab+bb} \\ \qquad 0 \qquad 0 \end{array}$$

And thus, to extract the Root out of $a^4+6a^3b+5a^2bb-12ab^3+4b^4$, first, set in the Quotient the Root of the first Term a^4, viz. aa, and having subtracted its Square $aa\times aa$, or a^4, there will remain $6a^3b+5aabb-12ab^3+4b^4$ to find the Remainder of the Root. Say therefore, How many times is $2aa$ contained in $6a^3b$? Answer $3ab$; wherefore write $3ab$ in the Quotient, and having subtracted the Product of $3ab$ into $2aa+3ab$, or $6a^3b+9aabb$, there will yet remain $-4aabb-12ab^3+4b^4$ to carry on the Work. Therefore say again, How many times is the Double of the Quotient, *viz.* $2aa+6ab$ contained in $-4aabb-12ab^3$, or, which is the same Thing, say, How many times is the Double of the first Term of the Quotient, or $2aa$, contained in the first Term of the Remainder $-4aabb$? Answer $-2bb$. Then having writ $-2bb$ in the Quotient, and subtracted the Product $-2bb$ into $2aa+6ab-2bb$, or $-4aabb-12ab^3+4b^4$, there will remain nothing. Whence it follows, That the Root is $aa+3ab-2bb$.

a^4+

$$\begin{array}{l} a^4+6a^3b+5aabb-12ab^3+4b^4\ (aa+3ab-2bb \\ \underline{a^4} \\ 0. \\ \quad \underline{+6a^3b+9aabb} \\ \qquad 0 \qquad -4aabb \\ \qquad\qquad \underline{-4aabb-12ab^3+4b^4} \\ \qquad\qquad\quad 0 \qquad\quad 0 \qquad 0 \end{array}$$

And thus the Root of the Quantity $xx-ax+\frac{1}{4}aa$ is $x-\frac{1}{2}a$; and the Root of the Quantity y^4+4y^3-8y+4 is $yy+2y-2$; and the Root of the Quantity $16a^4-24aaxx+9x^4+12bbxx-16aabb+4b^4$ is $3xx-4aa+2bb$, as may appear by the Diagrams underneath:

$$\begin{array}{l} xx-ax+\frac{1}{4}aa\ (x-\frac{1}{2}a \\ \underline{xx} \\ 0 \\ \quad \underline{-ax+\frac{1}{4}aa} \\ \qquad 0 \qquad 0 \end{array}$$

$$\begin{array}{l} 9x^4 \begin{matrix} -24aa \\ +12bb \end{matrix} x^2 \begin{matrix} +16a^4 \\ -16aab^2 \\ +4b^4 \end{matrix} \left(3x^2 \begin{matrix} -4aa \\ +2bb \end{matrix}\right. \\ \underline{9x^4} \\ 0 \\ \quad \underline{\begin{matrix} -24aa \\ +12bb \end{matrix} x^2 \begin{matrix} +16a^4 \\ -16a^2b^2 \\ +4b^4 \end{matrix}} \\ \qquad 0 \qquad\qquad 0 \end{array}$$

$$\begin{array}{l} y^4+4y^3 * -8y+4\ (yy+2y-2 \\ \underline{y^4} \\ 0 \\ \quad \underline{4y^3+4yy} \\ \quad 0 \quad -4yy \\ \qquad \underline{-yy-8y+4} \\ \qquad 0 \quad 0 \quad 0 \end{array}$$

F 2 If

If you would extract the Cube Root of $a^3 + 3aab + 3abb + b^3$, the Operation is performed thus:

$$\begin{array}{l} a^3 + 3aab + 3abb + b^3 \ (a+b \\ a^3 \\ 3aa)\ \overline{0 \ + 3aab} \ (b \\ \qquad \overline{a^3 + 3aab + 3abb + b^3} \\ \qquad 0 \quad 0 \quad 0 \quad 0 \end{array}$$

Extract first the Cube Root of the first Term a^3, viz. a, and set it down in the Quotient: Then, subtracting its Cube a^3, say, How many times is its triple Square, or $3aa$, contained in the next Term of the Remainder $3aab$? and there comes out b; wherefore write b in the Quotient, and subtracting the Cube of the Quotient, there will remain 0. Therefore $a+b$ is the Root.

After the same manner, if the Cube Root is to be extracted out of $z^6 + 6z^5 - 40z^3 + 96z - 64$, it will come out $zz + 2z - 4$. And so in higher Roots.

Of the REDUCTION *of* FRACTIONS *and* RADICAL *Quantities.*

THE Reduction of Fractions and Radical Quantities is of Use in the preceding Operations, and that either to the least Terms, or to the same Denomination.

Of the REDUCTION *of* FRACTIONS *to the least Terms.*

FRACTIONS *are reduced to the least Terms, by dividing the Numerators and Denominators by the greatest Divisor.* Thus the Fraction $\frac{aac}{bc}$ is reduced to a more Simple one $\frac{aa}{b}$ by dividing both aac and bc by c; and $\frac{203}{667}$ is reduced to a more Simple one $\frac{7}{23}$ by dividing both 203 and 667 by 29; and $\frac{203aac}{667bc}$ is reduced to $\frac{7aa}{23b}$ by dividing by $29c$. And so $\frac{6a^3 - 9acc}{6aa + 3ac}$ becomes $\frac{2aa - 3cc}{2a + c}$ by dividing by $3a$. And $\frac{a^3 - aab + abb - b^3}{aa - ab}$ becomes $\frac{aa + bb}{a}$ by dividing by $a - b$.

And after this Method, the Terms after Multiplication or Division, may be for the most part abridged. As if you were to multiply $\frac{2ab^3}{3ccd}$ by $\frac{9acc}{bdd}$, or divide it by $\frac{bdd}{9acc}$, there will come out $\frac{18aab^3cc}{3bccd^3}$, and by Reduction $\frac{6aabb}{d^3}$. But in these Cases, it is better to abbreviate the Terms before the Operation, by dividing those Terms first by the greatest common Divisor, which you would be obliged to do afterwards. Thus, in the Example before us, if I divide $2ab^3$ and bdd by the common Divisor b, and $3ccd$ and $9acc$ by the common Divisor $3cc$, there will come out the Fraction $\frac{2abb}{d}$ to be multiplied by $\frac{3a}{dd}$, or to be divided by $\frac{dd}{3a}$, there coming out $\frac{6aabb}{d^3}$ as above. And so $\frac{aa}{c}$ into $\frac{c}{b}$ becomes $\frac{aa}{1}$ into $\frac{1}{b}$, or $\frac{aa}{b}$. And $\frac{aa}{c}$ divided by $\frac{b}{c}$ becomes aa divided by b, or $\frac{aa}{b}$. And $\frac{a^3 - axx}{xx}$ into $\frac{cx}{aa + ax}$ becomes $\frac{a-x}{x}$, into $\frac{c}{1}$, or $\frac{ac}{x} - c$. And 28 divided by $\frac{7}{3}$ becomes 4 divided by $\frac{1}{3}$, or 12.

Of

Of the Invention of Diviſors.

TO this Head may be referred the Invention of Diviſors, by which any Quantity may be divided. *If it be a ſimple Quantity, divide it by its leaſt Diviſor, and the Quotient by its leaſt Diviſor, till there remain an indiviſible Quotient, and you will have all the prime Diviſors of that Quantity. Then multiply together each Pair of theſe Diviſors, each Ternary or three of them, each Quaternary,* &c. *and you will alſo have all the compounded Diviſors.* As, if all the Diviſors of the Number 60 are required, divide it by 2, and the Quotient 30 by 2, and the Quotient 15 by 3, and there will remain the indiviſible Quotient 5. Therefore the prime Diviſors are 1, 2, 2, 3, 5; thoſe compoſed of the Pairs 4, 6, 10, 15; of the Ternaries 12, 20, 30; and of all of them 60. Again, If all the Diviſors of the Quantity $21abb$ are deſired, divide it by 3, and the Quotient $7abb$ by 7, and the Quotient abb by a, and the Quotient bb by b, and there will remain the prime Quotient b. Therefore the prime Diviſors are 1, 3, 7, a, b, b; and thoſe compoſed of the Pairs 21, $3a$, $3b$, $7a$, $7b$, ab, bb; thoſe compoſed of the Ternaries $21a$, $21b$, $3ab$, $3bb$, $7ab$, $7bb$, abb; and thoſe of the Quaternaries $21ab$, $21bb$, $3abb$, $7abb$; that of the Quinaries $21abb$. After the ſame Way all the Diviſors of $2abb - 6aac$ are 1, 2, a, $bb - 3ac$, $2a$, $2bb - 6ac$, $abb - 3aac$, $2abb - 6aac$.

If after a Quantity is divided by all its ſimple Diviſors, it remains ſtill compounded, and you ſuſpect it has ſome compounded Diviſor, diſpoſe it according to the Dimenſions of any of the Letters in it, and in the Room of that Letter ſubſtitute ſucceſſively three or more Terms of this Arithmetical Progreſſion, viz. 3, 2, 1, 0, — 1, — 2, *and ſet the reſulting Terms together with all their Diviſors, by the correſponding Terms of the Progreſſion, ſetting down alſo the Signs of the Diviſors, both Affirmative and Negative. Then ſet alſo down the Arithmetical Progreſſions which run through the Diviſors of all the Numbers proceeding from the greater Terms to the leſs, in the Order that the Terms of the Progreſſion* 3, 2, 1, 0, — 1, — 2 *proceed, and whoſe Terms differ either by Unity, or by ſome Number which divides the higheſt Term of the Quantity propoſed. If any Progreſſion of this kind occurs, that Term of it which ſtands in the ſame Line with the Term* 0 *of the firſt Progreſſion, divided by the Difference of the Terms, and joined with its Sign to the aforeſaid Letter, will compoſe the Quantity by which you are to attempt the Diviſion.*

As if the Quantity be $x^3 - xx - 10x + 6$, by ſubſtituting, one by one, the Terms of this Progreſſion 1. 0. — 1, for x, there will ariſe the Numbers — 4, 6, + 14, which, together with all their Diviſors, I place right againſt the Terms of the Progreſſion 1. 0. — 1. after this Manner.

1	4	1. 2. 4.	+ 4.
0	6	1. 2. 3. 6	+ 3.
— 1	14	1. 2. 7. 14	+ 2.

Then, becauſe the higheſt Term x^3 is diviſible by no Number but Unity, I ſeek among the Diviſors a Progreſſion whoſe Terms differ by Unity, and (proceeding from the higheſt to the loweſt) decreaſe as the Terms of the lateral Progreſſion 1. 0. — 1. And I find only one Progreſſion of this Sort, *viz.* 4. 3. 2. whoſe Term therefore + 3 I chuſe, which ſtands in the ſame Line with the Term 0 of the firſt Progreſſion 1. 0. — 1. and I attemp the Diviſion by $x + 3$, and find it ſucceeds, there coming out $xx - 4x + 2$.

Again, if the Quantity be $6y^4 - y^3 - 21yy + 3y + 20$, for y I ſubſtitute ſucceſſively 2. 1. 0. — 1. — 2. and the reſulting Numbers 30. 7. 20. 3. 34. with all their Diviſors, I place by them as follows.

2	30	1. 2. 3. 5. 6. 10. 15. 30	+ 10.
1	7	1. 7.	+ 7.
0	20	1. 2. 4. 5. 10. 20	+ 4.
— 1	3	1. 3.	+ 1.
— 2	34	1. 2. 17. 34	— 2.

And among the Diviſors I perceive there is this decreaſing Arithmetical Progreſſion + 10. + 7. + 4. + 1. — 2. The Difference of the Terms of this Progreſſion, *viz.* 3, divides the higheſt Term of the Quantity $6y^4$. Wherefore I adjoin to the Letter y the Term + 4, which ſtands in the Row oppoſite to the Term 0, divided by the Difference of the Terms, *viz.* 3, and I attempt the Diviſion by $y + \frac{4}{3}$, or, which is the ſame Thing, by $3y + 4$, and the Buſineſs ſucceeds, there coming out $2y^3 - 3yy - 3y + 5$.

And ſo, if the Quantity be $24a^5 - 50a^4 + 49a^3 - 140a^2 + 64a + 30$; the Operation will be as follows.

2 | 24

2	42	1.2.3.6.7.14.21.42	+3.+3.+ 7.
1	23	1.23.	+1.—1.+ 1.
0	30	1.2.3.5.6.10.15.30.	—1.—5.— 5.
—1	297	1.3.9.11.27.33.99.297	—3.—9.—11.

Here are three Progreſſions, whoſe Terms —1. —5. —5, divided by the Differences of the Terms 2, 4, 6, give three Diviſors to be tried $a-\frac{1}{2}$, $a-\frac{5}{4}$, and $a-\frac{5}{6}$. And the Diviſion by the laſt Diviſor $a-\frac{5}{6}$, or $6a-5$, ſucceeds, there coming out $4a^4-5a^3+4aa-20a-6$.

If no Diviſor occur by this Method, or none that divides the Quantity propoſed, we are to conclude, that that Quantity does not admit a Diviſor of one Dimenſion. But perhaps it may, if it be a Quantity of more than three Dimenſions, admit a Diviſor of two Dimenſions. And if ſo, that Diviſor will be found by this Method. *Subſtitute in that Quantity for the Letter or Species as before, four or more Terms of this Progreſſion* 3, 2, 1, 0. — 1. — 2. — 3. *Let all the Diviſors of the Numbers that reſult be ſingly added to and ſubtracted from the Squares of the correſpondent Terms of that Progreſſion, multiplied into ſome Numeral Diviſor of the higheſt Term of the Quantity propoſed, and right againſt the Progreſſion let be placed the Sums and Differences. Then note all the collateral Progreſſions which run through thoſe Sums and Differences. Then ſuppoſe* ∓ C *to be a Term of ſuch like Progreſſions that ſtands againſt the Term* 0 *of the firſt Progreſſion, and* ∓ B *the Difference which ariſes by ſubducting* ∓ C *from the next ſuperior Term which ſtands againſt the Term* 1 *of the firſt Progreſſion, and* A *to be the aforeſaid Numeral Diviſor of the higheſt Term, and* l *to be the Letter which is the propoſed Quantity, then* $All \pm Bl \pm C$ *will be the Diviſor to be tried.*

Thus ſuppoſe the propoſed Quantity to be $x^4-x^3-5xx+12x-6$, for x I write ſucceſſively 3, 2, 1, 0. —1, —2, and the Numbers that come out 39. 6. 1. —6. —21. —26. I diſpoſe or place together with their Diviſors in the ſame Line with them, and I add and ſubtract the Diviſors to and from the Squares of the Terms of the firſt Progreſſion, multiplied by the Numeral Diviſor of the Term x^4, which is Unity, *viz.* to and from the Terms 9. 4. 1. 0. 1. 4, and I diſpoſe likewiſe the Sums and Differences on the Side. Then I write, as follows, the Progreſſions which occur among the ſame. Then I make uſe of the Terms of theſe Progreſſions 2 and

2 and — 3, which ſtands oppoſite to the Term 0 in that Progreſſion which is in the firſt Column, ſucceſſively for ∓ C,

3	39	1.3.13.39	9	—30.—4.6.8.10.12.22.48	—4. 6
2	6	1.2. 3. 6	4	—2.1.2.3.5.6.7.10.	—2. 3
1	1	1.	1	0. 2.	0. 0
0	6	1.2. 3. 6	0	—6.—3.—2.—1.1.2.3.6	2.—3
—1	21	1.3. 7.21	1	—20.—6.—2.0.2.4.8.22	4.—6
—2	26	1.2.13.26	4	—22.9.2.3.5.6.17.30	6.—9

and I make uſe of the Differences that ariſe by ſubtracting theſe Terms from the ſuperior Terms 0 and 0, *viz.* — 2 and + 3 reſpectively for ∓ B. Alſo Unity for A; and x for l. And ſo in the room of $All \pm Bl \pm C$, I have theſe two Diviſors to try, viz. $xx+2x-2$, and $xx-3x+3$, by both of which the Buſineſs ſucceeds.

Again, if the Quantity $3y^5-6y^4+y^3-8yy-14y+14$ be propoſed, the Operation will be as follows. Firſt, I attempt the Buſineſs by adding and ſubtracting the Diviſors to and from the Squares of the Terms of the Progreſſion 2. 1. 0. — 1, making uſe of 1 for A, but the Buſineſs does not

3	170		27		—7. 17
2	38	1.2.19.38	12	—16.—7.10.11.13.14.31.50.	—7.—11
1	10	1.2. 5.10	3	—7.2.1.2.4.5.8.13.	—7. 5
0	14	1.2. 7.14	0	—14.—7.—2.—1.1.2.7.14.	—7. —1
—1	10	1.2. 5.10	3	—7.—2.1.2.4.5.8.13.	—7. —7
—2	190		12		—7.—13

ſucceed. Wherefore in the room of A, I make uſe of 3, the other numeral Diviſor of the higheſt Term $3y^5$; and theſe Squares being multiplied by 3, I add and ſubtract the Diviſors to and from the Products, *viz.* 12. 3. 0. 3, and I find theſe two Progreſſions in the reſulting Terms, — 7. — 7. — 7. — 7, and 11. 5. — 1. — 7. For Expedition ſake, I neglected the Diviſors of the outermoſt Terms 170 and 190. Wherefore, the Progreſſions being continued upwards and downwards, I take the next Terms, *viz.* — 7 and 17 at the Top, and — 7 and — 13 at Bottom, and I try if theſe being ſubducted from the Numbers 27 and 12, which ſtand againſt them in the 4th Column, their Differences divide thoſe Numbers 170 and 190, which ſtand againſt them in the ſecond Column. And the Difference between 27 and — 7, that is, 34, divides 170; and the Difference of 12 and — 7, that is, 19, divides 190.

G Alſo

Alſo the Difference between 27 and 17, that is, 10, divides 170; but the Difference between 12 and — 13, that is, 25, does not divide 190. Wherefore I reject the latter Progreſſion. According to the former, ∓ C is — 7, and ∓ B is nothing; the Terms of the Progreſſion having no Difference. Wherefore the Diviſor to be tried $All + Bl + C$ will be $3yy + 7$. And the Diviſion ſucceeds, there coming out $y^3 - 2yy - 2y + 2$.

If after this way, there can be found no Diviſor which ſucceeds, we are to conclude, that the propoſed Quantity will not admit of a Diviſor of two Dimenſions. The ſame Method may be extended to the Invention of Diviſors of more Dimenſions, by ſeeking in the aforeſaid Sums and Differences not Arithmetical Progreſſions, but ſome others, the firſt, ſecond, and third, &c. Differences of whoſe Terms are in Arithmetical Progreſſion: But the Learner ought not to be detained about them.

Where there are two Letters in the propoſed Quantity, and all its Terms aſcend to equally high Dimenſions, put Unity for one of thoſe Letters; then, by the preceding Rules, ſeek a Diviſor, and compleat the deficient Dimenſions of this Diviſor, by reſtoring that Letter for Unity.

As if the Quantity be $6y^4 - cy^3 - 21ccyy + 3c^3y + 20c^4$, where all the Terms are of four Dimenſions; for c I put 1, and the Quantity becomes $6y^4 - y^3 - 21yy + 3y + 20$, whoſe Diviſor, as above, is $3y + 4$; and having compleated the deficient Dimenſion of the laſt Term by a correſpondent Dimenſion of c, you have $3y + 4c$ for the Diviſor ſought. So, if the Quantity be $x^4 - bx^3 - 5bbxx + 12b^3x - 6b^4$; putting 1 for b, and having found $xx + 2x - 2$ the Diviſor of the reſulting Quantity $x^4 - x^3 - 5xx + 12x - 6$, I compleat its deficient Dimenſions by reſpective Dimenſions of b, and ſo I have $xx + 2bx + 2bb$ the Diviſor ſought.

When there are three or more Letters in the Quantity propoſed, and all its Terms aſcend to the ſame Dimenſions, the Diviſor may be found by the precedent Rules; but more expeditiouſly after this way: *Seek all the Diviſors of all the Terms in which ſome one of the Letters is not, and alſo of all the Terms in which ſome other of the Letters is not; as alſo of all the Terms in which a third, fourth, and fifth Letter is not, if there are ſo many Letters; and ſo run over all the Letters: And in the ſame Line with thoſe Letters place the Diviſors reſpectively. Then ſee, if in any Series of Diviſors going through all the Letters, all the Parts involving only one Letter can be as often found as there are Letters (excepting only one) in the Quantity propoſed;* and likewiſe if the Parts involving two Letters *may be found as often as there are Letters (excepting two) in the Quantity propoſed. If ſo; all thoſe Parts taken together under their proper Signs will be the Diviſor ſought.*

As if there were propoſed the Quantity $12x^3 - 14bxx + 9cxx - 12bbx - 6bcx + 8ccx + 8b^3 - 12bbc - 4bcc + 6c^3$; the Diviſors of one Dimenſion of the Terms $8b^3 - 12bbc - 4bcc + 6c^3$, in which x is not, will be found by the preceding Rules to be $2b - 3c$ and $4b - 6c$; and of the Terms $12x^3 + 9cxx + 8ccx + 6c^3$, in which b is not, there will be only one Diviſor $4x + 3c$; and of the Terms $12x^3 - 14bxx - 12bbx + 8b^3$, in which there is not c, there will be the Diviſors $2x - b$ and $4x - 2b$. I diſpoſe theſe Diviſors in the ſame Lines with the Letters x, b, c, as you here ſee;

x	$2b - 3c.\ 4b - 6c.$
b	$4x + 3c.$
c	$2x - b.\ 4x - 2b.$

Since there are three Letters, and each of the Parts of the Diviſors only involve one of the Letters, thoſe Parts ought to be found twice in the Series of Diviſors. But the Parts $4b$, $6c$, $2x$, b of the Diviſors $4b - 6c$ and $2x - b$, only occur once, and are not found any where out of thoſe Diviſors whereof they are Parts. Wherefore I neglect thoſe Diviſors. There remain only three Diviſors $2b - 3c$, $4x + 3c$ and $4x - 2b$. Theſe are in the Series going through all the Letters x, b, c, and each of the Parts $2b$, $3c$, $4x$, are found in them twice, as ought to be, and that with the ſame Signs, provided the Signs of the Diviſor $2b - 3c$ be changed, and in its Place you write $-2b + 3c$. For you may change the Signs of any Diviſor. I take therefore all the Parts of theſe, viz. $2b$, $3c$, $4x$, once apiece under their proper Signs, and the Aggregate $-2b + 3c + 4x$ will be the Diviſor which was to be found. For if by this you divide the propoſed Quantity, there will come out $3xx - 2bx + 2cc - 4bb$.

G 2 Again

Again, if the Quantity be $12x^5 - 10ax^4 - 9bx^4 - 26a^2x^3 + 12abx^3 + 6bbx^3 + 24a^3xx - 8aabxx - 8abbxx - 24b^3xx - 4a^3bx + 6aabbx - 12ab^3x + 18b^4x + 12a^4b + 32aab^3 - 12b^5$; I place the Diviſors of the Terms in which x is not, by x; and thoſe Terms in which a is not, by a; and thoſe in which b is not, by b, as you here ſee. Then I perceive that all thoſe that

x	$b.\ 2b.\ 4b.\ aa+3bb.\ 2aa+6bb.\ 4aa+12bb.$ $bb-3aa.\ 2bb-6aa.\ 4bb-12aa.$
a	$4xx-3bx+2bb.\ 12xx-9bx+6bb.$
b	$x.\ 2x.\ 3x-4a.\ 6x-8a.\ 3xx-4ax.\ 6xx-8ax.$ $2xx+ax-3aa.\ 4xx+2ax-6aa.$

are but of one Dimenſion are to be rejected, becauſe the Simple ones, $b.\ 2b.\ 4b.\ x.\ 2x$, and the Parts of the compounded ones, $3x-4a.\ 6x.-8a$, are found but once in all the Diviſors; but there are three Letters in the propoſed Quantity, and thoſe Parts involve but one, and ſo ought to be found twice. In like manner, the Diviſors of two Dimenſions, $aa+3bb.\ 2aa+6bb.\ 4aa+12bb.\ bb-3aa.$ and $4bb-12aa$ I reject, becauſe their Parts $aa.\ 2aa.\ 4aa.\ bb.$ and $4bb.$ involving only one Letter a or b, are not found more than once. But the Parts $2bb$ and $6aa$ of the Diviſor $2bb-6aa$, which is the only remaining one in the Line with x, and which likewiſe involve only one Letter, are found again or twice, *viz.* the Part $2bb$ in the Diviſor $4xx-3bx+2bb$, and the Part $6aa$ in the Diviſor $4xx+2ax-6aa$. Moreover, theſe three Diviſors are in a Series ſtanding in the ſame Lines with the three Letters x, a, b; and all their Parts $2bb$, $6aa$, $4xx$, which involve only one Letter, are found twice in them, and that under their proper Signs; but the Parts $3bx$, $2ax$, which involve two Letters, occur but once in them. Wherefore, all the divers Parts of theſe three Diviſors, $2bb$, $6aa$, $4xx$, $3bx$, $2ax$, connected under their proper Signs, will make the Diviſors ſought, *viz.* $2bb-6aa+4xx-3bx+2ax$. I therefore divide the Quantity propoſed by this Diviſor, and there ariſes $3x^3-4axx-2aab-6b^3$.

If all the Terms of any Quantity are not equally high, the deficient Dimenſions muſt be filled up by the Dimenſions of any aſſumed Letter; then having found a Diviſor by the precedent Rules, the aſſumed Letter is to be blotted out.

As

As if the Quantity be $12x^3 - 14bxx + 9xx - 12bbx - 6bx + 8x + 8b^3 - 12b^2 - 4b + 6$; aſſume any Letter, as c, and fill up the Dimenſions of the Quantity propoſed by its Dimenſions, after this Manner, $12x^3 - 14bxx + 9cxx - 12bbx - 6bcx + 8ccx + 8b^3 - 12bbc - 4bcc + 6c^3$. Then having found out its Diviſor $4x - 2b + 3c$, blot out c; and you will have the Diviſor required, *viz.* $4x - 2b + 3$.

Sometimes Diviſors may be found more eaſily than by theſe Rules. As if ſome Letter in the propoſed Quantity be of only one Dimenſion; you may ſeek for the greateſt common Diviſor of the Terms in which that Letter is found, and of the remaining Terms in which it is not found; for that Diviſor will divide the whole. And if there is no ſuch common Diviſor, there will be no Diviſor of the whole. For Example, if there be propoſed the Quantity $x^4 - 3ax^3 - 8aaxx + 18a^3x + cx^3 - acxx - 8aacx + 6a^3c - 8a^4$; let there be ſought the common Diviſor of the Terms $+cx^3 - acxx - 8aacx + 6a^3c$, in which c is only of one Dimenſion, and of the remaining Terms $x^4 - 3ax^3 - 8aaxx + 18a^3x - 8a^4$, and that Diviſor, *viz.* $xx + 2ax - 2aa$, will divide the whole Quantity.

But the greateſt common Diviſor of two Numbers, if it is not known, or does not appear at firſt Sight, it is found by a perpetual Subtraction of the leſs from the greater, and of the Remainder from the laſt Quantity ſubtracted. For that will be the ſought Diviſor, which at length leaves nothing. Thus, to find the greateſt common Diviſor of the Numbers 203 and 667, ſubtract thrice 203 from 667, and the Remainder 58 thrice from 203, and the Remainder 29 twice from 58, and there will remain nothing; which ſhews, that 29 is the Diviſor ſought.

After the ſame Manner the common Diviſor in Species, when it is compounded, is found, by ſubtracting either Quantity, or its Multiple, from the other; provided both thoſe Quantities and the Remainder be ranged according to the Dimenſions of any Letter, as is ſhewn in Diviſion, and be each Time managed by dividing them by all their Diviſors, which are either Simple, or divide each of its Terms as if it were a Simple one. Thus, to find the greateſt common Diviſor of the Numerator and Denominator of this Fraction

2 x^4

$\frac{x^4 - 3ax^3 - 8aaxx + 18a^2x - 8a^4}{x^3 - axx - 8aax + 6a^3}$, multiply the Denominator by x, that its first Term may become the same with the first Term of the Numerator. Then subtract it, and there will remain $-2ax^3 + 12a^3x - 8a^4$, which being rightly ordered by dividing by $-2a$, it becomes $x^3 - 6a^2x + 4a^3$. Subtract this from the Denominator, and there will remain $-axx - 2aax + 2a^3$; which again divided by $-a$, becomes $xx + 2ax - 2aa$. Multiply this by x, that its first Term may become the same with the first Term of the last subtracted Quantity $x^3 - 6aax + 4a^3$, from which it is to be likewise subtracted, and there will remain $-2axx - 4aax + 4a^3$, which divided by $-2a$, becomes also $xx + 2ax - 2aa$. And since this is the same with the former Remainder, and consequently being subtracted from it, will leave nothing, it will be the Divisor sought; by which the proposed Fraction, by dividing both the Numerator and Denominator by it, may be reduced to a more Simple one, *viz.* to $\frac{xx - 5ax + 4aa}{x - 3a}$.

And so, if you have the Fraction

$$\frac{6a^5 + 15a^4b - 4a^3cc - 10aabcc}{9a^3b - 27aabc - 6abcc + 18bc^3},$$

its Terms must be first abbreviated, by dividing the Numerator by aa, and the Denominator by $3b$: Then subtracting twice $3a^3 - 9aac - 2acc + 6c^3$ from $6a^3 + 15aab - 4acc - 10bcc$, there will remain $\begin{matrix} 15b \\ +18c \end{matrix} aa \begin{matrix} -10bcc \\ -12c^3 \end{matrix}$. Which being ordered, by dividing each Term by $5b + 6c$ after the same Way as if $5b + 6c$ was a simple Quantity, it becomes $3aa - 2cc$. This being multiplied by a, subtract it from $3a^3 - 9aac - 2acc + 6c^3$, and there will remain $-9aac + 6c^3$, which being again ordered by a Division by $-3c$, becomes also $3aa - 2cc$, as before. Wherefore $3aa - 2cc$ is the Divisor sought. Which being found, divide by it the Parts of the proposed Fraction, and you will have $\frac{2a^3 + 5aab}{3ab - 9bc}$.

Now,

Now, if a common Divisor cannot be found after this Way, it is certain there is none at all; unless, perhaps, it may arise out of the Terms that abbreviate the Numerator and Denominator of the Fraction. As, if you have the Fraction $\frac{aadd - ccdd - aacc + c^4}{4aad - 4acd - 2acc + 2c^3}$, and so dispose its Terms, according to the Dimensions of the Letter d, that the Numerator may become $\begin{matrix} aa \\ -cc \end{matrix} dd \begin{matrix} -aacc \\ +c^4 \end{matrix}$, and the Denominator $\begin{matrix} 4aa \\ -4ac \end{matrix} d \begin{matrix} -2acc \\ +2c^3 \end{matrix}$. These must first be abbreviated by dividing each Term of the Numerator by $aa - cc$, and each of the Denominator by $2a - 2c$, just as if $aa - cc$ and $2a - 2c$ were simple Quantities. And so, in Room of the Numerator there will come out $dd - cc$, and in Room of the Denominator $2ad - cc$, from which, thus prepared, no common Divisor can be obtained. But, out of the Terms $aa - cc$ and $2a - 2c$, by which both the Numerator and Denominator are abbreviated, there comes out a Divisor, *viz.* $a - c$, by which the Fraction may be reduced to this, *viz.* $\frac{add + cdd - acc - c^3}{4ad - 2cc}$. Now, if neither the Terms $aa - cc$ and $2a - 2c$ had not had a common Divisor, the proposed Fraction would have been irreducible.

And this is a general Method of finding common Divisors: *But most commonly they are more expeditiously found by seeking all the prime Divisors of either of the Quantities, that is, such as cannot be divided by others, and then by trying if any of them will divide the other without a Remainder.* Thus, to reduce $\frac{a^3 - aab + abb - b^3}{aa - ab}$ to the least Terms, you must find the Divisors of the Quantity $aa - ab$, viz. a and $a - b$; then you must try whether either a, or $a - b$, will also divide $a^3 - aab + abb - b^3$ without any Remainder.

Of

Of the REDUCTION *of* FRACTIONS *to a common Denominator.*

FRACTIONS *are reduced to a common Denominator by multiplying the Terms of each by the Denominator of the other.*

Thus, having $\frac{a}{b}$ and $\frac{c}{d}$ multiply the Terms of one $\frac{a}{b}$ by d, and also the Terms of the other $\frac{c}{d}$ by b, and they will become $\frac{ad}{bd}$ and $\frac{bc}{bd}$, whereof the common Denominator is bd. And thus a and $\frac{ab}{c}$, or $\frac{a}{1}$ and $\frac{ab}{c}$ become $\frac{ac}{c}$ and $\frac{ab}{c}$. But where the Denominators have a common Divisor, it is sufficient to multiply them alternately by the Quotients. Thus the Fraction $\frac{a^3}{bc}$ and $\frac{a^3}{bd}$ are reduced to these $\frac{a^3 d}{bcd}$, and $\frac{a^3 c}{bcd}$, by multiplying alternately by the Quotients c and d, arising by the Division of the Denominators by the common Divisor b.

This Reduction is mostly of Use in the Addition and Subtraction of Fractions, which, if they have different Denominators, must be first reduced to the same Denominator before they can be added. Thus $\frac{a}{b} + \frac{c}{d}$ by Reduction becomes $\frac{ad}{bd} + \frac{bc}{bd}$, or $\frac{ad+bc}{bd}$, and $a + \frac{ab}{c}$ becomes $\frac{ac+ab}{c}$. And $\frac{a^3}{bc} - \frac{a^3}{bd}$ becomes $\frac{a^3 d - a^3 c}{bcd}$, or $\frac{d-c}{bcd}a^3$. And $\frac{c^4+x^4}{cc-xx} - cc - xx$ becomes $\frac{2x^4}{cc-xx}$. And so $\frac{2}{3} + \frac{5}{7}$ becomes $\frac{14}{21} + \frac{15}{21}$, or $\frac{14+15}{21}$, that is, $\frac{29}{21}$. And $\frac{11}{6} - \frac{3}{4}$ becomes $\frac{22}{12} - \frac{9}{12}$, or $\frac{13}{12}$. And $\frac{3}{4} - \frac{5}{12}$ becomes $\frac{9}{12} - \frac{5}{12}$, or $\frac{4}{12}$, that is $\frac{1}{3}$. And $3\frac{4}{7}$, or $\frac{3}{1} + \frac{4}{7}$ becomes $\frac{21}{7} + \frac{4}{7}$, or $\frac{25}{7}$. And $25\frac{1}{2}$ becomes $\frac{51}{2}$.

Where there are more Fractions than two, they are to be added gradually. Thus, having $\frac{aa}{x} - a + \frac{2xx}{3a} - \frac{ax}{a-x}$; from $\frac{aa}{x}$, take a, and there will remain $\frac{aa-ax}{x}$, to this add $\frac{2xx}{3a}$, and there will come out $\frac{3a^3 - 3aax + 2x^3}{3ax}$, from whence, lastly, take away $\frac{ax}{a-x}$, and there will remain $\frac{3a^4 - 6a^3 x + 2ax^3 - 2x^4}{3aax - 3axx}$. And so if you have $3\frac{4}{7} - \frac{2}{3}$, first, you are to find the Aggregate of $3\frac{4}{7}$, *viz.* $\frac{25}{7}$, and then to take from it $\frac{2}{3}$ and there will remain $\frac{61}{21}$.

Of the REDUCTION *of* RADICAL *Quantities to their least Terms.*

A *Radical Quantity, where the Root of the whole cannot be extracted, is reduced by extracting the Root of some Divisor of it.*

Thus $\sqrt{aabc}$, by extracting the Root of the Divisor aa, becomes $a\sqrt{bc}$. And $\sqrt{48}$, by extracting the Root of the Divisor 16, becomes $4\sqrt{3}$. And $\sqrt{48aabc}$, by extracting the Root of the Divisor $16aa$, becomes $4a\sqrt{3bc}$. And $\sqrt{\frac{a^3 b - 4aabb + 4ab^3}{cc}}$, by extracting the Root of its Divisor $\frac{aa - 4ab + 4bb}{cc}$, becomes $\frac{a-2b}{c}\sqrt{ab}$. And $\sqrt{\frac{aaoomm}{ppzz} + \frac{4aammm}{pzz}}$, by extracting the Root of the

H Divisor

Diviſor $\frac{aamm}{ppzz}$, becomes $\frac{am}{pz}\sqrt{oo+4mp}$. And $6\sqrt{\frac{75}{98}}$, by extracting the Root of the Diviſor $\frac{25}{49}$, becomes $\frac{30}{7}\sqrt{\frac{3}{2}}$, or $\frac{30}{7}\sqrt{\frac{6}{4}}$, and by farther extracting the Root of the Denominator, it becomes $\frac{15}{7}\sqrt{6}$. And ſo $a\sqrt{\frac{b}{a}}$, or $a\sqrt{\frac{ab}{aa}}$, by extracting the Root of the Denominator, becomes $\sqrt{ab}$. And $\sqrt[3]{8a^3b+16a^4}$, by extracting the Cube Root of its Diviſor $8a^3$, becomes $2a\sqrt[3]{b+2a}$. After the ſame manner $\sqrt[4]{a^3x}$, by extracting the Square Root of its Diviſor aa, becomes $\sqrt{a}$ into $\sqrt[4]{ax}$, or by extracting the Biquadratick Root of the Diviſor a^4, it becomes $a\sqrt[4]{\frac{x}{a}}$. And ſo $\sqrt[6]{a^7x^5}$ is changed into $a\sqrt[6]{ax^5}$, or into $ax\sqrt[6]{\frac{a}{x}}$, or into $\sqrt{ax}\times\sqrt[3]{aax}$.

Moreover, this Reduction is not only of uſe for abbreviating of Radical Quantities, but alſo for their Addition and Subtraction, if they agree in their Roots when they are reduced to the moſt ſimple Form; for then they may be added, which otherwiſe they cannot. Thus, $\sqrt{48}+\sqrt{75}$ by Reduction becomes $4\sqrt{3}+5\sqrt{3}$, that is $9\sqrt{3}$. And $\sqrt{48}-\sqrt{\frac{16}{27}}$ by Reduction becomes $4\sqrt{3}-\frac{4}{9}\sqrt{3}$, that is, $\frac{32}{9}\sqrt{3}$. And thus, $\sqrt{\frac{4ab^3}{cc}}+\sqrt{\frac{a^3b-4aabb+4ab^3}{cc}}$, by extracting what is Rational in it, becomes $\frac{2b}{c}\sqrt{ab}+\frac{a-2b}{c}\sqrt{ab}$, that is, $\frac{a}{c}\sqrt{ab}$. And $\sqrt[3]{8a^3b+16a^4}-\sqrt[3]{b^4+2ab^3}$ becomes $2a\sqrt[3]{b+2a}-b\sqrt[3]{b+2a}$, that is, $2a-b\sqrt[3]{b+2a}$.

Of

Of the Reduction *of* Radical *Quantities to the ſame Denomination.*

WHEN you are to multiply or divide Radicals of a different Denomination, you muſt firſt reduce them to the ſame Denomination, by prefixing that radical Sign whoſe Index is the leaſt Number, which their Indices divide without a Remainder, and by multiplying the Quantities under the Signs ſo many times, excepting one, as that Index is become greater.

For ſo $\sqrt{ax}$ into $\sqrt[3]{aax}$ becomes $\sqrt[6]{a^3x^3}$ into $\sqrt[6]{a^4xx}$, that is $\sqrt[6]{a^7x^5}$. And $\sqrt{a}$ into $\sqrt[4]{ax}$ becomes $\sqrt[4]{aa}$ into $\sqrt[4]{ax}$, that is, $\sqrt[4]{a^3x}$. And $\sqrt{6}$ into $\sqrt[4]{\frac{5}{6}}$ becomes $\sqrt[4]{36}$ into $\sqrt[4]{\frac{5}{6}}$, that is, $\sqrt[4]{30}$. By the ſame Reaſon, $a\sqrt{bc}$ becomes $\sqrt{aa}$ into $\sqrt{bc}$, that is $\sqrt{aabc}$. And $4a\sqrt{3bc}$ becomes $\sqrt{16aa}$ into $\sqrt{3bc}$, that is, $\sqrt{48aabc}$. And $2a\sqrt[3]{b+2a}$ becomes $\sqrt[3]{8a^3}$ into $\sqrt[3]{b+2a}$, that is, $\sqrt[3]{8a^3b+16a^4}$. And ſo $\frac{\sqrt{ac}}{b}$ becomes $\frac{\sqrt{ac}}{\sqrt{bb}}$, or $\sqrt{\frac{ac}{bb}}$. And $\frac{6ab}{\sqrt{18ab^3}}$ becomes $\frac{\sqrt{36aab^4}}{\sqrt{18ab^3}}$, or $\sqrt{2ab}$. And ſo in others.

Of the Reduction *of* Radicals *to more ſimple Radicals, by the Extraction of Roots.*

THE Roots of Quantities, which are compoſed of Integers and Radical Quadraticks, extract thus:

Let A *denote the greater Part of any Quantity, and* B *the leſſer Part*; and $\frac{A+\sqrt{AA-BB}}{2}$ *will be the Square of the greater Part of the Root; and* $\frac{A-\sqrt{AA-BB}}{2}$ *will be the Square of the leſſer Part, which is to be joined to the greater Part with the Sign of* B.

H 2

As

As if the Quantity be $3+\sqrt{8}$, by writing 3 for A, and $\sqrt{8}$ for B, $\sqrt{AA-BB}=1$, and thence the Square of the greater Part of the Root $\frac{3+1}{2}$, that is, 2, and the Square of the leſs $\frac{3-1}{2}$, that is, 1. Therefore the Root is, $1+\sqrt{2}$. Again if you are to extract the Root of $\sqrt{32}-\sqrt{24}$, by putting $\sqrt{32}$ for A, and $\sqrt{24}$ for B, $\sqrt{AA-BB}$ will be $=\sqrt{8}$, and thence $\frac{\sqrt{32}+\sqrt{8}}{2}$, and $\frac{\sqrt{32}-\sqrt{8}}{2}$, that is, $3\sqrt{2}$ and $\sqrt{2}$ will be the Squares of the Parts of the Root. The Root therefore is $\sqrt[4]{18}-\sqrt[4]{2}$. After the ſame manner, if out of $aa+2x\sqrt{aa-xx}$ you are to extract the Root, for A write aa, and for B write $2x\sqrt{aa-xx}$, and $AA-BB$ will be $=a^4-4aaxx+4x^4$, the Root whereof is $aa-2xx$. Whence the Square of one Part of the Root will be $aa-xx$, and that of the other xx; and ſo the Root will be $x+\sqrt{aa-xx}$. Again, if you have $aa+5ax-2a\sqrt{ax+4xx}$, by writing $aa+5ax$ for A, and $2a\sqrt{ax+4xx}$ for B, $AA-BB$ will be $=a^4+6a^3x+9aaxx$, whoſe Root is $aa+3ax$. Whence the Square of the greater Part of the Root will be $aa+4ax$, and that of the leſſer Part ax, and the Root $\sqrt{aa+4ax}-\sqrt{ax}$. Laſtly, If you have $6+\sqrt{8}-\sqrt{12}-\sqrt{24}$, putting $6+\sqrt{8}=A$, and $-\sqrt{12}-\sqrt{24}=B$, $AA-BB$ will be $=8$; whence the greater Part of the Root is $\sqrt{3+\sqrt{8}}$, that is as above $1+\sqrt{2}$, and the leſſer Part $\sqrt{3}$, and conſequently the Root itſelf $1+\sqrt{2}-\sqrt{3}$. But where there are more of this ſort of Radical Terms, the Parts of the Root may be ſooner found, by dividing the Product of any two of the Radicals by ſome third Radical, which ſhall produce a Rational and Integer Quotient. For the Root of twice that Quotient will be double of the Part of the Root ſought. As in the laſt Example, $\frac{\sqrt{8}\times\sqrt{12}}{\sqrt{24}}=2$, $\frac{\sqrt{8}\times\sqrt{24}}{\sqrt{12}}=4$, And $\frac{\sqrt{12}\times\sqrt{24}}{\sqrt{8}}=6$. Therefore the Parts of the Root are 1, $\sqrt{2}$, $\sqrt{3}$ as above.

There is alſo a Rule of extracting higher Roots out of Numeral Quantities conſiſting of two Parts, whoſe Squares are commenſurable.

Let there be the Quantity $A\pm B$. *And its greater Part* A. *And the Index of the Root to be extracted* c. Seek the leaſt Number n, *whoſe Power* n^c *may be divided by* $AA-BB$ *without any Remainder*, and let the Quotient be Q. *Compute* $\sqrt[c]{A+B\times\sqrt{Q}}$ *in the neareſt Integer Numbers. Let it be* r. *Divide* $A\sqrt{Q}$ *by the greateſt rational Diviſor. Let the Quotient be* s, *and let* $\frac{r+\frac{n}{r}}{2s}$ *in the next greateſt Integers be called* t. And $\frac{ts\pm\sqrt{ttss-n}}{\sqrt[2c]{Q}}$ *will be the Root ſought, if the Root can be extracted.*

As if the Cube Root be to be extracted out of $\sqrt{968}+25$; $AA-BB$ will be $=343$; and 7, 7, 7, will be its Diviſors; therefore $n=7$, and $Q=1$. Moreover, $\overline{A+B}\times\sqrt{Q}$, or $\sqrt{968}+25$, having extracted the former Part of the Root, is a little greater than 56; and its Cube Root in the neareſt Numbers is 4; therefore r 4. Moreover, $A\sqrt{Q}$ or $\sqrt{968}$, by taking out whatever is Rational, becomes $22\sqrt{2}$. Therefore $\sqrt{2}$ its Radical Part is s, and $\frac{r+\frac{n}{r}}{2s}$, or $\frac{5\frac{3}{4}}{2\sqrt{2}}$ in the neareſt Integer Numbers is 2. Therefore $t=2$. Laſtly, ts is $2\sqrt{2}$, $\sqrt{ttss-n}$ is 1, and $\sqrt[2c]{Q}$, or $\sqrt[6]{1}$, is 1. Therefore $2\sqrt{2}+1$ is the Root ſought, if it can be extracted. I try therefore by Multiplication if the Cube of $2\sqrt{2}+1$ be $\sqrt{968}+25$, and it ſucceeds.

Again, if the Cube Root is to be extracted out of $68-\sqrt{4374}$, $AA-BB$ will be $=250$, whoſe Diviſors are 5, 5, 5, 2. Therefore $n=5\times2=10$, and $Q=4$. And $\sqrt[c]{A+B\times\sqrt{Q}}$, or $\sqrt[3]{68+\sqrt{4374}\times 2}$ in the neareſt Integer Numbers is $7=r$. Moreover, $A\sqrt{Q}$, or $68\sqrt{4}$, by ex-

extracting or taking out what is Rational, becomes $136\sqrt{1}$.

Therefore $s=1$, and $\frac{r+\frac{n}{r}}{2s}$, or $\frac{7+\frac{10}{7}}{2}$ in the neareſt Integer Numbers is $4=t$. Therefore $ts=4$, $\sqrt{ttss-n}=\sqrt{6}$, and $\sqrt[2c]{Q}=\sqrt[6]{4}$, or $\sqrt[3]{2}$; and ſo the Root to be try'd is $\frac{4-\sqrt{6}}{\sqrt[3]{2}}$.

Again, if the fifth Root be to be extracted out of $29\sqrt{6}+41\sqrt{3}$; $AA-BB$ will be $=3$, and conſequently $n=3$, $Q=81$, $r=5$, $s=\sqrt{6}$, $t=1$, $ts=\sqrt{6}$, $\sqrt{ttss-n}=\sqrt{3}$, and $\sqrt[2c]{Q}=\sqrt[10]{81}$, or $\sqrt[5]{9}$; and ſo the Root to be tried is $\frac{\sqrt{6}+\sqrt{3}}{\sqrt[5]{9}}$.

But if in theſe Sorts of Operations, the Quantity be a Fraction, or its Parts have a common Diviſor, extract ſeparately the Roots of the Terms, and of the Factors. As if the Cube Root be to be extracted out of $\sqrt{242}-12\frac{1}{2}$, this, having reduced its Parts to a common Denominator, will become $\frac{\sqrt{968}-25}{2}$. Then having extracted ſeparately the Cube Root of the Numerator and the Denominator, there will come out $\frac{2\sqrt{2}-1}{\sqrt[3]{2}}$. Again, if you are to extract any Root out of $\sqrt[3]{3993}+\sqrt[6]{17578125}$; divide the Parts by the common Diviſor $\sqrt[3]{3}$, and there will come out $11+\sqrt{125}$. Whence the propoſed Quantity is $\sqrt[3]{3}$ into $11+\sqrt{125}$, whoſe Root will be found by extracting ſeparately the Root of each Factor $\sqrt[3]{3}$, and $11+\sqrt{125}$.

Of

Of the Form of an EQUATION.

EQUATIONS are Ranks of Quantities either equal to one another, or, taken together, equal to nothing. Theſe are to be conſidered chiefly after two Ways; either as the laſt Concluſions to which you come in the Reſolution of Problems; or as Means, by the Help whereof you are to obtain final Equations. An Equation of the former Kind is compoſed only out of one unknown Quantity involved with known ones, if the Problem be determined, and propoſes ſomething certain to be found out. But thoſe of the latter Kind involve ſeveral unknown Quantities, which, for that Reaſon, muſt be compared among one another, and ſo connected, that out of all there may emerge a new Equation, in which there is only one unknown Quantity which we ſeek mixed with known Quantities. Which Quantity, that it may be the more eaſily diſcovered, that Equation muſt be transformed moſt commonly various Ways, until it becomes the moſt Simple that it can, and alſo like ſome of the following Degrees of them, in which x denotes the Quantity ſought, according to whoſe Dimenſions the Terms, as you ſee, are ordered, and p, q, r, s denote any other Quantities from which, being known and determined, x is alſo determined, and may be inveſtigated by Methods hereafter to be explained.

$x=p$	Or, $x-p=0$.
$xx=px+q$.	$xx-px-q=0$.
$x^3=px^2+qx+r$.	$x^3-pxx-qx-r=0$.
$x^4=px^3+qx^2+rx+s$.	$x^4-px^3-qx^2-rx-s=0$.
&c.	&c.

After this Manner therefore the Terms of Equations are to be ordered according to the Dimenſions of the unknown Quantity, ſo that thoſe may be in the firſt Place, in which the unknown Quantity is of the moſt Dimenſions, as x, xx, x, x^4, &c. and thoſe in the ſecond Place, in which x is of the next greateſt Dimenſion, as p, px, px^2, px^3, and ſo on. As to what regards the Signs, they may ſtand any how; and one or more of the intermediate Terms may be ſometimes wanting. Thus, $x^3 * -bbx+b^3=0$, or $x^3=bbx-b^3$, is an Equation of the third Degree, and

2 Z4

$Z^4 \begin{matrix}+a\\-b\end{matrix} Z^3 * \begin{matrix}+ab^3\\-b^4\end{matrix} = 0$, is an Equation of the fourth Degree: For the Degree of an Equation is always eſtimated by the greateſt Dimenſion of the unknown Quantity, without any regard to the known ones, or to the intermediate Terms. But by the Defect of the intermediate Terms, the Equation is moſt commonly rendered much more ſimple, and may be ſometimes depreſſed to a lower Degree. For thus, $x^4 = qxx + s$ is to be reckoned an Equation of the ſecond Degree, becauſe it may be reſolved into two Equations of the ſecond Degree. For, ſuppoſing $xx = y$, and y being accordingly writ for xx in that Equation, there will come out in its ſtead $yy = qy + s$, an Equation of the ſecond Degree; by the Help whereof when y is found, the Equation $xx = y$ alſo of the ſecond Degree, will give x.

And theſe are the Concluſions to which Problems are to be brought. But before I go upon their Reſolution, it will be neceſſary to ſhew the Methods of transforming and reducing Equations into Order, and the Methods of finding the final Equations. I ſhall comprize the Reduction of a Single Equation in the following Rules.

Of ordering a Single EQUATION.

RULE I. IF *there are any Quantities that may deſtroy one another, or may be joined into one by Addition or Subtraction, the Terms are that Way to be diminiſhed.*

As if you have $5b - 3a + 2x = 5a + 3x$, take from each Side $2x$, and add $3a$, and there will come out $5b = 8a + x$. And thus, $\frac{2ab + bx}{a} - b = a + b$, by ſtriking out the equivalent Quantities $\frac{2ab}{a} - b = b$, becomes $\frac{bx}{a} = a$.

To this Rule may alſo be referred the Ordering of the Terms of an Equation, which is uſually performed by the Tranſpoſition of the Members to the contrary Sides under the contrary Sign. As if you had the Equation $5b = 8a \quad x$, you are to find x; take from each Side $8a$, or, which is the ſame Thing, tranſpoſe $8a$ to the contrary Side with its Sign changed, and there will come out $5b - 8a = x$. After the ſame way, if you have $aa - 3ay = ab - bb + by$, and you are to find y; tranſpoſe $-3ay$ and $ab - bb$, ſo that there may be the Terms multiplied by y on the one Side, and the other Terms on the other Side, and there will come out $aa - ab + bb = 3ay + by$, whence you will have y by the fifth Rule following, *viz.* by dividing each Part by $3a + b$, for there will come out $\frac{aa - ab + bb}{3a + b} = y$. And thus the Equation $abx + a^3 - aax = abb - 2abx - x^3$, by due ordering and tranſpoſition becomes $x^3 = \begin{matrix}aa\\-3ab\end{matrix} x \begin{matrix}-a^3\\+abb\end{matrix}$ or $x^3 \begin{matrix}-aa\\+3ab\end{matrix} x \begin{matrix}+a^3\\-abb\end{matrix} = 0$.

RULE II. *If there is any Quantity by which all the Terms of the Equation are multiplied, all of them muſt be divided by that Quantity; or, if all are divided by the ſame Quantity, all muſt be multiplied by it too.*

Thus, having $15bb = 24ab + 3bx$, divide all the Terms by b, and you will have $15b = 24a + 3x$; then by 3, and you will have $5b = 8a + x$. Or having $\frac{b^3}{ac} - \frac{bbx}{cc} = \frac{xx}{c}$, multiply all by c, and there comes out $\frac{b^3}{a} - \frac{bbx}{c} = xx$.

RULE III. *If there be any irreducible Fraction, in whoſe Denominator there is found the Letter, according to whoſe Dimenſions the Equation is to be ordered, all the Terms of the Equation muſt be multiplied by that Denominator, or by ſome Diviſor of it.*

As if the Equation $\frac{ax}{a-x} + b = x$ be to be ordered according to x, multiply all its Terms by $a - x$ the Denominator of the Fraction $\frac{ax}{a-x}$ ſeeing x is contained therein, and there comes out $ax + ab - bx = ax - xx$, or $ab - bx = -xx$, and tranſpoſing each Part you will have $xx = bx - ab$. And ſo if you have $\frac{a^3 - aab}{2cy - cc} = y - c$, and the Terms are to be ranged according to the Dimenſions of y, multiply them by the Denominator $2cy - cc$, or, at

I leaſt,

least, by its Divisor $2y - c$, that y may vanish in the Denominator, and there will come out $\frac{a^3 - abb}{c} = 2yy - 3cy + cc$, and by farther ordering $\frac{a^3 - abb}{c} - cc + 3cy = 2yy$. After the same manner $\frac{aa}{x} - a = x$, by being multiplied by x, becomes $aa - ax = xx$, and $\frac{aabb}{cxx} = \frac{xx}{a + b - x}$, by multiplying first by xx, and then by $a + b - x$, becomes $\frac{a^3bb + aab^3 - aabbx}{c} = x^4$.

Rule IV. *If that particular Letter, according to whose Dimensions the Equation is to be ordered, be involved with an irreducible Surd, all the other Terms are to be transposed to the other Side, their Signs being changed, and each Part of the Equation must be once multiplied by itself, if the Root be a* Square one, *or* twice, *if it be a* Cubick one, *&c.*

Thus, to order the Equation $\sqrt{aa - ax} + a = x$ according to the Letter x, transpose a to the other Side, and you have $\sqrt{aa - ax} = x - a$; and having squared the Parts, $aa - ax = xx - 2ax + aa$, or $0 = xx - ax$, that is, $x = a$. So also $\sqrt[3]{aax + 2axx - x^3} - a + x = 0$, by transposing $-a + x$, becomes $\sqrt[3]{aax + 2axx - x^3} = a - x$, and multiplying the Parts cubically, $aax + 2axx - x^3 = a^3 - 3aax + 3axx - x^3$, or $xx = 4ax - aa$. And so $y = \sqrt{ay + yy - a\sqrt{ay - yy}}$, having squared the Parts, becomes $yy = ay + yy - a\sqrt{ay - yy}$, and the Terms being rightly transposed, it becomes $ay = a\sqrt{ay - yy}$, or $y = \sqrt{ay - yy}$, and the Parts being again squared $yy = ay - yy$, and lastly by transposing $2yy = ay$, or $2y = a$.

Rule V. *The Terms, by help of the preceding Rules, being disposed according to the Dimensions of some one of the Letters, if the highest Dimension of that Letter be multiplied by any known Quantity, the whole Equation must be divided by that Quantity.*

Thus, $2y = a$, by dividing by 2, becomes $y = \frac{1}{2}a$. And $\frac{bx}{a} = a$, by dividing by $\frac{b}{a}$, becomes $x = \frac{aa}{b}$. And $\begin{matrix} 2ac \\ -cc \end{matrix} x^3 \begin{matrix} +a^3 \\ +aac \end{matrix} xx \begin{matrix} -2a^3c \\ +aacc \end{matrix} x - a^3cc = 0$, by dividing by $2ac - cc$, becomes $x^3 + \frac{\begin{matrix} a^3 \\ aac \end{matrix} x^2 \begin{matrix} -2a^3c \\ +aacc \end{matrix} x - a^3cc}{2ac - cc} = 0$, or $x^3 + \frac{a^3 + aac}{2ac - cc} xx - aax - \frac{a^3c}{2a - c} = 0$.

Rule VI. *Sometimes the Reduction may be performed by dividing the Equation by some compounded Quantity.*

For thus $y^3 = \begin{matrix} -2c \\ +b \end{matrix} yy + 3bcy - bbc$, is reduced to this, *viz.* $yy = -2cy + bc$; by transferring all the Terms to the same Side thus, $y^3 \begin{matrix} +2c \\ -b \end{matrix} yy - 3bcy + bbc = 0$, and dividing by $y - b$, as is shewn in the Chapter of *Division*, for there will come out $yy + 2cy - bc = 0$. But the Invention of this sort of Divisors is difficult, and we have taught it already.

Rule VII. *Sometimes also the Reduction is performed by Extraction of the Root out of each Part of the Equation.*

As if you have $xx = \frac{1}{4}aa - bb$, having extracted the Root on both Sides, there comes out $x = \sqrt{\frac{1}{4}aa - bb}$. If you have $xx + aa = 2ax + bb$, transpose $2ax$, and there will arise $xx - 2ax + aa = bb$, and extracting the Roots of the Parts $x - a = +$ or $-b$, or $x = a \pm b$. So also having $xx = ax - bb$, add on each Side $-ax + \frac{1}{4}aa$, and there comes out $xx - ax + \frac{1}{4}aa = \frac{1}{4}aa - bb$, and extracting the Root on each Side $x - \frac{1}{2}a = \pm\sqrt{\frac{1}{4}aa - bb}$, or $x = \frac{1}{2}a \pm \sqrt{\frac{1}{4}aa - bb}$.

And thus universally if you have $xx = .px.q$; x will be $= .\frac{1}{2}p \pm \sqrt{\frac{1}{4}pp.q}$. Where $\frac{1}{2}p$ and q are to be affected with the same Signs as p and q in the former Equation; but $\frac{1}{4}pp$ must be always made Affirmative. And this Example is a Rule according to which all Quadratick Equations may be reduced to the Form of Simple ones. For example,

I 2

ample, having proposed the Equation $yy = \frac{2xxy}{a} + xx$, to extract the Root y, compare $\frac{2xx}{a}$ with p, and xx with q, that is, write $\frac{xx}{a}$ for $\frac{1}{2}p$, and $\frac{x^4}{aa} + xx$ for $\frac{1}{4}pp.q$, and there will arise $y = \frac{xx}{a} + \sqrt{\frac{x^4}{aa} + xx}$ or $y = \frac{xx}{a} - \sqrt{\frac{x^4}{aa} + xx}$. After the same way, the Equation $yy = ay - 2cy + aa - cc$, by comparing $a - 2c$ with p, and $aa - cc$ with q, will give $y = \frac{1}{2}a - c \pm \sqrt{\frac{5}{4}aa - ac}$.

Moreover, the Biquadratick Equation $x^4 = -aaxx + ab^3$, whose odd Terms are wanting, by help of this Rule becomes $xx = -\frac{1}{2}aa \pm \sqrt{\frac{1}{4}a^4 + ab^3}$, and extracting again the Root $x = \sqrt{-\frac{1}{2}aa \pm \sqrt{\frac{1}{4}a^4 + ab^3}}$. And so in others.

And these are the Rules for ordering one only Equation, the Use whereof, when the Analyst is sufficiently acquainted with, so that he knows how to dispose any proposed Equation according to any of the Letters contained in it, and to obtain the Value of that Letter if it be of one Dimension, or of its greatest Power if it be of more: The Comparison of several Equations among one another will not be difficult to him; which I am now going to shew.

Of the Transformation of two or more EQUATIONS *into one, in order to exterminate the unknown Quantities.*

WHEN, in the Solution of any Problem, there are more Equations than one to comprehend the State of the Question, in each of which there are several unknown Quantities; those Equations (two by two, if there are more than two) are to be so connected, that one of the unknown Quantities may be made to vanish at each of the Operations, and so produce a new Equation. Thus, having the Equations $2x = y + 5$, and $x = y + 2$, by taking equal Things out of equal Things, there will come out $x = 3$. And you are to know, that by each Equation one unknown Quantity may be taken away, and consequently, when there are as many Equations as unknown Quantities, all may at length be reduc'd into one, in which there shall be only one Quantity unknown. But if there be more unknown Quantities by one than there are Equations, then there will remain in the Equation last resulting two unknown Quantities; and if there are more unknown Quantities by two than there are Equations, then in the last resulting Equation there will remain three, and so on.

There may also, perhaps, two or more unknown Quantities be made to vanish, by only two Equations. As if you have $ax - by = ab - az$, and $bx + by = bb + az$: Then adding Equals to Equals, there will come out $ax + bx = ab + bb$, both y and z being exterminated. But such Cases either argue some Fault to lie hid in the State of the Question, or that the Calculation is erroneous, or not artificial enough. The Method by which one unknown Quantity may be exterminated or taken away by each of the Equations, will appear by what follows.

The Extermination of an unknown Quantity by an Equality of its Values.

WHEN the Quantity to be exterminated is only of one Dimension in both Equations, both its Values are to be sought by the Rules already delivered, and the one made equal to the other.

Thus, putting $a + x = b + y$ and $2x + y = 3b$, that y may be exterminated, the first Equation will give $a + x - b = y$, and the second will give $3b - 2x = y$. Therefore $a + x - b$ is $= 3b - 2x$, or by due ordering $x = \frac{4b - a}{3}$.

And thus, $2x = y$ and $5 + x = y$ give $2x = 5 + x$ or $x = 5$.

And $ax - 2by = ab$ and $xy = bb$ give $\frac{ax - ab}{2b} (= y) = \frac{bb}{x}$; or by due ordering the Terms $xx - bx - \frac{2b^3}{a} = 0$.

Also

Alſo $\frac{bbx-aby}{a}=ab+xy$, and $bx+\frac{ayy}{c}=2aa$, by taking away x, give $\frac{aby+aab}{bb-ay}(=x)=\frac{2aac-ayy}{bc}$; and by Reduction $y^3-\frac{bb}{a}yy-\frac{2aac+bbc}{a}y+bbc=0$.

Laſtly, $x+y-z=0$ and $ay=xz$ by taking away z give $x+y(=z)=\frac{ay}{x}$ or $xx+xy=ay$.

The ſame is alſo performed by ſubtracting either of the Values of the unknown Quantities from the other, and making the Remainder equal to nothing. Thus, in the firſt of the Examples, take away $3b-2x$ from $a+x-b$, and there will remain $a+3x-4b=0$, or $x=\frac{4b-a}{3}$.

The Extermination of an unknown Quantity, by ſubſtituting its Value for it.

WHEN, at leaſt, in one of the Equations the Quantity to be exterminated is only of one Dimenſion, its Value is to be ſought in that Equation, and then to be ſubſtituted in its room in the other Equation. Thus, having propoſed $xyy=b^3$, and $xx+yy=by-ax$; to exterminate x, the firſt will give $\frac{b^3}{yy}=x$; wherefore I ſubſtitute in the ſecond $\frac{b^3}{yy}$ in the room of x, and there comes out $\frac{b^6}{y^4}+yy=by-\frac{ab^3}{yy}$, and by Reduction $y^6-by^5+ab^3yy+b^6=0$.

But having propoſed $ayy+aay=z^3$, and $yz-ay=az$, to take away y, the ſecond will give $y=\frac{az}{z-a}$. Wherefore for y I ſubſtitute $\frac{az}{z-a}$ into the firſt, and there comes out $\frac{a^3zz}{zz-2az+aa}+\frac{a^3z}{z-a}=z^3$. And by Reduction, $z^4-2az^3+aazz-2a^3z+a^4=0$. In

In the like manner, having propoſed $\frac{xy}{c}=z$ and $cy+zx=cc$, to take away z, I ſubſtitute in its room $\frac{xy}{c}$ in the ſecond Equation, and there comes out $cy+\frac{xxy}{c}=cc$.

But a Perſon uſed to theſe Sorts of Computations, will oftentimes find ſhorter Methods than theſe by which the unknown Quantity may be exterminated. Thus, having $ax=\frac{bbx-b^3}{z}$ and $x=\frac{az}{x-b}$ if equal Quantities are multiplied by Equals, there will come out equal Quantities, *viz.* $axx=abb$, or $x=b$.

But I leave particular Caſes of this kind to be found out by the Students as Occaſion ſhall offer.

The Extermination of an unknown Quantity of ſeveral Dimenſions in each Equation.

WHEN the Quantity to be taken away is of more than one Dimenſion in both the Equations, the Value of its greateſt Power muſt be ſought in both; then if thoſe Powers are not the ſame, the Equation that involves the leſſer Power muſt be multiplied by the Quantity to be taken away, or by its Square, or Cube, &c. that it may become of the ſame Power with the other Equation. Then the Values of thoſe Powers are to be made Equal, and there will come out a new Equation, where the greateſt Power or Dimenſion of the Quantity to be taken away is diminiſhed. And by repeating this Operation, the Quantity will at length be taken away.

As if you have $xx+5x=3yy$ and $2xy-3xx=4$; to take away x, the firſt Equation will give $xx=-5x+3yy$, and the ſecond $xx=\frac{2xy-4}{3}$. I put therefore $3yy-5x=\frac{2xy-4}{3}$, and ſo x is reduced to only one Dimenſion, and ſo may be taken away by what I have before ſhewn, *viz.* by a due Reduction of the laſt Equation there comes out $9yy-15x=2xy-4$, or $x=\frac{9yy+4}{2y+15}$.

I there-

I therefore substitute this Value for x in one of the Equations first proposed (as in $xx + 5x = 3yy$) and there arises $\frac{81y^4 + 72yy + 16}{4yy + 60y + 225} + \frac{45yy + 20}{2y + 15} = 3yy$. To reduce which into order, I multiply by $4yy + 60yy + 225$, and there comes out $81y^4 + 72yy + 16 + 90y^3 + 40y + 675yy + 300 = 12y^4 + 180y^3 + 675yy$, or $69y^4 - 90y^3 + 72yy + 40y + 316 = 0$.

Moreover, if you have $y^3 = xyy + 3x$, and $yy = xx - xy - 3$; to take away y, I multiply the latter Equation by y, and you have $y^3 = xxy - xyy - 3y$, of as many Dimensions as the former. Now, by making the Values of y^3 equal to one another, I have $xyy + 3x = xxy - xyy - 3y$, where y is depressed to two Dimensions. By this therefore, and the most Simple one of the Equations first proposed $yy = xx - xy - 3$, the Quantity y may be wholly taken away by the same Method as in the former Example.

There are moreover other Methods by which this may be done, and that oftentimes more concisely. As if there be given $yy = \frac{2x^2y}{a} + xx$, and $yy = 2xy + \frac{x^4}{aa}$; that y may be extirpated, extract the Root y in each, as is shewn in the 7th Rule, and there will come out $y = \frac{xx}{a} + \sqrt{\frac{x^4}{aa} + xx}$, and $y = x + \sqrt{\frac{x^4}{aa} + xx}$. Now, by making these two Values of y equal you will have $\frac{xx}{a} + \sqrt{\frac{x^4}{aa} + xx} = x + \sqrt{\frac{x^4}{aa} + xx}$, and by rejecting the equal Quantities $\sqrt{\frac{x^4}{aa} + xx}$, there will remain $\frac{xx}{a} = x$, or $xx = ax$, and $x = a$.

Moreover, to take x out of the Equations $x + y + \frac{yy}{x} = 20$, and $xx + yy + \frac{y^4}{xx} = 140$, take away y from the

I Parts

Parts of the first Equation, and there remains $x + \frac{yy}{x} = 20 - y$, and squaring the Parts, it becomes $xx + 2yy + \frac{y^4}{xx} = 400 - 40y + yy$, and taking away yy on both Sides, there remains $xx + yy + \frac{yyyy}{xx} = 400 - 40y$. Wherefore, since $400 - 40y$ and 140 are equal to the same Quantities, $400 - 40y$ will be equal to 140, or $y = 6\frac{1}{2}$; and so you may contract the Matter in most other Equations.

But when the Quantity to be exterminated is of several Dimensions, sometimes there is required a very laborious Calculus to exterminate it out of the Equations; but then the Labour will be much diminished by the following Examples made use of as Rules.

Rule I.

From $axx + bx + c = 0$, and $fxx + gx + h = 0$,
x being exterminated, there comes out

$$\overline{ah - bg - 2cf} \times ah : + \overline{bh - cg} \times bf : \times \overline{agg + cff} \times c = 0.$$

Rule II.

From $ax^3 + bxx + cx + d = 0$, and $fxx + gx + h = 0$,
x being exterminated, there comes out

$$\overline{ah - bg - 2cf} \times ahh : + \overline{bh - cg - 2df} \times bfh : + \overline{ch - dg} \times \overline{agg + cff} : + \overline{3agh + bgg + dff} \times df = 0.$$

Rule III.

From $ax^4 + bx^3 + cxx + dx + e = 0$, *and* $fxx + gx + h = 0$,
x being exterminated, there comes out

$$\overline{ah - bg - 2cf} \times ah^3 : + \overline{bh - cg - 2df} \times bfhh : + \overline{agg + cff} \times \overline{chh + dgh + egg - 2efh + 3agh + bgg + dff} \times dfh : + \overline{2ahh + 3bgh - dfg + eff} \times eff : - \overline{bg - 2ah} \times efgg = 0.$$

K Rule

Rule IV.

From $ax^3+bxx+cx+d=0$, and $fx^3+gx^2+hx+k=0$.

x being exterminated, there comes out

$$\overline{ah-bg-2cf}\times\overline{adhh-achk}:+\overline{ak+bh-cg-2df}\times bdfh:-\overline{ak+bh+2cg+3df}\times aakk:+\overline{cdh-ddg-cck+2bdk}\times\overline{agg+cff}:+\overline{3agh+bgg+dff-3afk}\times ddf:-\overline{3ak-bh+cg+df}\times bcfk:+\overline{bk-2dg}\times bbfk-\overline{bbk-3adh-cdf}\times agk=0.$$

For Example, to exterminate x out of the Equations $xx+5x-3yy=0$, and $3xx-2xy+4=0$: I reſpectively ſubſtitute in the firſt Rule for $a, b, c; f, g,$ and h theſe Quantities, $1, 5, -3yy; 3, -2y$ and 4; and duly obſerving the Signs $+$ and $-$, there ariſes $\overline{4+10y+18yy}\times 4:+\overline{20-6y^3}\times 15:+\overline{4yy-27yy}\times -3yy=0$, or $16+40y+72yy+300-90y^3+69y^4=0$.

By the like Reaſon that y may be expunged out of the Equations $y^3-xyy-3x=0$, and $yy+xy-xx+3=0$, I ſubſtitute into the ſecond Rule for $a, b, c, d; f, g, h,$ and x, theſe Quantities $1, -x, 0, -3x; 1, x, -xx+3$, and y reſpectively, and there comes out $\overline{3-xx+xx}\times\overline{9-6xx+x^4}:-\overline{3x+x^3+6x}\times\overline{-3x+x^3}:+3xx\times xx:+\overline{9x-3x^3-x^3-3x}\times -3x=0$: Then blotting out the ſuperfluous Quantities and multiplying, you have $27-18xx+3x^4, -9xx+x^6, +3x^4-18x^2+12x^4=0$. And ordering $x^6+18x^4-45xx+27=0$.

Hitherto we have diſcourſed of taking away one unknown Quantity out of two Equations. Now, if ſeveral are to be taken out of ſeveral, the Buſineſs muſt be done by degrees: Out of the Equations $ax=yz$, $x+y=z$ and $5x=y+3z$; if the Quantity y is to be found, firſt, take out one of the Quantities x or z, ſuppoſe x, by ſubſtituting for it its Value $\frac{yz}{a}$ (found by the firſt Equation) in the ſecond and

third

third Equations; and then you will have $\frac{yz}{a}+y=z$, and $\frac{5yz}{a}=y+3z$, out of which take away z as above.

Of the Method of taking away any Number of Surd Quantities out of Equations.

Hitherto may be referred the Extermination of Surd Quantities, by making them equal to any Letters. As if you have $\sqrt{ay}-\sqrt{aa-ay}=2a+\sqrt[3]{ayy}$, by writing t for $\sqrt{ay}$, and v for $\sqrt{aa-ay}$, and x for $\sqrt[3]{ayy}$, you will have the Equations $t-v=2a+x$, $tt=ay$, $vv=aa-ay$, and $x^3=ayy$, out of which taking away by degrees t, v, and x, there will reſult an Equation entirely free from Surdity.

How a Queſtion may be brought to an Equation.

After the Learner has been ſome time exerciſed in managing and transforming Equations, Order requires that he ſhould try his Skill in bringing Queſtions to an Equation. And any Queſtion being propoſed, his Skill is particularly required to denote all its Conditions by ſo many Equations. To do which he muſt firſt conſider whether the Propoſitions or Sentences in which it is expreſſed, be all of them fit to be denoted in Algebraick Terms, juſt as we expreſs our Conceptions in *Latin* or *Greek* Characters. And if ſo, (as will happen in Queſtions converſant about Numbers or abſtract Quantities) then let him give Names to both known and unknown Quantities, as far as occaſion requires; and expreſs the Senſe of the Queſtion in the Analytick Language, if I may ſo ſpeak. And the Conditions thus tranſlated to Algebraick Terms will give as many Equations as are neceſſary to ſolve it.

As if there are required three Numbers in continual Proportion, whoſe Sum is 20, and the Sum of their Squares 140; putting x, y, and z for the Names of the three Numbers ſought, the Queſtion will be tranſlated out of the Verbal to the Symbolical Expreſſion, as follows:

K 2 The

The Queſtion in Words.	*The ſame in Symbols.*
There are ſought three Numbers on theſe Conditions:	x, y, z?
That they ſhall be continually proportional.	$x : y :: y : z$, or $xz = yy$.
That the Sum ſhall be 20.	$x + y + z = 20$.
And the Sum of their Squares 140.	$xx + yy + zz = 140$.

And ſo the Queſtion is brought to theſe Equations, *viz.* $xz = yy$, $x + y + z = 20$, and $xx + yy + zz = 140$, by the Help whereof x, y, and z, are to be found by the Rules delivered above.

But you muſt note, That the Solutions of Queſtions are (for the moſt part) ſo much the more expedite and artificial, by how fewer unknown Quantities you have at firſt. Thus, in the Queſtion propoſed, putting x for the firſt Number, and y for the ſecond, $\frac{yy}{x}$ will be the third Proportional; which then being put for the third Number, I bring the Queſtion into Equations, as follows:

The Queſtion in Words.	*Symbolically.*
There are ſought three Numbers in continual Proportion.	$x, y, \frac{yy}{x}$?
Whoſe Sum is 20.	$x + y + \frac{yy}{x} = 20$.
And the Sum of their Squares 140.	$xx + yy + \frac{y^4}{xx} = 140$.

You have therefore the Equations $x + y + \frac{yy}{x} = 20$, and $xx + yy + \frac{y^4}{xx} = 140$, by the Reduction whereof x and y are to be determined.

Take another Example. A certain Merchant encreaſes his Eſtate yearly by a third Part, abating 100 *l.* which he ſpends yearly in his Family; and after three Years he finds his Eſtate doubled. *Query*, What was he worth?

To reſolve this, you muſt know there are or lie hid ſeveral Propoſitions, which are all thus found out and laid down.

In Engliſh.	*Algebraically.*
A Merchant has an Eſtate - - -	x.
Out of which the firſt Year he expends 100 *l.*	$x - 100$.
And augments the reſt by one third.	$x - 100 + \frac{x-100}{3}$ or $\frac{4x-400}{3}$.
And the ſecond Year expends 100 *l.* - -	$\frac{4x-400}{3} - 100$ or $\frac{4x-700}{3}$.
And augments the reſt by a third - -	$\frac{4x-700}{3} + \frac{4x-700}{9}$ or $\frac{16x-2800}{9}$.
And ſo the third Year expends 100 *l.* - -	$\frac{16x-2800}{9} - 100$ or $\frac{16x-3700}{9}$.
And by the reſt gains likewiſe one third Part - - - -	$\frac{16x-3700}{9} + \frac{16x-3700}{27}$, or $\frac{64x-14800}{27}$.
And he becomes at length twice as rich as at firſt - -	$\frac{64x-14800}{27} = 2x$.

Therefore the Queſtion is brought to this Equation, $\frac{64x - 14800}{27} = 2x$, by the Reduction whereof you are to find x; *viz.* multiply it by 27, and you have $64x = 14800 = 54x$; ſubtract $54x$, and there remains $10x - 14800 = 0$, or $10x = 14800$, and dividing by 10, you have $x = 1480$. Wherefore, 1480 *l.* was his Eſtate at firſt, as alſo his Profit or Gain ſince.

You ſee therefore, that to the Solution of Queſtions which only regard Numbers, or the abſtracted Relations of Quantities, there is ſcarce any Thing elſe required, than that the Problem be tranſlated out of the *Engliſh*, or any other Tongue it is propoſed in, into the Algebraical Language, that is, into Characters fit to denote our Conceptions of the Relations of Quantities. But it may ſometimes happen, that the Language or the Words wherein the State of the Queſtion is

is expressed, may seem unfit to be turned into the Algebraical Language; but making Use of a few Changes, and attending to the Sense, rather than the Sound of the Words, the Version will become easy. Thus, the Forms of Speech among different Nations have their proper Idioms; which, where they happen, the Translation out of one into another is not to be made literally, but to be determined by the Sense. But that I may illustrate these Sorts of Problems, and make familiar the Method of reducing them to Equations; and since Arts are more easily learned by Examples than Precepts, I have thought fit to adjoin the Solutions of the following Problems.

PROBLEM I.

Having given the Sum of two Numbers, a, *and the Difference of their Squares* b, *to find the Numbers?*

Let the least of them be x, the other will be $a-x$, and their Squares xx, and $aa-2ax+xx$: the Difference whereof $aa-2ax$ is supposed b. Therefore $aa-2ax=b$, and then by Reduction $aa-b=2ax$, or $\frac{aa-b}{2a}\left(=\frac{1}{2}a-\frac{b}{2a}\right)=x$.

For Example, if the Sum of the Numbers or a be 8, and the Difference of the Squares or b be 16; $\frac{1}{2}a-\frac{b}{2a}$ $(=4-1)$ will be $=3=x$, and $a-x=5$. Wherefore the Numbers are 3 and 5.

PROBLEM II.

To find three Quantities, x, y, *and* z, *the Sum of any two of which shall be given.*

If the Sum of two of them, *viz.* x and y be a; of x and z, b; and of y and z, c; there will be had three Equations to determine the three Quantities sought, x, y, and z, *viz.* $x+y=a$, $x+z=b$, and $y+z=c$. Now, that two of the unknown Quantities, *viz.* y and z may be exterminated, take away x on both Sides in the first and second Equation, and you will have $y=a-x$, and $z=b-x$, which Values substitute for y and z in the third Equation, and there will come out $a-x+b-x=c$, and by Reduction $x=\frac{a+b-c}{2}$; and having found x, the Equations above $y=a-x$ and $z=b-x$ will give y and z.

EXAMPLE. If the Sum of x and y be 9, of x and z, 10, and y and z, 13; then, in the Values of x, y, and z, write 9 for a, 10 for b, and 13 for c; and you will have $a+b-c=6$, and consequently $x\left(=\frac{a+b-c}{2}\right)=3$, y $(=a-x)=6$, and z $(=b-x)=7$.

PROBLEM III.

To divide a given Quantity into as many Parts as you please, so that the greater Parts may exceed the least by any given Differences.

Let a be a Quantity to be divided into four such Parts, and its first or least Part call x, and the Excess of the second Part above this call b, and of the third Part c, and of the fourth d; and $x+b$ will be the second Part, $x+c$ the third, and $x+d$ the fourth, the Aggregate of all which $4x+b+c+d$ is equal to the whole Line a. Take away on both Sides $b+c+d$, and there remains $4x=a-b-c-d$, or $x=\frac{a-b-c-d}{4}$.

EXAMPLE. Let there be proposed a Line of 20 Foot, so to be divided into four Parts, that the Excess of the second above the first Part shall be 2 Foot, of the third 3 Foot, and of the fourth 7 Foot; and the four Parts will be $x\left(=\frac{a-b-c-d}{4}\text{ or }\frac{20-2-3-7}{4}\right)=2$, $x+b=4$, $x+c=5$, and $x+d=9$.

After the same Manner a Quantity is divided into more Parts on the same Conditions.

PROBLEM IV.

A Person being willing to distribute some Money among Beggars, wanted eight Pence to give three Pence a piece to them; he therefore gave to each two Pence, and had three Pence remaining over and above. To find the Number of the Beggars.

Let the Number of the Beggars be x, and there will be wanting eight Pence to give all $3x$ Pence; he has therefore $\overline{3x-8}$ Pence. Out of these he gives $2x$ Pence, and the remaining Pence $\overline{x-8}$ are three. That is, $x-8=3$, or $x=11$.

PRO-

EXAMPLE.

PROBLEM V.

If two Post-Boys, A *and* B, *at* 59 *Miles Distance from one another, set out in the Morning in order to meet. And* A *rides* 7 *Miles in two Hours, and* B 8 *Miles in three Hours, and* B *begins his Journey one Hour later than* A; *to find what Number of Miles* A *will ride before he meets* B.

Call that Length x, and you will have $59-x$, the Length of B's Journey. And since A travels 7 Miles in two Hours, he will make the Space x in $\frac{2x}{7}$ Hours, because 7 Miles : 2 Hours : : x Miles : $\frac{2x}{7}$ Hours. And so, since B rides 8 Miles in 3 Hours, he will describe his Space or ride his Journey $59-x$ in $\frac{177-3x}{8}$ Hours. Now, since the Difference of these Times is one Hour; to the End they may become equal, add that Difference to the shorter Time $\frac{177-3x}{8}$, and you will have $1+\frac{177-3x}{8}=\frac{2x}{7}$, and by Reduction $35=x$. For, multiplying by 8 you have $185-3x=\frac{16x}{7}$. Then multiplying also by 7 you have $1295-21x=16x$, or $1295=37x$. And, lastly, dividing by 37, there arises $35=x$. Therefore, 35 Miles is the Distance that A must ride before he meets B.

The same more generally.

Having given the Velocities of two moveable Bodies, A *and* B, *tending to the same Place, together with the Interval or Distance of the Places and Times from, and in which they begin to move; to determine the Place they shall meet in.*

Suppose, the Velocity of the Body A to be such, that it shall pass over the Space c in the Time f; and of the Body B to be such as it shall pass over the Space d in the Time g; and that the Interval of the Places is e, and h the Interval of the Times in which they begin to move.

CASE I. Then if both tend to the same Place, [or the same Way] and A be the Body that, at the Beginning of the Motion, is farthest distant from the Place they tend to: call that Distance x, and subtract from it the Distance e, and there will remain $x-e$ for the Distance of B from the Place it tends to. And since A passes through the Space c in the Time f, the Time in which it will pass over the Space x will be $\frac{fx}{c}$, because the Space c is to the Time f, as the Space x to the Time $\frac{fx}{c}$. And so, since B passes the Space d in the Time g, the Time in which it will pass the Space $x-e$ will be $\frac{gx-ge}{d}$. Now since the Difference of these Times is supposed h, that they may become equal, add h to the shorter Time, *viz.* to the Time $\frac{fx}{c}$ if B begins to move first, and you will have $\frac{fx}{c}+h=\frac{gx-ge}{d}$, and by Reduction $\frac{cge+cdh}{cg-df}$ or $\frac{ge+dh}{g-\frac{d}{c}f}=x$. But if A begins to move first, add h to the Time $\frac{gx-ge}{d}$, and you will have $\frac{fx}{c}=h+\frac{gx-ge}{d}$, and by Reduction $\frac{cge-cdh}{cg-df}=x$.

CASE II. If the moveable Bodies proceed towards one another, and x, as before, be made the initial Distance of the moveable Body A, from the Place it is to move to, then $e-x$ will be the initial Distance of the Body B from the same Place; and $\frac{fx}{c}$ the Time in which A will describe the Distance x, and $\frac{ge-gx}{d}$ the Time in which B will describe its Distance $e-x$. To the lesser of which Times, as above, add the Difference h, *viz.* to the Time $\frac{fx}{c}$ if B begin first to move, and so you will have $\frac{fx}{c}+h=\frac{ge-gx}{d}$, and by Reducti-

L

on $\frac{cge-cdh}{cg+df}=x$. But if *A* begins first to move, add *h* to the Time $\frac{ge-gx}{d}$ and it will become $\frac{fx}{c}=h+\frac{ge-gx}{d}$, and by Reduction $\frac{cge+cdh}{cg+df}=x$.

EXAMPLE I. If the Sun moves every Day one Degree, and the Moon thirteen, and at a certain Time the Sun be at the Beginning of *Cancer*, and, in three Days after, the Moon in the Beginning of *Aries*, the Place of their next following Conjunction is demanded. Answer, in $10\frac{3}{4}$ Deg. of *Cancer*: For since they both are going towards the same Parts, and the Motion of the Moon, which is farther distant from the Conjunction, hath a later *Epocha*, the Moon will be *A*, the Sun *B*, and $\frac{cge+cdh}{cg-df}$ the Length of the Moon's Way, which, if you write 13 for *c*, 1 for *f*, *d*, and *g*, 90 for *e*, and 3 for *h*, will become $\frac{13\times1\times90+13\times1\times3}{13\times1-1\times1}$, that is, $\frac{1209}{12}$, or $100\frac{3}{4}$ Degrees; and then add these Degrees to the Beginning of *Aries*, and there will come out $10\frac{3}{4}$ Deg. of *Cancer*.

EXAMPLE II. If two Post-Boys, *A* and *B*, being in the Morning 59 Miles asunder, set out to meet each other, and *A* goes 7 Miles in 2 Hours, and *B* 8 Miles in 3 Hours, and *B* begins his Journey 1 Hour later than *A*, it is demanded how far *A* will have gone before he meets *B*? Answer, 35 Miles. For since they go towards each other, and *A* sets out first, $\frac{cge+cdh}{cg+df}$ will be the Length of his Journey; and writing 7 for *c*, 2 for *f*, 8 for *d*, 3 for *g*, 59 for *e*, and 1 for *h*, this will become $\frac{7\times3\times59+7\times8\times1}{7\times3+8\times2}$, that is, $\frac{1295}{37}$ or 35.

PROBLEM VI.

Giving the Power of any Agent, to find how many such Agents will perform a given Effect a, *in a given Time* b.

Let the Power of the Agent be such that it can produce the Effect *c* in the Time *d*, and it will be as the Time *d* to the Time *b*, so the Effect *c*, which that Agent can produce in the Time *d*, to the Effect which he can produce in the Time *b*, which therefore will be $\frac{bc}{d}$. Again, as the Effect of one Agent $\frac{bc}{d}$ to the Effect of all *a*; so that single Agent to all the Agents; and thus the Number of the Agents will be $\frac{ad}{bc}$.

EXAMPLE. If a Scribe can in 8 Days write 15 Sheets, how many such Scribes must there be to write 405 Sheets in 9 Days? Answer 24. For if 8 be substituted for *d*, 15 for *c*, 405 for *a*, and 9 for *b*, the Number $\frac{ad}{bc}$ will become $\frac{405\times8}{9\times15}$, that is, $\frac{3240}{135}$, or 24.

PROBLEM VII.

The Forces of several Agents being given, to determine x *the Time, wherein they will jointly perform a given Effect* d.

Let the Forces of the Agents A, B, C, be supposed, which in the Times *e*, *f*, *g* can produce the Effects *a*, *b*, *c* respectively; and these in the Time *x* will produce the Effects $\frac{ax}{e}$, $\frac{bx}{f}$, $\frac{cx}{g}$; wherefore is $\frac{ax}{e}+\frac{bx}{f}+\frac{cx}{g}=d$, and by Reduction $x=\frac{d}{\frac{a}{e}+\frac{b}{f}+\frac{c}{g}}$.

EXAMPLE. Three Workmen can do a Piece of Work in certain Times, *viz.* *A* once in 3 Weeks, *B* thrice in 8 Weeks, and *C* five times in 12 Weeks. It is desired to know in what Time they can finish it jointly? Here then are the Forces of the Agents *A*, *B*, *C*, which in the Times 3, 8, 12 can produce the Effects 1, 3, 5, respectively, and the Time is sought where-

L 2 in

in they can do one Effect. Wherefore, for a, b, c; d; e, f, g write 1, 3, 5, 1, 3, 8, 12, and there will ariſe $x = \frac{1}{\frac{1}{3}+\frac{3}{8}+\frac{5}{12}}$, or $\frac{8}{9}$ of a Week, that is, [allowing 6 working Days to a Week, and 12 Hours to each Day] 5 Days and 4 Hours, the Time wherein they will jointly finiſh it.

Problem VIII.

So, to compound unlike Mixtures of two or more things, that the Things mixed together may have a given Ratio to one another.

Let the given Quantity of one Mixture be $dA+eB+fC$, the ſame Quantity of another Mixture $gA+hB+kC$, and the ſame of a third $lA+mB+nC$, where A, B, C denote the Things mixed, and d, e, f, g, h, &c. the Proportions of the ſame in the Mixtures. And let $pA+qB+rC$ be the Mixture which muſt be compoſed of theſe three Mixtures; and ſuppoſe x, y and z to be the Numbers, by which if the three given Mixtures be reſpectively multiplied, their Sum will become $pA+qB+rC$.

Therefore is $\left\{\begin{array}{l} dxA+exB+fxC \\ +gyA+hyB+kyC \\ +lzA+mzB+nzC \end{array}\right\} = pA+qB+rC$.

And then comparing the Terms by making $dx+gy+lz=p$, $ex+hy+mz=q$, and $fx+ky+nz=r$, and by Reduction $x = \frac{p-gy-lz}{d} = \frac{q-hy-mz}{e} = \frac{r-ky-nz}{f}$. And again, the Equations $\frac{p-gy-lz}{d} = \frac{q-hy-mz}{e}$, and $\frac{q-hy-mz}{e} = \frac{r-ky-nz}{f}$ by Reduction give $\frac{ep-dq+dmz-elz}{eg-dh} (=y) = \frac{fq-er+enz-fmz}{fh-ek}$: Which, if abbreviated by writing α for $ep-dq$, β for $dm-el$, γ for $eg-dh$, δ for $fq-er$, ζ for $en-fm$, and θ for $fh-ek$, will become $\frac{\alpha+\beta z}{\gamma} = \frac{\delta+\zeta z}{\theta}$, and by Reduction $\frac{\theta\alpha-\gamma\delta}{\gamma\zeta-\beta\theta} = z$. Having found z, put $\frac{\alpha+\beta z}{\gamma} = y$, and $\frac{p-gy-lz}{d} = x$.

Example. If there were three Mixtures of Metals melted down together; of the firſt of which a Pound [Averdupois] contains of Silver ℥ 12, of Braſs ℥ 1, and of Tin ℥ 3; of the ſecond, a Pound contains of Silver ℥ 1, of Braſs ℥ 12, and of Tin ℥ 3; and a Pound of the third contains of Braſs ℥ 14, of Tin ℥ 2, and no Silver; and let theſe Mixtures be ſo to be compounded, that a Pound of the Compoſition may contain of Silver ℥ 4, of Braſs ℥ 9, and of Tin ℥ 3: For d, e, f; g, h, k; l, m, n; p, q, r, write 12, 1, 3; 1, 12, 3; 0, 14, 2; 4, 9, 3 reſpectively, and α will be $(= ep-dq = 1\times 4 - 12\times 9) = -104$, and β $(= dm-el = 12\times 14 - 1\times 0) = 168$, and ſo $\gamma = -143$, $\delta = 24$, $\zeta = -40$, and $\theta = 33$. And therefore $z \left(= \frac{\theta\alpha-\gamma\delta}{\gamma\zeta-\beta\theta} = \frac{-3432+3432}{5720-5544}\right) = 0$; $y \left(= \frac{\alpha+\beta z}{\gamma} = \frac{-104+0}{-143}\right) = \frac{8}{11}$, and $x \left(= \frac{p-gy-lz}{d} = \frac{4-\frac{8}{11}}{12}\right) = \frac{3}{11}$. Wherefore, if there be mix'd $\frac{8}{11}$ Parts of a Pound of the ſecond Mixture, $\frac{3}{11}$ Parts of a Pound of the firſt, and nothing of the third, the Aggregate will be a Pound, containing four Ounces of Silver, nine of Braſs, and three of Tin.

Problem IX.

The Prices of ſeveral Mixtures of the ſame Things, and the Proportions of the Things mixed together being given, to determine the Price of each of the Things mixed.

Of each of the Things A, B, C, let the Price of the Mixture $dA+gB+lC$ be p, of the Mixture $eA+hB+mC$ the Price q, and of the Mixture $fA+kB+nC$ the Price r; and of thoſe Things A, B, C let the Prices x, y, z, be demanded. For the Things A, B, C ſubſtitute their Prices x, y, z, and there will ariſe the Equations $dx+gy+lz=p$, $ex+hy+mz=q$, and $fx+ky+nz=r$; from which, by proceeding as in the foregoing Problem, there will in like manner be got $\frac{\theta\alpha-\gamma\delta}{\gamma\zeta-\beta\theta} = z$, $\frac{\alpha+\beta z}{\gamma} = y$, and $\frac{p-gy-lz}{d} = x$.

Example

EXAMPLE. One bought 40 Bushels of Wheat, 24 Bushels of Barley, and 20 Bushels of Oats together, for 15 Pounds 12 Shillings. Again, he bought of the same Grain 26 Bushels of Wheat, 30 Bushels of Barley, and 50 Bushels of Oats together, for 16 Pounds. And thirdly, he bought of the like kind of Grain, 24 Bushels of Wheat, 120 Bushels of Barley, and 100 Bushels of Oats together, for 34 Pounds. It is demanded at what Rate a Bushel of each of the Grains ought to be valued. Answer, a Bushel of Wheat at 5 Shillings, of Barley at 3 Shillings, and of Oats at 2 Shillings. For instead of d, g, l; e, h, m; f, k, n; p, q, r, by writing respectively 40, 24, 20; 26, 30, 50; 24, 120, 100; $15\frac{3}{5}$, 16, and 34, there arises $\alpha\ (= ep - dq = 26 \times 15\frac{3}{5} - 40 \times 16) = -234\frac{2}{5}$; and $\beta\ (= dm - el = 40 \times 50 - 26 \times 20) = 1480$; and thus $\gamma = -576$, $\delta = -500$, $\zeta = 1400$, and $\theta = -2400$. Then $z \left(= \frac{\theta\alpha - \gamma\delta}{\gamma\zeta - \beta\theta} = \frac{562560 - 288000}{-806400 + 3552000} = \frac{274560}{2745600}\right) = \frac{1}{10}$; $y \left(= \frac{\alpha + \beta z}{\gamma} = \frac{-234\frac{2}{5} + 148}{-576}\right) = \frac{3}{20}$; and $x \left(= \frac{p - gy - lz}{d} = \frac{15\frac{3}{5} - \frac{18}{5} - 2}{40}\right) = \frac{1}{4}$. Therefore a Bushel of Wheat cost $\frac{1}{4}$ ℔, or 5 Shillings, a Bushel of Barley $\frac{3}{20}$ ℔, or 3 Shillings, and a Bushel of Oats $\frac{1}{10}$ ℔, or 2 Shillings.

PROBLEM X.

There being given the specifick Gravity both of the Mixture and the Things mixed, to find the Proportion of the mixed Things to one another.

Let e be the specifick Gravity of the Mixture A + B, a the specifick Gravity of A, and b the specifick Gravity of B; and since the absolute Gravity, or the Weight, is composed of the Bulk of the Body and the specifick Gravity, a A will be the Weight of A; b B of B; and e A + e B the Weight of the Mixture A + B; and therefore a A + b B = e A + e B; and from thence a A − e A = e B − b B or $e - b : a - e$ :: A : B.

EXAMPLE.

EXAMPLE. Suppose the Gravity or specifick Weight of Gold to be as 19, and of Silver as $10\frac{1}{3}$, and King *Hiero's* Crown as 17; and it will be 10 : 3 ($e - b : a - e$ :: A : B) :: Bulk of Gold in the Crown : Bulk of Silver, or 190 : 31 (:: $19 \times 10 : 10\frac{1}{3} \times 3$ :: $a \times \overline{e - b} : b \times \overline{a - e}$) :: the Weight of Gold in the Crown, to the Weight of Silver, and 221 : 31 :: the Weight of the Crown, to the Weight of the Silver.

PROBLEM XI.

If the Number of Oxen a *eat up the Meadow* b *in the Time* c; *and the Number of Oxen* d *eat up as good a Piece of Pasture* e *in the Time* f, *and the Grass grows uniformly; to find how many Oxen will eat up the like Pasture* g *in the Time* h.

If the Oxen a in the Time c eat up the Pasture b; then, by Proportion, the Oxen $\frac{e}{b}a$ in the same Time c, or the Oxen $\frac{ec}{bf}a$ in the Time f, or the Oxen $\frac{ec}{bh}a$ in the Time h will eat up the Pasture e; supposing the Grass did not grow at all after the Time c. But since, by reason of the Growth of the Grass, all the Oxen d in the Time f can eat up only the Meadow e, therefore that Growth of the Grass in the Meadow e in the Time $f - c$ will be so much as alone would be sufficient to feed the Oxen $d - \frac{eca}{bf}$ the Time f, that is as much as would suffice to feed the Oxen $\frac{df}{h} - \frac{eca}{bh}$ in the Time h. And in the Time $h - c$, by Proportion so much would be the Growth of the Grass as would be sufficient to feed the Oxen $\frac{h-c}{f-c}$ into $\frac{df}{h} - \frac{eca}{bh}$ or $\frac{bdfh - ecah - bdcf + aecc}{bfh - bch}$. Add this Increment to the Oxen $\frac{aec}{bh}$, and there will come out $\frac{bdfh - ecah - bdcf + ecfa}{bfh - bch}$, the Number of Oxen which the Pasture e will suffice to feed in the Time h. And so

L

ſo in Proportion the Meadow g will ſuffice to feed the Oxen $\frac{gbdfh - ecagh - bdcgf + ecfga}{befh - bceh}$ during the ſame Time h.

Example. If 12 Oxen eat up $3\frac{1}{3}$ Acres of Paſture in 4 Weeks, and 21 Oxen eat up ten Acres of like Paſture in 9 Weeks; to find how many Oxen will eat up 24 Acres in 18 Weeks? Anſwer 36; for that Number will be found by ſubſtituting in $\frac{bdfgh - ecagh - bdcgf + ecfga}{befh - bceh}$ the Numbers 12, $3\frac{1}{3}$, 4, 21, 10, 9, 24, and 18 for the Letters a, b, c, d, e, f, g, and h reſpectively; but the Solution, perhaps, will be no leſs expedite, if it be brought out from the firſt Principles, in Form of the precedent literal Solution. As if 12 Oxen in 4 Weeks eat up $3\frac{1}{3}$ Acres, then by Proportion 36 Oxen in 4 Weeks, or 16 Oxen in 9 Weeks, or 8 Oxen in 18 Weeks, will eat up 10 Acres, on Suppoſition that the Graſs did not grow. But ſince by reaſon of the Growth of the Graſs 21 Oxen in 9 Weeks can eat up only 10 Acres, that Growth of the Graſs in 10 Acres for the laſt 5 Weeks will be as much as would be ſufficient to feed the Exceſs of 21 Oxen above 16, that is 5 Oxen for 9 Weeks, or what is the ſame Thing, to feed $\frac{5}{2}$ Oxen for 18 Weeks. And in 14 Weeks (the Exceſs of 18 above the firſt 4) the Increaſe of the Graſs, by Analogy, will be ſuch, as to be ſufficient to feed 7 Oxen for 18 Weeks; for it is 5 Weeks : 14 Weeks :: $\frac{5}{2}$ Oxen : 7 Oxen. Wherefore add theſe 7 Oxen, which the Growth of the Graſs alone would ſuffice to feed, to the 8, which the Graſs without Growth after 4 Weeks would feed, and the Sum will be 15 Oxen. And, laſtly, if 10 Acres ſuffice to feed 15 Oxen for 18 Weeks, then, in Proportion, 24 Acres would ſuffice 36 Oxen for the ſame Time.

Problem XII.

Having given the Magnitudes and Motions of Spherical Bodies perfectly elaſtick, moving in the ſame right Line, and ſtriking againſt one another, to determine their Motions after Reflexion.

The Reſolution of this Queſtion depends on theſe Conditions, that each Body will ſuffer as much by Re-action as the Action

Action of each is upon the other, and that they muſt recede from each other after Reflexion with the ſame Velocity or Swiftneſs as they met before it. Theſe Things being ſuppoſed, let the Velocity of the Bodies A and B, be a and b reſpectively; and their Motions (as being compoſed of their Bulk and Velocity together) will be aA and bB. And if the Bodies tend the ſame Way, and A moving more ſwiftly, follows B, make x the Decrement of the Motion aA, and the Increment of the Motion bB ariſing by the Percuſſion; and the Motions after Reflexion will be $aA - x$ and $bB + x$; and the Celerities $\frac{aA - x}{A}$ and $\frac{bB + x}{B}$, whoſe Difference is $= a - b$ the Difference of the Celerities before Reflexion. Therefore there ariſes this Equation $\frac{bB + x}{B} - \frac{aA - x}{A} = a - b$, and thence by Reduction x becomes $= \frac{2aAB - 2bAB}{A + B}$, which being ſubſtituted for x in the Celerities $\frac{aA - x}{A}$, and $\frac{bB + x}{B}$, there comes out $\frac{aA - aB + 2bB}{A + B}$ for the Celerity of A, and $\frac{2aA - bA + bB}{A + B}$ for the Celerity of B after Reflexion.

But if the Bodies move towards one another, then changing every where the Sign of b, the Velocities after Reflexion will be $\frac{aA - aB - 2bB}{A + B}$ and $\frac{2aA + bA - bB}{A + B}$; either of which, if they come out, by Chance, Negative, it argues that Motion, after Reflexion, to tend a contrary Way to that which A tended to before Reflexion. Which is alſo to be underſtood of A's Motion in the former Caſe.

Example. If the homogeneous Bodies [or Bodies of the ſame Sort] A of 3 Pounds with 8 Degrees of Velocity, and B a Body of 9 Pounds with 2 Degrees of Velocity, tend the ſame Way; then for A, a, B and b, write 3, 8, 9 and 2; and $\left(\frac{aA - aB + 2bB}{A + B}\right)$ beomes -1, and

M (2 a

$\left(\frac{2aA - bA + bB}{A + B}\right)$ becomes 5. Therefore A will return back with one Degree of Velocity after Reflexion, and B will go on with 5 Degrees.

PROBLEM XIII.

To find three Numbers in continual Proportion, whose Sum shall be 20, *and the Sum of their Squares* 140?

Make the first of the Numbers $= x$, and the second $= y$, and the third will be $\frac{yy}{x}$, and consequently $x + y + \frac{yy}{x} = 20$; and $xx + yy + \frac{y^4}{xx} = 140$. And by Reduction $xx \begin{matrix} +y \\ -20 \end{matrix} x + yy = 0$, and $x^4 \begin{matrix} +yy \\ -140 \end{matrix} xx + y^4 = 0$. Now to exterminate x, for a, b, c, d, e, f, g, h, in the third Rule, substitute respectively $1, 0, yy - 140, 0, y^4; 1, y - 20$, and yy; and there will come out $-yy + 280 \times y^6 : +\overline{2yy - 40y + 260} \times \overline{260y^4 - 40y^5} : +3y^4 \times y^4 : -2yy \times y^3 - 40y^5 + 400y^4 : = 0$; and by Multiplication $1600y^5 - 20800y^5 - 67600y = 0$. And by Reduction $4yy - 52y + 169 = 0$. Or (the Root being extracted) $2y - 13 = 0$, or $y = 6\frac{1}{2}$. Which is found more short by another Method before, but not so obvious as this. Moreover, to find x, substitute $6\frac{1}{2}$ for y in the Equation $xx \begin{matrix} +y \\ -20 \end{matrix} x + yy = 0$, and there will arise $xx - 13\frac{1}{2}x + 42\frac{1}{4} = 0$, or $xx = 13\frac{1}{2}x + 42\frac{1}{4}$, and having extracted the Root $x = 6\frac{3}{4} +$ or $- \sqrt{3\frac{5}{16}}$; *viz.* $6\frac{3}{4} + \sqrt{3\frac{5}{6}}$ is the greatest of the three Numbers sought, and $6\frac{3}{4} - \sqrt{3\frac{5}{16}}$ the least. For x denotes ambiguously either of the extreme Numbers, and thence there will come out two Values, either of which may be x, the other being $\frac{yy}{x}$.

The same otherwise. Putting the Numbers x, y and $\frac{yy}{x}$

as before, you will have $x + y + \frac{yy}{x} = 20$, or $xx = \begin{matrix} 20 \\ -y \end{matrix} x - yy$, and extracting the Root $x = 10 - \frac{1}{2}y + \sqrt{100 - 10y - \frac{3}{4}yy}$ for the first Number: Take away this and y from 20, and there remains $\frac{yy}{x} = 10 - \frac{1}{2}y - \sqrt{100 - 10y - \frac{3}{4}yy}$ the third Number. And the Sum of the Squares arising from these three Numbers is $400 - 40y$, and so $400 - 40y = 140$, or $y = 6\frac{1}{2}$. And having found the mean Number $6\frac{1}{2}$, substitute it for y in the first and third Number above found; and the first will become $6\frac{3}{4} + \sqrt{3\frac{5}{16}}$, and the third $6\frac{3}{4} - \sqrt{3\frac{5}{16}}$, as before.

PROBLEM XIV.

To find four Numbers in continual Proportion, the two Means whereof together make 12, *and the two Extremes* 20.

Let x be the second Number; and $12 - x$ will be the third; $\frac{xx}{12 - x}$ the first; and $\frac{144 - 24x + xx}{x}$ the fourth; and consequently $\frac{xx}{12 - x} + \frac{144 - 24x + xx}{x} = 20$. And by Reduction $xx = 12x - 30\frac{6}{7}$, or $x = 6 + \sqrt{5\frac{1}{7}}$. Which being found, the other Numbers are given from those above.

PROBLEM XV.

To find four Numbers continually proportional, whereof the Sum a *is given, and also the Sum of their Squares* b.

Although we ought for the most Part to seek the Quantities required immediately, yet if there are two that are ambiguous, that is, that involve both the same Conditions, (as here the two Means and two Extremes of the four Proportionals) the best Way is to seek other Quantities that are not ambiguous, by which these may be determined, as suppose their Sum, or Difference, or Rectangle. Let us therefore make the Sum of the two mean Numbers to be s, and the Rectangle r; and the Sum of the Extremes will be $a - s$, and the Rectangle also r, because of the Proportionality. Now that from hence these four Numbers may be found, make x the first, and y the second;

M 2 and

and $s-y$ will be the third; and $a-s-x$ the fourth; and the Rectangle under the Means $sy-yy=r$, and thence one Mean $y=\frac{1}{2}s+\sqrt{\frac{1}{4}ss-r}$, the other $s-y=\frac{1}{2}s-\sqrt{\frac{1}{4}ss-r}$. Alſo, the Rectangle under the Extremes $ax-sx-xx=r$,

and thence one Extreme $x=\frac{a-s}{2}+\sqrt{\frac{ss-2as+aa}{4}-r}$,

and the other $a-s-x=\frac{a-s}{2}-\sqrt{\frac{ss-2as+aa}{4}-r}$.

The Sum of the Squares of theſe four Numbers is $2ss-2as+aa-4r$ which is $=b$. Therefore $r=\frac{1}{2}ss-\frac{1}{2}as+\frac{1}{4}aa-\frac{1}{4}b$, which being ſubſtituted for r, there come out the four Numbers as follows:

The two Means $\begin{cases}\frac{1}{2}s+\sqrt{\frac{1}{4}b-\frac{1}{4}ss+\frac{1}{2}as-\frac{1}{4}aa} \\ \frac{1}{2}s-\sqrt{\frac{1}{4}b-\frac{1}{4}ss+\frac{1}{2}as-\frac{1}{4}aa}.\end{cases}$

The two Extremes $\begin{cases}\frac{a-s}{2}+\sqrt{\frac{1}{4}b-\frac{1}{4}ss} \\ \frac{a-s}{2}-\sqrt{\frac{1}{4}b-\frac{1}{4}ss}.\end{cases}$

Yet there remains the Value of s to be found. Wherefore, to abbreviate the Terms, for theſe Quantities ſubſtitute

$$\frac{1}{2}s+p. \qquad \frac{a-s}{2}+q$$

and

$$\frac{1}{2}s-p. \qquad \frac{a-s}{2}-q$$

And make the Rectangle under the ſecond and fourth equal to the Square of the third, ſince this Condition of the Queſtion is not yet ſatisfied, and you will have $\frac{as-ss}{4}-\frac{1}{2}qs+\frac{pa-ps}{2}-pq=\frac{1}{4}ss-ps+pp$. Make alſo the Rectangle under the firſt and third equal to the Square of the ſecond, and you will have $\frac{as-ss}{4}+\frac{1}{2}qs+\frac{-pa+ps}{2}-pq=\frac{1}{4}ss+ps+pp$. Take the firſt of theſe Equations from the latter, and there will remain $qs-pa+ps=2ps$, or $qs=pa+ps$. Reſtore now $\sqrt{\frac{1}{4}b-\frac{1}{4}ss+\frac{1}{2}as-\frac{1}{4}aa}$ in the Place of p, and $\sqrt{\frac{1}{4}b-\frac{1}{4}ss}$ in the Place of q, and you will have $s\sqrt{\frac{1}{4}b-\frac{1}{4}ss}=\overline{a+s}\sqrt{\frac{1}{4}b-\frac{1}{4}ss+\frac{1}{2}as-\frac{1}{4}aa}$, and by ſquaring $ss=-\frac{b}{a}s+\frac{1}{2}aa-\frac{1}{2}b$, or $s=-\frac{b}{2a}+\sqrt{\frac{bb}{4aa}+\frac{1}{2}aa-\frac{1}{2}b}$; which being found, the four Numbers ſought are given from what has been ſhewn above.

Problem XVI.

If an annual Penſion of the Number of Pounds a, *to be paid in the five next following Years, be bought for the ready Money* c, *to find what the Compound Intereſt of* 100 l. per Annum *will amount to?*

Make $1-x$ the Compound Intereſt of the Money x for a Year, that is, that the Money 1 to be paid after one Year is worth x in ready Money: and, by Proportion, the Money a to be paid after one Year will be worth ax in ready Money, and after two Years it will be worth axx, and after three Years ax^3, and after four Years ax^4, and after five Years ax . Add theſe five Terms, and you will have $ax^5+ax^4+ax^3+axx+ax=c$, or $x^5+x^4+x^3+x^2+x=\frac{c}{a}$ an Equation of five Dimenſions, by Help of which when x is found by the † Rules to be taught hereafter, put $x:1::100:y$, and $y-100$ will be the Compound Intereſt of 100 *l. per Annum.*

It is ſufficient to have given theſe Inſtances in Queſtions where only the Proportions of Quantities are to be conſidered, without the Poſitions of Lines: Let us now proceed to the Solutions of Geometrical Problems.

† Viz. *by finding the firſt Figures of the Root by any mechanical Conſtruction, and the remaining Figures by the Method of* Vieta.

How

How Geometrical Queſtions may be reduced to Equations.

GEometrical Queſtions may be reduced ſometimes to Equations with as much Eaſe, and by the ſame Laws, as thoſe we have propoſed concerning abſtracted Quantities. As if the right Line [See *Fig. 6.*] AB be to be divided in mean and extreme Proportion in C, that is, ſo that BE the Square of the greateſt Part ſhall be equal to the Rectangle BD contained under the whole and the leaſt Part; having put $AB = a$, and $BC = x$, then will AC be $= a - x$, and $xx = a$ into $a - x$; an Equation which by Reduction gives $x = -\frac{1}{2}a + \sqrt{\frac{5}{4}aa}$.

But in Geometrical Affairs, which more frequently occur, they ſo much depend on the various Poſitions and complex Relations of Lines, that they require ſome farther Invention and Artifice to bring them into Algebraick Terms. And though it is difficult to preſcribe any Thing in theſe Sorts of Caſes, and every Perſon's own Genius ought to be his Guide in theſe Operations; yet I will endeavour to ſhew the Way to Learners. You are to know therefore, that Queſtions about the ſame Lines, related after any definite Manner to one another, may be variouſly propoſed, by making different Quantities the *Quæſita* or Things ſought, from different *Data* or Things given. But of what *Data* or *Quæſita* ſoever the Queſtion be propoſed, its Solution will follow the ſame Way by an Analytick Series, without any other Variation of Circumſtance beſides the feigned Species of Lines, or the Names by which we are uſed to diſtinguiſh the given Quantities from thoſe ſought.

As if the Queſtion be of an *Iſoſceles* Triangle CBD [See *Fig. 7.*] inſcribed in a Circle, whoſe Sides BC, BD, and Baſe CD, are to be compared with the Diameter of the Circle AB. This may either be propoſed of the Inveſtigation of the *Diameter* from the given Sides and Baſe, or of the Inveſtigation of the *Baſis* from the given Sides and Diameter; or laſtly, of the Inveſtigation of the *Sides* from the given Baſe and Diameter; but however it be propoſed, it will be reduced to an Equation by the ſame Series of an Analyſis, *viz.* If the *Diameter* be ſought, I put $AB = x$, $CD = a$, and BC or $BD = b$. Then (having drawn AC) by reaſon of the ſimilar Triangles ABC, and CBE, it will be AB : BC :: BC : BE, or $x : b :: b : BE$. Wherefore $BE = \frac{bb}{x}$. Moreover CE is $= \frac{1}{2}CD$ or $\frac{1}{2}a$; and by reaſon of the right Angle CEB, $CEq + BEq = BCq$, that is $\frac{1}{4}aa + \frac{b^4}{xx} = bb$. Which Equation, by Reduction, will give the Quantity x ſought.

But if the *Baſe* be ſought, put $AB = c$, $CD = x$, and BC or $BD = b$. Then (AC being drawn) becauſe of the ſimilar Triangles ABC and CBE, there is AB : BC :: BC : BE, or $c : b :: b : BE$. Wherefore $BE = \frac{bb}{c}$; and alſo $CE = \frac{1}{2}CD$, or $\frac{1}{2}x$. And becauſe the Angle CEB is right, $CEq + BEq = BCq$, that is, $\frac{1}{4}xx + \frac{b^4}{cc} = bb$; an Equation which will give by Reduction the ſought Quantity x.

But if the Side BC or BD be ſought, put $AB = c$, $CD = a$, and BC or $BD = x$. And (AC being drawn as before) by reaſon of the ſimilar Triangles ABC and CBE, it is AB : BC :: BC : BE; or $c : x :: x : BE$. Wherefore $BE = \frac{xx}{c}$. Moreover CE is $= \frac{1}{2}CD$ or $\frac{1}{2}a$; and by reaſon of the right Angle CEB, $CEq + BEq$ is $= BCq$, that is, $\frac{1}{4}aa + \frac{x^4}{cc} = xx$; and the Equation, by Reduction, will give the Quantity ſought, *viz.* x.

You ſee therefore that in every Caſe, the Calculus, by which you come to the Equation, is the ſame every where, and brings out the ſame Equation, excepting only that I have denoted the Lines by different Letters according as I made the *Data* and *Quæſita* different. And from different *Data* and *Quæſita* there ariſes a Diverſity in the Reduction of the Equation found: For the Reduction of the Equation $\frac{1}{4}aa + \frac{b^4}{xx} = bb$, in order to obtain $x = \frac{2bb}{\sqrt{4bb - aa}}$ the Value of AB, is different from the Reduction of the Equation

Equation $\frac{1}{4}xx+\frac{b^4}{cc}=bb$, in order to obtain $x=\frac{2b}{c}\sqrt{cc-bb}$, the Value of C D; and the Reduction of the Equation $\frac{1}{4}aa+\frac{x^4}{cc}=xx$ very different to obtain $x=\sqrt{\frac{1}{4}cc\pm\frac{1}{2}c\sqrt{cc-aa}}$ the Value of B C or B D: (as well as this alſo, $\frac{1}{4}aa+\frac{b^4}{cc}=bb$, to bring out c, a, or b, ought to be reduced after different Methods) but there was no Difference in the Inveſtigation of theſe Equations. And hence it is that Analyſts order us to make no Difference between the given and ſought Quantities. For ſince the ſame Computation agrees to any Caſe of the given and ſought Quantities, it is convenient that they ſhould be conceived and compared without any Difference, that we may the more rightly judge of the Methods of computing them; or rather it is convenient that you ſhould imagine, that the Queſtion is propoſed of thoſe *Data* and *Quæſita* given and ſought Quantities, by which you think it is moſt eaſy for you to make out your Equation.

Having therefore any Problem propoſed, compare the Quantities which it involves, and making no Difference between the given and ſought ones, conſider how they depend one upon another, that you may know what Quantities if they are aſſumed, will, by proceeding ſynthetically, give the reſt. To do which, there is no need that you ſhould at firſt of all conſider how they may be deduced from one another Algebraically; but this general Conſideration will ſuffice, that they may be ſome how or other deduced by a direct Connexion with one another. For Example; If the Queſtion be put of the Diameter of the Circle A D, [See *Fig.* 8.] and the three Lines A B, B C, and C D inſcribed in a Semi-circle, and from the reſt given you are to find B C; at firſt Sight it is manifeſt, that the Diameter A D determines the Semi-circle, and then that the Lines A B and C D by Inſcription determine the Points B and C, and conſequently the Quantity ſought B C, and that by a direct Connexion; and yet after what Manner B C is to be had from theſe *Data* or given Quantities, is not ſo evident to be found by an Analyſis. The ſame Thing is alſo to be underſtood of A B or C D if they were to be ſought from the other *Data*. Now, if A D were to be found from the given Quantities A B, B C, and C D, it

2 is

is equally evident it could not be done Synthetically; for the Diſtance of the Points A and D depends on the Angles B and C, and thoſe Angles on the Circle in which the given Lines are to be inſcribed, and that Circle is not given without knowing the Diameter A D. The Nature of the Thing therefore requires, that A D be ſought, not Synthetically, but by aſſuming it as given to make thence a Regreſſion to the Quantities given.

When you ſhall have thoroughly perceived the different Orderings of the Proceſs by which the Terms of the Queſtion may be explained, *make Uſe of any of the Synthetical Methods by aſſuming Lines as given, from which the Proceſs to others ſeems very eaſy, and the Regreſſion to them very difficult.* For the Computation, though it may proceed through various Mediums, yet will begin from thoſe Lines; and will be ſooner performed by ſuppoſing the Queſtion to be ſuch, as if it was propoſed of thoſe *Data*, and ſome Quantity ſought that would eaſily come out from them, than by thinking of the Queſtion as it is really propoſed. Thus, in the propoſed Example, if from the reſt of the Quantities given you were to find A D. Since I perceive that it cannot be done Synthetically, but yet provided it was given, I could proceed in my Ratiocination in a direct Connexion from that to other Things, I aſſume A D as given, and then I begin to compute as if it was given indeed, and ſome of the other Quantities, *viz.* ſome of the given ones, as A B, B C, or C D, were ſought. And by this Method, by carrying on the Computation from the Quantities aſſumed after this Way to the others, as the Relations of the Lines to one another direct, there will always be obtained an Equation between two Values of ſome one Quantity, whether one of thoſe Values be a Letter ſet down as a Repreſentation or Name at the Beginning of the Work for that Quantity, and the other a Value of it found out by Computation, or whether both be found by a Computation made after different Ways.

But when you have compared the Terms of the Queſtion thus generally, there is more Art and Invention required to find out the particular Connexions or Relations of the Lines that ſhall accommodate them to Computation. For thoſe Things, which to a Perſon that does not ſo thoroughly conſider them, may ſeem to be immediately, and by a very near Relation connected together, when we have a Mind to expreſs that Relation Algebraically, require a great deal more round-about Proceeding, and oblige you to begin your Schemes

N anew

anew, and carry on your Computation Step by Step; as may appear by finding BC from AD, AB, and CD. For you are only to proceed by ſuch Propoſitions or Enunciations that can fitly be repreſented in Algebraick Terms, whereof in particular you have ſome from *Eucl. Ax.* 19. *Prop.* 4. *Book* 6. and *Prop.* 47. of the firſt.

In the firſt Place therefore, the Calculus may be aſſiſted by the Addition and Subtraction of Lines, ſo that from the Values of the Parts you may find the Values of the Whole, or from the Value of the Whole and one of the Parts you may obtain the Value of the other Part.

In the ſecond Place, the Calculus is promoted by the Proportionality of Lines; for we ſuppoſe (as above) that the Rectangle of the mean Terms, divided by either of the Extremes, gives the Value of the other; or, which is the ſame Thing, if the Values of all four of the Proportionals are firſt had, we make an Equality between the Rectangles of the Extremes and Means. But the Proportionality of Lines is beſt found out by the Semilarity of Triangles, which, as it is known by the Equality of their Angles, the Analyſt ought in particular to be converſant in comparing them, and conſequently not to be ignorant of *Eucl. Prop.* 5, 13, 15, 29, and 32 of the firſt Book, and of *Prop.* 4, 5, 6, 7, and 8 of the ſixth Book, and of the 20, 21, 22, 27, and 31 of the third Book of his *Elem.* To which alſo may be added the 3d *Prop.* of the ſixth Book, wherein, from the Proportion of the Sides is inferred the Equality of the Angles, and *è contra.* Sometimes likewiſe the 36 and 37th *Prop.* of the third Book will do the ſame Thing.

In the third Place, the Calculus is promoted by the Addition or Subtraction of Squares, *viz.* In right angled Triangles we add the Squares of the leſſer Sides to obtain the Square of the greateſt, or from the Square of the greateſt Side we ſubtract the Square of one of the leſſer, to obtain the Square of the other.

And on theſe few Foundations (if we add to them *Prop.* 1. of the 6th *Elem* when the Buſineſs relates to Superficies, as alſo ſome Propoſitions taken out of the 11th and 12th of *Euclid*, when Solids come in Queſtion) the whole Analytick Art, as to right-lined Geometry, depends. Moreover, all the Difficulties of Problems may be reduced to the ſole Compoſition of Lines out of Parts, and the Similarity of Triangles; ſo that there is no Occaſion to make uſe of other Theorems; becauſe they may all be reſolved into theſe two, and conſequently into the Solutions that may be drawn from them. And, for an Inſtance of this, I have ſubjoined a Problem about letting fall a Perpendicular upon the Baſe of an oblique-angled Triangle, which is ſolved without the Help of the 47th *Prop.* of the firſt Book of *Euclid.* But although it may be of Uſe not to be ignorant of the moſt ſimple Principles on which the Solutions of Problems depend, and though by only their Help any Problems may be ſolved; yet, for Expedition ſake, it will be convenient not only that the 47th *Prop.* of the firſt Book of *Euclid*, whoſe Uſe is moſt frequent, but alſo that other *Theorems* ſhould ſometimes be made Uſe of.

As if, for Example, a Perpendicular being let fall upon the Baſe of an oblique-angled Triangle, the Queſtion were (for the ſake of promoting Algebraick Calculus) to find the Segments of the Baſe; here it would be of Uſe to know, that the Difference of the Squares of the Sides is equal to the double Rectangle under the Baſe, and the Diſtance of the Perpendicular from the Middle of the Baſis.

If the Vertical Angle of any Triangle be biſected, it will not only be of Uſe to know, that the Baſe is divided in Proportion to the Sides, but alſo that the Difference of the Rectangles made by the Sides, and the Segments of the Baſe is equal to the Square of the Line that biſects the Angle.

If the Problem relate to Figures inſcribed in a Circle, this Theorem will frequently be of Uſe, *viz.* That in any quadrilateral Figure inſcribed in a Circle, the Rectangle of the Diagonals is equal to the Sum of the Rectangles of the oppoſite Sides.

The Analyſt may obſerve ſeveral Theorems of this Nature in his Practice, and reſerve them for his Uſe; but let him uſe them ſparingly, if he can, with equal Facility, or not much more Difficulty, deduce the Solution from more ſimple Principles of Computation. Wherefore let him take eſpecial Notice of the three Principles firſt propoſed, as being more known, more ſimple, more general, but a few, and yet ſufficient for all Problems, and let him endeavour to reduce all Difficulties to them before others.

But that theſe Theorems may be accommodated to the Solution of Problems, the *Schemes* are oft times to be farther conſtructed, and that moſt frequently, by producing out ſome of

N 2

of the Lines till they cut others, or become of an aſſigned Length; or by drawing from ſome remarkable Point, Lines parallel or perpendicular to others, or by conjoining ſome remarkable Points; as alſo ſometimes by conſtructing after other Methods, according as the State of the Problem, and the Theorems which are made uſe of to ſolve it, ſhall require. As for Example, If two Lines that do not meet each other, make given Angles with a certain third Line, perhaps we produce them ſo, that when they concur, or meet, they ſhall form a Triangle, whoſe Angles, and conſequently the Ratio's of their Sides, ſhall be given; or, if any Angle is given, or be equal to any one, we often complete it into a Triangle given in Specie, or ſimilar to ſome other, and that by producing ſome of the Lines in the Scheme, or by drawing a Line ſubtending an Angle. If the Triangle be an oblique angled one, we often reſolve it into two right angled ones, by letting fall a Perpendicular. If the Buſineſs concerns multilateral or many ſided Figures, we reſolve them into Triangles, by drawing Diagonal Lines; and ſo in others; always aiming at this End, *viz. that the Scheme may be reſolved either into given, or ſimilar, or right angled Triangles.* Thus, in the Example propoſed, [See *Fig.* 9.] I draw the Diagonal BD, and the Trapezium ABCD may be reſolved into the two Triangles, ABD a right angled one, and BDC an oblique angled one. Then I reſolve the oblique angled one into two right angled Triangles, by letting fall a Perpendicular from any of its Angles, B, C or D, upon the oppoſite Side; as from B upon CD produced to E, that BE may meet it perpendicularly. But ſince the Angles BAD and BCD make in the mean while two right ones (by 22 *Prop.* 3. *Elem.*) as well as BCE and BCD, I perceive the Angles BAD and BCE to be equal; conſequently the Triangles BCE and DAB to be ſimilar. And ſo I ſee that the Computation (by aſſuming AD, AB, and BC as if CD were ſought) may be thus carried on, *viz.* AD and AB (by reaſon of the right-angled Triangle ABD) give you BD. AD, AB, BD, and BC (by reaſon of the ſimilar Triangles ABD and CEB) give BE and CE. BD and BE (by reaſon of the right angled Triangle BED) give ED; and ED — EC gives CD. Whence there will be obtained an Equation between the Value of CD ſo found out, and the Algebraick Letter that was put for it. We may alſo (and for the greateſt Part it is better ſo to do, than to follow the Work too far in one continued Series) begin the Computation from different Principles, or at leaſt promote it by divers Methods to any one and the ſame Concluſion, that at length there may be obtained two Values of any the ſame Quantity, which may be made equal to one another. Thus, AD, AB, and BC, give BD, BE, and CE as before; then CD + CE gives ED; and laſtly, BD, and ED (by reaſon of the right angled Triangle BED) give BE. You might alſo very well form the Computation thus, that the Values of thoſe Quantities ſhould be ſought between which any other known Relation interceeds, and then that Relation will bring it to an Equation. Thus, ſince the Relation between the Lines BD, DC, BC, and CE, is manifeſt from the 12th *Prop.* of the ſecond Book of the *Elem. viz.* that $BDq - BCq - CDq$ is $= 2\,CD \times CE$: I ſeek BDq from the aſſumed AD and AB; and CE from the aſſumed AD, AB, and BC. And, laſtly, aſſuming CD I make $BDq - BCq - CDq = 2\,CD \times CE$. After ſuch Ways, and led by theſe Sorts of Conſultations, you ought always to take care of the Series of the Analyſis, and of the Scheme to be conſtructed in order to it, at once.

Hence, I believe, it will be manifeſt what Geometricians mean, when they bid you imagine that to be already done which is ſought. For making no Difference between the known and unknown Quantities, you may aſſume any of them to begin your Computation from, as much as if all had indeed been known by a previous Solution, and you were no longer to conſult the Solution of the Problem, but only the Proof of that Solution. Thus, in the firſt of the three Ways of computing already deſcribed, although perhaps AD be really ſought, yet I imagine CD to be the Quantity ſought, as if I had a mind to try whether its Value derived from AD will coincide with its Quantity before known. So alſo in the two laſt Methods, I do not propoſe, as my Aim, any Quantity to be ſought, but only ſome how or other to bring out an Equation from the Relations of the Lines: And, for ſake of that Buſineſs, I aſſume all the Lines AD, AB, BC, and CD as known, as much as if (the Queſtion being before ſolved) the Buſineſs was to enquire whether ſuch and ſuch Lines would tiſfy the Conditions of it, by agreeing with any Equations which the Relations of the Lines can exhibit. I entered upon the Buſineſs at firſt Sight after this Way, and with ſuch Sort of Conſultations; but when I arrive at an Equation, I change my Method, and endeavour to

to find the Quantity ſought by the Reduction and Solution of that Equation. Thus, laſtly, we aſſume often more Quantities as known, than what are expreſſed in the State of the Queſtion. Of this you may ſee an eminent Example in the 55th of the following Problems, where I have aſſumed a, b, and c, in the Equation $aa + bx + cx^2 = yy$ for determining the Conick Section; as alſo the other Lines r, s, t, v, of which the Problem, as it is propoſed, hints nothing. For you may aſſume any Quantities by the Help whereof it is poſſible to come to Equations; only taking this Care, that you obtain as many Equations from them as you aſſume Quantities really unknown.

After you have conſulted your Method of Computation, and drawn up your Scheme, give Names to the Quantities that enter into the Computation, (that is, from which being aſſumed, the Values of others are to be derived, until at laſt you come to an Equation) chuſing ſuch as involve all the Conditions of the Problem, and ſeem accommodated before others to the Buſineſs, and that ſhall render the Concluſion (as far as you can gueſs) more ſimple, but yet not more than what ſhall be ſufficient for your Purpoſe. Wherefore, do not give proper Names to Quantities which may be denominated from Names already given. Thus, from a whole Line and its Parts, from the three Sides of a right angled Triangle, and from three or four Proportionals, ſome one of the leaſt conſiderable we leave without a Name, becauſe its Value may be derived from the Names of the reſt. As in the Example already brought, if I make $AD = x$, and $AB = a$, I denote BD by no Letter, becauſe it is the third Side of a right angled Triangle ABD, and conſequently its Value is $\sqrt{xx - aa}$. Then if I call $BC = b$, ſince the Triangles DAB and BCE are ſimilar, and thence the Lines $AD : AB :: BC : CE$ proportional, to three whereof, $viz.$ to AD, AB, and BC there are already Names given; for that reaſon I leave the fourth CE without a Name, and in its room I make Uſe of $\frac{ab}{x}$ diſcovered from the foregoing Proportionality. And ſo if DC be called c, I give no Name to DE, becauſe from its Parts, DC and CE, or c and $\frac{ab}{x}$, its Value $c + \frac{ab}{x}$ comes out. [*See Figure* 10.]

But

But while I am talking of theſe Things, the Problem is almoſt reduced to an Equation. For, after the aforeſaid Letters are ſet down for the Species of the principal Lines, there remains nothing elſe to be done, but that out of thoſe Species the Values of other Lines be made out according to a preconceived Method, until after ſome foreſeen Way they come out to an Equation. And I ſee nothing wanting in this Caſe, except that by means of the right angled Triangles BCE and BDE I can bring out a double Value of BE, $viz.$ $BCq - CEq$ (or $bb - \frac{aabb}{xx}$) $= BEq$; as alſo $BDq - DEq$ (or $xx - aa - cc - \frac{2abc}{x} - \frac{aabb}{xx}$) $= BEq$. And hence (blotting out on both Sides $\frac{aabb}{xx}$) I ſhall have the Equation $bb = xx - aa - cc - \frac{2abc}{x}$; which being reduced, becomes $x^3 = \begin{array}{c} +aa \\ +bb \\ +cc \end{array} x + 2abc$.

But ſince I have reckoned up ſeveral Methods for the Solution of this Problem, and thoſe not much unlike one another in the precedent Paragraphs, of which that taken from *Prop.* 12. of the ſecond Book of the *Elem.* being ſomething more elegant than the reſt, we will here ſubjoin it. Make therefore $AD = x$, $AB = a$, $BC = b$, and $CD = c$, and you will have $BDq = xx - aa$, and $CE = \frac{ab}{x}$ as before. Theſe Species therefore being ſubſtituted in the Theorem $BDq - BCq - CDq = 2CD \times CE$, there will ariſe $xx - aa - bb - cc = \frac{2abc}{x}$; and after Reduction, $x^3 = \begin{array}{c} +aa \\ +bb \\ +cc \end{array} x + 2abc$, as before.

But that it may appear how great a Variety there is in the Invention of Solutions, and that it is not very difficult for a prudent Geometrician to light upon them; I have thought fit to ſhew other Ways of doing the ſame Thing. And having drawn the Diagonal BD, if in room of the Perpendicular BE, which before was let fall from the Point B upon the Side DC, you now let fall a Perpendicular from the Point D

upon

upon the Side B C, or from the Point C upon the Side B D, by which the oblique angled Triangle B C D may any how be resolved into two right angled Triangles, you may come almost by the same Methods I have already described to an Equation. And there are other Methods very different from these.

As if there are drawn two Diagonals, A C and B D, [*See Figure* 11.] B D will be given by assuming A D and A B; as also A C by assuming A D and C D; then, by the known Theorem of Quadrilateral Figures inscribed in a Circle, *viz.* That $AD \times BC + AB \times CD$ is $= AC \times BD$, you will obtain an Equation. [*See Figure* 11.] The Names therefore of the Lines A D, A B, B C, C D, remaining, *viz.* x, a, b, c; B D will be $= \sqrt{xx-aa}$, and $AC = \sqrt{xx-cc}$, by the 47th *Prop.* of the first *Elem.* and these Species of the Lines being substituted in the Theorem we just now mentioned, there will come out $xb + ac = \sqrt{xx-cc} \times \sqrt{xx-aa}$. The Parts of which Equation being squared and reduced, you will again have $x^3 = \begin{matrix} +aa \\ +bb \\ +cc \end{matrix} x + 2abc$.

But, moreover, that it may be manifest after what Manner the Solutions drawn from that Theorem may be thence reduced to only the Similarity of Triangles; erect B H perpendicular to B C, and meeting A C in H, and there will be formed the Triangles B C H, B D A similar, by reason of the right Angles at B, and equal Angles at C and D, (by the 21. 3. *Elem.*); as also the Triangles B C D, B H A similar, by reason of the equal Angles both at B, (as may appear by taking away the common Angle D B H from the two right ones) as also at D and A (by 21.3. *Elem.*) You may see therefore, that from the Proportionality B D : A D : : H C, there is given the Line H C; as also A H from the Proportionality B D : C D : : A B : A H. Whence, since $AH + HC = AC$, you have an Equation. The Names therefore aforesaid of the Lines remaining, *viz.* x, a, b, c, as also the Values of the Lines A C and B D, *viz.* $\sqrt{xx-cc}$ and $\sqrt{xx-aa}$, the first Proportionality will give $HC = \frac{bx}{\sqrt{xx-aa}}$, and the second will give $AH = \frac{ac}{\sqrt{xx-aa}}$. Whence, by reason of $AH + HC = AC$, you will have $\frac{bx+ac}{\sqrt{xx-aa}} = \sqrt{xx-cc}$; an Equation which (by multiplying by $\sqrt{xx-aa}$, and by squaring) will be reduced to a Form often described in the preceeding Pages.

But that it may yet farther appear what a Plenty of Solutions may be found, produce B C and A D [*See Figure* 12.] till they meet in F, and the Triangles A B F and C D F will be similar, because the Angle at F is common, and the Angles A B F and C D F (while they compleat the Angle C D A to two right ones, by 13, 1. and 22, 3 *Elem.*) are equal. Wherefore, if besides the four Terms which compose the Question, there was given A F, the Proportion A B : A F : : C D : C F would give C F. Also $AF - AD$ would give D F, and the Proportion C D : D F : : A B : B F would give B F; whence (since $BF - CF$ is $= BC$) there would arise an Equation. But since there are assumed two unknown Quantities A D and D F as if they were given, there remains another Equation to be found. I let fall therefore B G at right Angles upon A F, and the Proportion A D : A B : : A B : A G will give A G; which being had, the Theorem borrowed from the 13, 2 *Eucl. viz.* that $BFq + 2FAG$ is $= ABq + AFq$ will give another Equation. a, b, c, x, remaining therefore as before, and making $AF = y$, you will have (by insisting on the Steps already laid down) $\frac{cy}{a} = CF$. $\overline{y-x} = DF$. $\frac{\overline{y-x} \times a}{c} = BF$. And thence $\frac{\overline{y-x} \times a}{c} - \frac{cy}{a} = b$, the first Equation. Also $\frac{aa}{x}$ will be $= AG$, and consequently $\frac{aayy - 2a^2xy + a^2x^2}{cc} + \frac{2aay}{x} = aa + yy$ for the second Equation. Which two, by Reduction, will give the Equation sought, *viz.* The Value of y found by the first Equation is $\frac{abc + aax}{aa - cc}$, which being substituted in the second, will give an Equation, from which rightly ordered will come out $x^3 = \begin{matrix} +aa \\ +bb \\ +cc \end{matrix} x + 2abc$, as before.

O And

And so, if A B and D C are produced till they meet one another, the Solution will be much the same, unless perhaps it be something easier. Wherefore I will rather subjoyn another Specimen of this Problem drawn from a Fountain very unlike the former, *viz.* by seeking the Area of the Quadrilateral Figure proposed, and that doubly. I draw therefore the Diagonal B D, and the Quadrilateral Figure may be resolved into two Triangles. Then using the Names of the Lines x, a, b, c, as before, I find $BD = \sqrt{xx - aa}$, and thence $\frac{1}{2} a \sqrt{xx - aa}$ $(= \frac{1}{2} AB \times BD)$ the Area of the Triangle A B D. Moreover, having let fall B E perpendicularly upon C D you will have (by reason of the similar Triangles A B D, B C E) $AD : BD :: BC : BE$, and consequently $BE = \frac{b}{x} \sqrt{xx - aa}$. Wherefore also $\frac{bc}{2x} \sqrt{xx - aa}$ $(= \frac{1}{2} CD \times BE)$ will be the Area of the Triangle B C D. Now, by adding these Area's, there will arise $\frac{ax + bc}{2x} \sqrt{xx - aa}$, the Area of the whole Quadrilateral. After the same Way, by drawing the Diagonal A C, and seeking the Area's of the Triangles A C D and A C B, and adding them, there will again be obtained the Area of the Quadrilateral Figure $\frac{cx + ba}{2x} \sqrt{xx - cc}$. Wherefore, by making these Area's equal, and multiplying both by $2x$, you will have $\overline{ax + bc}\sqrt{xx - aa} = \overline{cx + ba}\sqrt{xx - cc}$, an Equation which, by squaring and dividing by $aax - ccx$, will be reduced to the Form already often found out, $x^3 \begin{matrix} + aa \\ + bb \\ + cc \end{matrix} x + 2abc$.

Hence it may appear how great a Plenty of Solutions may be had, and that some Ways are much more neat than others. Wherefore, if the Method you take from your first Thoughts, for solving a Problem, be but ill accommodated to Computation, you must again consider the Relations of the Lines, until you shall have hit on a Way as fit and elegant as possible. For those Ways that offer themselves at first Sight, may often create sufficient Trouble if they are made use of. Thus, in the Problem we have been upon, it would not have been more difficult to have fallen upon the following Method than upon one of the precedent ones. [*See Figure* 13.] Having let fall B R and C S perpendicular to A D, as also C T to B R, the Figure will be resolved into right angled Triangles. And it may be seen, that A D and A B give A R, A D and C D give S D, A D — A R — S D gives R S or T C. Also A B and A R give B R, C D and S D give C S or T R, and B R — T R gives B T. Lastly, B T and T C give B C, whence an Equation will be obtained. But if any one should go to compute after this Rate, he would fall into larger and more perplexed Algebraick Terms than are any of the former, and more difficult to be brought to a final Equation.

So much for the Solution of Problems in right lined Geometry; unless it may perhaps be worth while to note moreover, that when Angles, or Positions of Lines, expressed by Angles, enter the State of the Question, Lines, or the Proportions of Lines, ought to be used instead of Angles, *viz.* such as may be derived from given Angles by a Trigonometrical Calculation; or from which being found, the Angles sought will come out by the same Calculus. Several Instances of which may be seen in the following Pages.

As for what belongs to the Geometry of Curve Lines, we use to denote them, either by describing them by the local Motion of right Lines, or by using Equations indefinitely expressing the Relation of right Lines disposed according to some certain Law, and ending at the Curve Lines. The Antients did the same by the Sections of Solids, but less commodiously. But the Computations that regard Curves described after the first Way, are no otherwise performed than in the precedent Pages. [*See Figure* 14.] As if A K C be a Curve Line described by K the Vertical Point of the Square A K ϕ, whereof one Leg A K freely slides through the Point A given by Position, while the other K ϕ of a determinate Length is carried along the right Line A D also given by Position, and you are to find the Point C in which any right Line C D given also by Position shall cut this Curve: I draw the right Lines A C, C F, which may represent the Square in the Position sought, and the Relation of the Lines (without any Difference or Regard of what is given or sought, or any Respect had to the Curve) being considered, I perceive the Dependency of the others upon C F and any of these four, *viz.* B C, B F, A F, and A C to be Synthetical; two whereof I therefore assume, as $CF = a$, and

O 2 C B

CB $=x$, and beginning the Computation from thence, I presently obtain BF $=\sqrt{aa-xx}$, and AB $=\frac{xx}{\sqrt{aa-xx}}$, by reaſon of the right Angle CBF, and that the Lines BF : BC :: BC : AB are continual Proportionals. Moreover, from the given Poſition of CD, AD is given, which I therefore call b; there is alſo given the Ratio of BC to BD, which I make as d to e, and you have BD $=\frac{ex}{d}$, and AB $=b-\frac{ex}{d}$. Therefore $b-\frac{ex}{d}$ is $=\frac{xx}{\sqrt{aa-xx}}$, an Equation which (by ſquaring its Parts and multiplying by $aa-xx$, &c.) will be reduced to this Form, $x^4=$

$$\frac{2bdex^3 \begin{matrix}-bbdd\\+aaee\end{matrix} xx-2aabdex+aabbdd}{dd+ee}.$$

Whence, laſtly, from the given Quantities a, b, d, and e, there may be found x, by Rules hereafter to be given, and at that Interval or Diſtance x or BC, a right Line drawn parallel to AD will cut CD in the Point ſought C.

But if we do not uſe Geometrical Deſcriptions but Equations to denote the Curve Lines by, the Computations will thereby become as much ſhorter and eaſier, as the gaining of thoſe Equations can make them. [See *Fig.* 15.] As if the Interſection C of the given Ellipſis ACE with the right Line CD given by Poſition, be ſought. To denote the Ellipſis, I take ſome known Equation proper to it, as $rx-\frac{r}{q}xx=yy$, where x is indefinitely put for any Part of the Axis Ab or AB, and y for the Perpendicular bc or BC terminated at the Curve; and r and q are given from the given Species of the Ellipſis. Since therefore CD is given by Poſition, AD will be alſo given, which call a; and BD will be $a-x$; alſo the Angle ABC will be given, and thence the Ratio of BD to BC, which call 1 to e, and BC (y) will be $=ea-ex$, whoſe Square $eeaa-2eeax+eexx$ will be equal to $rx-\frac{r}{q}xx$. And thence by Reduction there will ariſe $xx=\frac{2aeex+rx-aaee}{ee+\frac{r}{q}}$, or

$$x=\frac{aee+\frac{1}{2}r\pm e\sqrt{ar+\frac{rr}{4ee}-\frac{aar}{q}}}{ee+\frac{r}{q}}.$$

Moreover, although a Curve be denoted by a Geometrical Deſcription, or by a Section of a Solid, yet thence an Equation may be obtained, which ſhall define the Nature of the Curve, and conſequently all the Difficulties of Problems propoſed about it may be reduced hither.

Thus, in the former Example, [See *Fig.* 14.] if AB be called x, and BC y, the third Proportional BF will be $\frac{yy}{x}$, whoſe Square, together with the Square of BC, is equal to CFq, that is, $\frac{y^4}{xx}+yy=aa$; or $y^4+xxyy=aaxx$. And this is an Equation by which every Point C of the Curve AKC, agreeing or correſponding to any Length AB of the Baſe (and conſequently the Curve it ſelf) is defined, and from whence therefore you may obtain the Solutions of Problems propoſed concerning this Curve.

After the ſame Manner almoſt, when a Curve is not given in Specie, but propoſed to be determined, you may feign an Equation at Pleaſure, that may generally contain its Nature; and aſſume this to denote it as if it was given, that from its Aſſumption you can any Way come to Equations by which the Aſſumptions may at length be determined: Examples whereof you have in ſome of the following Problems, which I have collected for a more full Illuſtration of this Doctrine, and for the Exerciſe of Learners, and which I now proceed to deliver.

PRO-

Problem I.

Having a finite right Line BC *given, from whose Ends the two right Lines* BA, CA *are drawn in the given Angles* ABC, ACB; *to find* AD *the Height of their Concourse* A, *above the given Line* BC. [*See* Figure 16.]

Make $BC = a$, and $AD = y$; and since the Angle ABD is given, there will be given (from the Table of Sines or Tangents) the Ratio between the Lines AD and BD which make as d to e. Therefore $d : e :: AD\ (y) : BD$. Wherefore $BD = \frac{ey}{d}$. In like manner by reason of the given Angle ACD there will be given the Ratio between AD and DC, which make as d to f, and you will have $DC = \frac{fy}{d}$. But $BD + DC = BC$, that is, $\frac{ey}{d} + \frac{fy}{d} = a$. Which reduced, by multiplying both Parts of the Equation by d, and dividing by $e + f$ becomes $y = \frac{ad}{e+f}$.

Problem II.

The Sides AB, AC *of the Triangle* ABC *being given, and also the Base* BC, *which the Perpendicular* AD *let fall from the Vertical Angle cuts in* D, *to find the Segments* BD *and* DC. [*See* Figure 17.]

Let $AB = a$, $AC = b$, $BC = c$, and $BD = x$, and DC will $= c - x$. Now since $ABq - BDq\ (aa - xx) = ADq$; and $ACq - DCq\ (bb - cc + 2cx - xx) = ADq$; you will have $aa - xx = bb - cc + 2cx - xx$; which by Reduction becomes $\frac{aa - bb + cc}{2c} = x$.

But that it may appear that all the Difficulties of all Problems may be resolved by only the Proportionality of Lines, without the Help of the 47 of 1 *Eucl.* although not without round-about Methods, I thought fit to subjoin the following Solution of this Problem over and above. From the Point

Point D let fall the Perpendicular DE upon the Side AB, and the Names of the Lines, already given, remaining, you will have $AB : BD :: BD : BE$.

$a : x :: x : \frac{xx}{a}$. And $BA - BE \left(a - \frac{xx}{a}\right) = EA$. Also $EA : AD :: AD : AB$, and consequently $EA \times AB\ (aa - xx) = ADq$. And so, by reasoning about the Triangle ACD, there will be found again $ADq = bb - cc + 2cx - xx$. Whence you will obtain as before $x = \frac{aa - bb + cc}{2c}$.

Problem III.

The Area and Perimeter of the right angled Triangle ABC *being given, to find the Hypothenuse* BC. [*See* Figure 18.]

Let the Perimeter be called a, the Area bb, make $BC = x$, and $AC = y$; then will be $AB = \sqrt{xx - yy}$; whence again the Perimeter $(BC + AC + AB)$ is $x + y + \sqrt{xx - yy}$, and the Area $(\frac{1}{2} AC \times AB)$ is $\frac{1}{2} y \sqrt{xx - yy}$. Therefore $x + y + \sqrt{xx - yy} = a$, and $\frac{1}{2} y \sqrt{xx - yy} = bb$.

The latter of these Equations gives $\sqrt{xx - yy} = \frac{2bb}{y}$; wherefore I write $\frac{2bb}{y}$ for $\sqrt{xx - yy}$ in the former Equation, that the Asymmetry may be taken away; and there comes out $x + y + \frac{2bb}{y} = a$, or multiplying by y, and ordering the Equation $yy = ay - xy - 2bb$. Moreover from the Parts of the former Equation I take away $x + y$ and there remains $\sqrt{xx - yy} = a - x - y$, and squaring the Parts to take away again the Asymmetry, there comes out $xx - yy = aa - 2ax - 2ay + xx + 2xy + yy$, which ordered and divided by 2 becomes $yy = ay - xy + ax - \frac{1}{2} aa$. Lastly, making an Equality between the two Values of yy, I have $ay - xy - 2bb = ay - xy + ax - \frac{1}{2} aa$, which reduced becomes $\frac{1}{2} a - \frac{2bb}{a} = x$.

The

The same otherwise.

Let $\frac{1}{2}$ the Perimeter be $= a$, the Area $= bb$, and $BC = x$, and it will be $AC + AB = 2a - x$. Now since xx (BCq) is $= ACq + ABq$, and $4bb = 2\,AC \times AB$, $xx + 4bb$ will be $= ACq + ABq + 2\,AC \times AB =$ to the Square of $\overline{AC + AB} =$ to the Square of $\overline{2a - x} = 4aa - 4ax + xx$. That is, $xx + 4bb = 4aa - 4ax + xx$, which reduced becomes $a - \frac{bb}{a} = x$.

PROBLEM IV.

Having given the Perimeter and Perpendicular of a right angled Triangle, to find the Triangle. [*See* Figure 67.]

Let C be the right Angle of the Triangle ABC and CD a Perpendicular let fall thence to the Base AB. Let there be given $AB + BC + AC = a$, and $CD = b$. Make the Base $AB = x$, and the Sum of the Sides will be $a - x$. Put y for the Difference of the Legs, and the greater Leg AC will be $= \frac{a - x + y}{2}$; the less $BC = \frac{a - x - y}{2}$. Now from the Nature of a right angled Triangle you have $ACq + BCq = ABq$, that is $\frac{aa - 2ax + xx + yy}{2} = xx$. And also $AB : AC :: BC : DC$; therefore $AB \times DC = AC \times BC$, that is $bx = \frac{aa - 2ax + xx - yy}{4}$. By the former Equation yy is $= xx + 2ax - aa$. By the latter $yy = xx - 2ax + aa - 4bx$. And consequently $xx + 2ax - aa = xx - 2ax + aa - 4bx$. And by Reduction $4ax + 4bx = 2aa$, or $x = \frac{aa}{2a + 2b}$.

Geometrically thus. In every right angled Triangle, as the Sum of the Perimeter and Perpendicular is to the Perimeter, so is half the Perimeter to the Base.

Subtract $2x$ from a, and there will remain $\frac{ab}{a + b}$ the Excess of the Sides above the Base. Whence again, as in every right angled Triangle, the Sum of the Perimeter and Perpendicular is to the Perimeter, so is the Perpendicular to the Excess of the Sides above the Base. PRO-

PROBLEM V.

Having given the Base AB *of a right angled Triangle, and the Sum of the Perpendicular, and the Legs* $CA + CB + CD$; *to find the Triangle.*

Let be $CA + CB + CD = a$, $AB = b$, $CD = x$, and $AC + CB$ will be $= a - x$. Put $AC - CB = y$, and AC will be $= \frac{a - x + y}{2}$, and $CB = \frac{a - x - y}{2}$. But $ACq + CBq$ is $= ABq$; that is $\frac{aa - 2ax + xx + yy}{2} = bb$.

Moreover it is $AC \times CB = AB \times CD$, that is $\frac{aa - 2ax + xx - yy}{4} = bx$. Which being compared, you have $2bb - aa + 2ax - xx = yy = aa - 2ax + xx - 4bx$. And by Reduction, $xx = 2ax + 2bx - aa + bb$, and $x = a + b - \sqrt{2ab + 2bb}$.

Geometrically thus. In any right-angled Triangle, from the Sum of the Legs and Perpendicular subtract the mean Proportional between the said Sum and the Double of the Base, and there will remain the Perpendicular.

The same otherwise.

Make $CA + CB + CD = a$, $AB = b$, and $AC = x$, and BC will be $= \sqrt{bb - xx}$, $CD = \frac{x\sqrt{bb - xx}}{b}$. And $x + CB + CD = a$, or $CB + CD = a - x$. And therefore $\frac{b + x}{b}\sqrt{bb - xx} = a - x$. And the Parts being squared and multiplied by bb, there will be made $-x^4 - 2bx^3 + 2b^3x + b^4 = aabb - 2abbx + bbxx$. Which Equation being ordered, by Transposition of Parts, after this Manner, $x^4 + 2bx^3 \begin{matrix} +3bb \\ +2ab \end{matrix} xx \begin{matrix} +2b^3 \\ +2abb \end{matrix} x \begin{matrix} +b^4 \\ +2ab^3 \\ +aabb \end{matrix} = \begin{matrix} 2bb \\ 2ab \end{matrix} xx \begin{matrix} +4b^3 \\ +4abb \end{matrix} x \begin{matrix} +2b^4 \\ +3ab^3 \end{matrix}$ and extracting the Roots on

P

both

both Sides, there will arise $xx + bx + bb + ab = \overline{x+b}\sqrt{2ab+2bb}$. And the Root being again extracted $x = -\frac{1}{2}b + \sqrt{\frac{1}{2}bb + \frac{1}{2}ab} \pm \sqrt{b\sqrt{\frac{1}{2}bb + \frac{1}{2}ab} - \frac{1}{4}bb - \frac{1}{2}ab}$.

The Geometrical Construction. [*See* Figure 68.]

Take therefore $AB = \frac{1}{2}b$, $BC = \frac{1}{2}a$, $CD = \frac{1}{2}AB$, AE a mean Proportional between b and AC, and EF on both sides a mean Proportional between b and DE, and BF, BF will be the two Legs of the Triangle.

PROBLEM VI.

Having given in the right-angled Triangle ABC, *the Sum of the Sides* AC + BC, *and the Perpendicular* CD, *to find the Triangle.*

Let be $AC + BC = a$, $CD = b$, $AC = x$, and BC will be $= a - x$, $AB = \sqrt{aa - 2ax + 2xx}$. Moreover CD : AC :: BC : AB. Therefore again $AB = \frac{ax - xx}{b}$. Wherefore $ax - xx = b\sqrt{aa - 2ax + 2xx}$; and the Parts being squared and ordered $x^4 - 2ax^3 \begin{smallmatrix}+aa\\-2bb\end{smallmatrix} xx + 2abbx - aabb = 0$. Add to both Parts $aabb + b^4$, and there will be made $x^4 - 2ax^3 \begin{smallmatrix}+aa\\-2bb\end{smallmatrix} xx + 2abbx + b^4 = aabb + b^4$. And the Root being extracted on both Sides, $xx - ax - bb = -b\sqrt{aa+bb}$, and the Root being again extracted $x = \frac{1}{2}a \pm \sqrt{\frac{1}{4}aa + bb - b\sqrt{aa+bb}}$.

The Geometrical Construction. [*See* Figure 69.]

Take $AB = BC = \frac{1}{2}a$. At C erect the Perpendicular $CD = b$. Produce DC to E, so that DE shall be = DA. And between CD and CE take a mean Proportional CF. And let a Circle GH described from the Center F and the Radius BC, cut the right Line BC in G and H, and BG and BH will be the two Sides of the Triangle.

The

The same otherwise.

Let be $AC + BC = a$, $AC - BC = y$, $AB = x$, and $DC = b$, and $\frac{a+y}{2}$ will be $= AC$, $\frac{a-y}{2} = BC$, $\frac{aa+yy}{2} = ACq + BCq = ABq = xx$. $\frac{aa-yy}{4b} = \frac{AC \times BC}{DC} = AB = x$. Therefore $2xx - aa = yy = aa - 4bx$, and $xx = aa - 2bx$, and the Root being extracted $x = -b + \sqrt{bb + aa}$. Whence in the Construction above CE is the Hypothenuse of the Triangle sought. But the Base and Perpendicular, as well in this as the Problem above being given, the Triangle is thus expeditiously constructed. [*See Figure* 70.] Make a Parallelogram CG, whose Side CE shall be the Basis of the Triangle, and the other Side CF the Perpendicular. And upon CE describe a Semicircle, cutting the opposite Side FG in H. Draw CH, EH, and CHE will be the Triangle sought.

PROBLEM VII.

In a right-angled Triangle, having given the Sum of the Legs, and the Sum of the Perpendicular and Base, to find the Triangle.

Let the Sum of the Legs AC and BC be a, the Sum of the Base AB and of the Perpendicular CD be b, the Leg $AC = x$, the Base $AB = y$, and BC will be $= a - x$, $CD = b - y$, $aa - 2ax + 2xx = ACq + BCq = ABq = yy$, $ax - xx = AC \times BC = AB \times CD = by - yy = by - aa + 2ax - 2xx$, and $by = aa - ax + xx$. Make its Square $a^4 - 2a^3x + 3aaxx - 2ax^3 + x^4$ equal to $yy \times bb$, that is, equal to $aabb - 2abbx + 2bbxx$. And ordering the Equation, there will come out $x^4 - 2ax^3 \begin{smallmatrix}+3aa\\-2bb\end{smallmatrix} xx \begin{smallmatrix}-2a^3\\+2abb\end{smallmatrix} x \begin{smallmatrix}+a^4\\-aabb\end{smallmatrix} = 0$. Add to each Side of the Equation $b^4 - aabb$, and there will come out $x^4 - 2ax^3 \begin{smallmatrix}+3aa\\-2bb\end{smallmatrix} xx \begin{smallmatrix}-2a^3\\+2abb\end{smallmatrix} x \begin{smallmatrix}+a^4\\-2aabb\\+b^4\end{smallmatrix} = b^4 - aabb$. And the Root being extracted on both Sides $xx - ax + aa - bb = -b\sqrt{bb - aa}$, and the Root being again extracted $x = \frac{1}{2}a \pm \sqrt{bb - \frac{3}{4}aa - b\sqrt{bb - aa}}$.

P 2 *The*

The Geometrical Construction.

Take R a mean Proportional between $b+a$ and $b-a$, and S a mean Proportional between R and $b-$R, and T a mean Proportional between $\frac{1}{2}a+$S; and $\frac{1}{2}a-$S; and $\frac{1}{2}a+$T and $\frac{1}{2}a-$T will be the Sides of the Triangle.

PROBLEM VIII.

Having given the Area, Perimeter, and one of the Angles A *of any Triangle* A B C, *to determine the rest.* [*See* Figure 19.]

Let the Perimeter be $=a$, and the Area $=bb$, and from either of the unknown Angles, as C, let fall the Perpendicular C D to the opposite Side A B; and by reason of the given Angle A, A C will be to C D in a given Ratio, suppose as d to e. Call therefore A C $=x$, and C D will be $=\frac{ex}{d}$, by which divide the Double of the Area, and there will come out $\frac{2bbd}{ex}=$ AB. Add AD (*viz.* $\sqrt{ACq-CDq}$, or $\frac{x}{d}\times\sqrt{dd-ee}$) and there will come out B D $=\frac{2bbd}{ex}+\frac{x}{d}\times\sqrt{dd-ee}$; to the Square whereof add CDq, and there will arise $\frac{4b^4dd}{eexx}+xx+\frac{4bb}{e}\sqrt{dd-ee}=$ BCq. Moreover from the Perimeter take away AC and AB, and there will remain $a-x-\frac{2bbd}{ex}=$ B C, the Square whereof $aa-2ax+xx-\frac{4abbd}{ex}+\frac{4bbd}{e}+\frac{4b^4dd}{eexx}$ make equal to the Square before found; and neglecting the Equivalents, you will have $\frac{4bb}{e}\sqrt{dd-ee}=aa-2ax-\frac{4abbd}{ex}+\frac{4bbd}{e}$. And this, by assuming $4af$ for the given Terms

$aa+$

$aa+\frac{4bbd}{e}-\frac{4bb}{e}\sqrt{dd-ee}$, and by reducing, becomes $xx=2fx-\frac{2bbd}{e}$, or $x=f\pm\sqrt{ff-\frac{2bbd}{e}}$.

The same Equation would have come out also by seeking the Leg A B; for the Sides A B and A C are indifferently alike to all the Conditions of the Problem. Wherefore if A C be made $=f-\sqrt{ff-\frac{2bbd}{e}}$, A B will be $=f+\sqrt{ff-\frac{2bbd}{e}}$, and reciprocally; and the Sum of these $2f$ subtracted from the Perimeter, leaves the third Side B C$=a-2f$.

PROBLEM IX.

Having given the Altitude, Base, and Sum of the Sides, to find the Triangle.

Let the Altitude C D be $=a$, half the Basis A B $=b$, half the Sum of the Sides $=c$, and their Semi-difference $=z$; and the greater Side as B C will be $=c+z$, and the lesser A C$=c-z$. Subtract C Dq from C Bq, and also from A Cq, and hence will B D be $=\sqrt{cc+2cz+zz-aa}$, and thence A D $=\sqrt{cc-2cz+zz-aa}$. Subtract also A B from B D, and A D will again be $=\sqrt{cc+2cz+zz-aa}-2b$. Having now squared the Values of A D, and ordered the Terms, there will arise $bb+cz=b\sqrt{cc+2cz+zz-aa}$. Again, by squaring and reducing into Order, you will obtain $cczz-bbzz=bbcc-bbaa-b^4$. And $z=b\times\sqrt{1-\frac{aa}{cc-bb}}$. Whence the Sides are given.

PRO-

PROBLEM X.

Having given the Base AB, *and the Sum of the Sides* AC+BC, *and also the Vertical Angle* C, *to determine the Sides.* [*See* Figure 20.]

Make the Base $=a$, half the Sum of the Sides $=b$, and half the Difference $=x$, and the greater Side BC will be $=b+x$, and the lesser $AC=b-x$. From either of the unknown Angles A let fall the Perpendicular AD to the opposite Side BC, and by reason of the given Angle C there will be given the Ratio of AC to CD, suppose as d to e, and then CD will be $=\frac{eb-ex}{d}$. Also, by 13. 2 *Elem.* $\frac{ACq-ABq+BCq}{2BC}$ that is $\frac{2bb+2xx-aa}{2b+2x}=CD$; and so you have an Equation between the Values of CD. And this reduced, x becomes $=\sqrt{\frac{daa+2ebb-2dbb}{2d+2e}}$, whence the Sides are given.

If the Angles at the Base were sought, the Conclusion would be more neat, as draw EC bisecting the given Angle and meeting the Base in E; and it will be AB : AC+BC (: : AE : AC) : : Sine Angle ACE : Sine Angle AEC. And if from the Angle AEC, and also from its Complement BEC you subtract $\frac{1}{2}$ the Angle C, there will be left the Angles ABC and BAC.

PROBLEM XI.

Having the Sides of a Triangle given, to find the Angles. [*See* Figure 72.]

Let the given Sides AB be $=a$, $AC=b$, $BC=c$, to find the Angle A. Having let fall to AB the Perpendicular CD, which is opposite to that Angle, you will have in the first Place, $bb-cc=ACq-BCq=ADq-BDq=\overline{AD+BD}\times\overline{AD-BD}=AB\times\overline{2AD-AB}=2AD\times a-aa$. And consequently $\frac{1}{2}a+\frac{bb-cc}{2a}=AD$. Whence comes out this *first Theorem.*

I. As AB to AC+BC so AB−BC to a fourth Proportional N. $\frac{AB+N}{2}=AD$. As AC to AD so Radius to the Cosine of the Angle A.

Moreover $DCq=ACq-ADq=$
$$\frac{2aabb+2aacc+2bbcc-a^4-b^4-c^4}{4aa}=\frac{\overline{a+b+c}\times\overline{a+b-c}\times\overline{a-b+c}\times\overline{-a+b+c}}{4aa}.$$
Whence having multiplied the Roots of the Numerator and Denominator by b, there is made this *second Theorem.*

II. As $2ab$ to a mean Proportional between $\overline{a+b+c}\times\overline{a+b-c}$ and $\overline{a-b+c}\times\overline{-a+b+c}$, so is Radius to the Sine of the Angle A.

Moreover on AB take AE = AC, and draw CE, and the Angle ECD will be equal to half the Angle A. Take AD from AE, and there will remain $DE=b-\frac{1}{2}a-\frac{bb-cc}{2a}=\frac{cc-aa+2ab-bb}{2a}=\frac{\overline{c+a-b}\times\overline{c-a+b}}{2a}$.

Whence $DEq=\frac{\overline{c+a-b}\times\overline{c+a-b}\times\overline{c-a+b}\times\overline{c-a+b}}{4aa}$.

And hence is made the *third* and *fourth Theorem, viz.*

III. As $2ab$ to $\overline{c+a-b}\times\overline{c-a+b}$ (so AC to DE) so Radius to the versed Sine of the Angle A.

IV. And, as a mean Proportional between $a+b+c$, and $a+b-c$ to a mean Proportional between $c+a-b$, and $c-a+b$ (so CD to DE) so Radius to the Tangent of half the Angle A, or the Co-tangent of half the Angle to Radius.

Besides, CEq is $=CDq+DEq=\frac{2abb+bcc-baa-b^3}{a}=\frac{b}{a}\times\overline{c+a-b}\times\overline{c-a+b}$. Whence the *fifth* and *sixth Theorem.*

V. As a mean Proportional between $2a$ and $2b$ to a mean Proportional between $c+a-b$, and $c-a+b$, or as 1 to a mean Proportional between $\frac{c+a-b}{2a}$, and $\frac{c-a+b}{2b}$ (so AC to

to $\frac{1}{2}$ CE or CE to DE) so Radius to the Sine of $\frac{1}{2}$ the Angle A.

VI. And as a mean Proportional between $2a$ and $2b$ to a mean Proportional between $a+b+c$ and $a+b-c$ (so CE to CD) so Radius to the Cosine of half the Angle A.

But if besides the Angles, the Area of the Triangle be also sought, multiply CDq by $\frac{1}{4}ABq$, and the Root, *viz.* $\frac{1}{4}\sqrt{\overline{a+b+c}\times\overline{a+b-c}\times\overline{a-b+c}\times\overline{-a+b+c}}$ will be the Area sought.

Problem XII.

Having the Sides and Base of any right lined Triangle given, to find the Segments of the Base, the Perpendicular, the Area, and the Angles. [*See* Figure 40.]

Let there be given the Sides AC, BC, and the Base AB of the Triangle ABC. Bisect AB in I, and take on it (being produced on both Sides) AF and AE equal to AC, and BG and BH equal to BC. Join CE, CF; and from C to the Base let fall the Perpendicular CD. And $ACq - BCq$ will be $= ADq + CDq - CDq - BDq = ADq - BDq = \overline{AD+BD}\times\overline{AD-BD} = AB\times 2DI$. Therefore $\frac{ACq-BCq}{2AB} = DI$. And $2AB : AC + BC :: AC - BC : DI$. Which is a Theorem for determining the Segments of the Base.

From IE, that is, from $AC - \frac{1}{2}AB$, take away DI, and there will remain $DE = \frac{BCq - ACq + 2AC\times AB - ABq}{2AB}$, that is $= \frac{\overline{BC+AC-AB}\times\overline{BC-AC+AB}}{2AB}$, or $= \frac{HE\times EG}{2AB}$. Take away DE from FE, or $2AC$, and there will remain $FD = \frac{ACq + 2AC\times AB + ABq - BCq}{2AB}$, that is $= \frac{\overline{AC+AB+BC}\times\overline{AC+AB-BC}}{2AB}$, or $= \frac{FG\times FH}{2AB}$. And since CD is a mean Proportional between DE and DF, and CE a mean Proportional between DE and EF, and CF a mean Proportional between DF and EF, CD will be $= \frac{\sqrt{FG\times FH\times HE\times EG}}{2AB}$, CE $= \sqrt{\frac{AC\times HE\times EG}{AB}}$, and $CF = \sqrt{\frac{AC\times FG\times FH}{AB}}$. Multiply CD into $\frac{1}{2}AB$, and you will have the Area $= \frac{1}{4}\sqrt{FG\times FH\times HE\times EG}$. But for determining the Angle A, there come out several Theorems:

1. As $2AB\times AC : HE\times EG$ (:: AC : DE) :: Radius : versed Sine of the Angle A.

2. $2AB\times AC : FG\times FH$ (:: AC : FD) :: Radius : versed Cosine of A.

3. $2AB\times AC : \sqrt{FG\times FH\times HE\times EG}$ (:: AC : CD) :: Radius : Sine of A.

4. $\sqrt{FG\times FH} : \sqrt{HE\times EG}$ (:: CF : CE) :: Radius : Tangent of $\frac{1}{2}$ A.

5. $\sqrt{HE\times EG} : \sqrt{FG\times FH}$ (:: CE : FC) :: Radius : Cotangent of $\frac{1}{2}$ A.

6. $2\sqrt{AB\times AC} : \sqrt{HE\times EG}$ (:: FE : CE) :: Radius : Sine of $\frac{1}{2}$ A.

7. $2\sqrt{AB\times AC} : \sqrt{FG\times FH}$ (:: FE : FC) :: Radius : Cosine of $\frac{1}{2}$ A.

Q Pro-

PROBLEM XIII.

To subtend the given Angle CBD *with the given right Line* CD; *so that if* AD *be drawn from the End of that right Line* D *to the Point* A, *given on the right Line* CB *produced, the Angle* ADC *shall be equal to the Angle* ABD. [*See* Figure 71.]

Make $CD = a$, $AB = b$, $BD = x$, and it will be $BD : BA :: CD : DA = \frac{ab}{x}$. Let fall the Perpendicular DE, and BE will be $= \frac{BDq - ADq + BAq}{2BA} = \frac{xx - \frac{aabb}{xx} + bb}{2b}$. By reason of the given Triangle DBA, make $BD : BE :: b : c$, and you will have again $BE = \frac{ex}{b}$, therefore $xx - \frac{aabb}{xx} + bb = 2ex$. And $x^4 - 2ex^3 + bbxx - aabb = 0$.

PROBLEM XIV.

To find the Triangle ABC, *whose three Sides* AB, AC, BC, *and its Perpendicular* DC *are in Arithmetical Progression.* [*See* Figure 46.]

Make $AC = a$, $BC = x$, and DC will be $= 2x - a$, and $AB = 2a - x$. Also AD will be $(= \sqrt{ACq - DCq}) = \sqrt{4ax - 4xx}$, and BD $(= \sqrt{BCq - DCq}) = \sqrt{4ax - 3xx - aa}$. And so again $AB = \sqrt{4ax - 4xx} + \sqrt{4ax - 3xx - aa}$. Wherefore $2a - x = \sqrt{4ax - 4xx} + \sqrt{4ax - 3xx - aa}$, or $2a - x - \sqrt{4ax - 4xx} = \sqrt{4ax - 3xx - aa}$. And the Parts being squared, $4aa - 3xx - \overline{4a + 2x} \times \sqrt{4ax - 4xx} = 4ax - 3xx - aa$, or $5aa - 4ax = \overline{4a - 2x} \times \sqrt{4ax - 4xx}$. And the Parts being again squared, and the Terms rightly disposed, $16x^4 - 80ax^3 + 144aaxx - 104a^3x + 25a^4 = 0$. Divide this Equation by $2x - a$, and there will arise $8x^3 - 36axx + 54aax - 25a^3 = 0$, an Equation by the Solution whereof x is given from a, being any how assumed. a and x being had, make a Triangle, whose Sides shall be $2a - x$, a and x, and a Perpendicular let fall upon the Side $2a - x$ will be $2x - a$.

If I had made the Difference of the Sides of the Triangle to be d, and the Perpendicular to be x, the Work would have been something neater; this Equation at last coming out, *viz.* $x^3 = 24ddx - 48d^3$.

PROBLEM XV.

To find a Triangle ABC, *whose three Sides* AB, AC, BC, *and the Perpendicular* CD *shall be in a Geometrical Progression.*

Make $AC = x$, $BC = a$; and AB will be $= \frac{xx}{a}$. And $CD = \frac{aa}{x}$. And AD $(= \sqrt{ACq - CDq}) = \sqrt{xx - \frac{a^4}{xx}}$; and BD $(= \sqrt{BCq - DCq}) = \sqrt{aa - \frac{a^4}{xx}}$ and consequently $\frac{xx}{a}$ $(= AB) = \sqrt{xx - \frac{a^4}{xx}} + \sqrt{aa - \frac{a^4}{xx}}$, or $\frac{xx}{a} - \sqrt{aa - \frac{a^4}{xx}} = \sqrt{xx - \frac{a^4}{xx}}$; and the Parts of the Equation being squared, $\frac{x^4}{aa} - \frac{2xx}{a} \times \sqrt{aa - \frac{a^4}{xx}} + aa - \frac{a^4}{xx} = xx - \frac{a^4}{xx}$, that is, $x^4 - aaxx + a^4 = 2aax\sqrt{xx - aa}$. And the Parts being again squared, $x^8 - 2aax^6 + 3a^4x^4 - 2a^5xx + a^8 = 4a^4x^4 - 4a^6xx$. That is, $x^8 - 2aax^6 - a^4x^4 + 2a^6xx + a^8 = 0$. Divide this Equation by $x^4 - aaxx - a^4$, and there will arise $x^4 - aaxx - a^4$. Wherefore x^4 is $= aaxx + a^4$. And extracting the Root $xx = \frac{1}{2}aa + \sqrt{\frac{5}{4}a^4}$, or $x = a\sqrt{\frac{1}{2} + \sqrt{\frac{5}{4}}}$. Take therefore a or BC, of any

Q 2 Length,

Length, and make BC : AC :: AC : AB :: 1 : $\sqrt{\frac{1}{2}} + \sqrt{\frac{5}{4}}$, and the Perpendicular DC of a Triangle ABC made of theſe Sides, will be to the Side BC in the ſame Ratio.

The ſame otherwiſe. [*See* Figure 47.]

Since AB : AC :: BC : DC. I ſay the Angle ACB is a right one. For if you deny it, draw CE, making the Angle ECB a right one. Therefore the Triangles BCE, DBC are ſimiliar by 8. 6 *Elem.* and conſequently EB : EC :: BC : DC, that is, EB : EC :: AB : AC. Draw AF perpendicular to CE, and by reaſon of the parallel Lines AF, BC, EB will be : EC :: AE : FE :: AB : FC. Therefore by 9. 5 *Elem.* AC is $=$ FC, that is, the Hypothenuſe of a right-angled Triangle is equal to the Side, contrary to the 19. 1 *Elem.* Therefore the Angle ECB is not a right one; wherefore it is neceſſary ACB ſhould be a right one. Therefore $ACq + BCq$ is $= ABq$. But $ACq = AB \times BC$, therefore $AB \times BC + BCq = ABq$, and extracting the Root $AB = \frac{1}{2}BC + \sqrt{\frac{5}{4}BCq}$. Wherefore take BC : AB :: 1 : $\frac{1+\sqrt{5}}{2}$, and AC a mean Proportional between BC and AB, and a Triangle being made of theſe Sides, AB, AC, BC, DC will be continually Proportionals.

PROBLEM XVI.

To make the Triangle ABC *upon the given Baſe* AB, *whoſe Vertex* C *ſhall be in the right Line* EC *given in Poſition, and the Baſe an Arithmetical Mean between the Sides.* [*See* Figure 48.]

Let the Baſe AB be biſected in F, and produced until it meet the right Line given in Poſition EC in E, and let fall to it the Perpendicular CD; and making $AB = a$, $FE = b$, and $BC - AB = x$, BC will be $= a + x$, $AC = a - x$; and by the 13. 2 *Elem.* $BD \left(= \frac{BCq - ACq + ABq}{2AB}\right) = 2x + \frac{1}{2}a$. And conſequently, $FD = 2x$, $DE = b + 2x$, and $CD \left(= \sqrt{CBq - BDq}\right) = \sqrt{\frac{3}{4}aa - 3xx}$. But by reaſon of the given Poſitions of the right Lines CE and AB, the Angle CED is given; and conſequently the Ratio of DE to CD, which if it be put as d to e, will give the Proportion

$d : e :: b + 2x : \sqrt{\frac{3}{4}aa - 3xx}$. Whence the Means and Extremes being multiplied by each other, there ariſes the Equation $eb + 2ex = d\sqrt{\frac{3}{4}aa - 3xx}$, the Parts whereof being ſquared and rightly ordered, you have $xx = \frac{\frac{3}{4}d^2a^2 - eebb - 4eebx}{4ee + 3dd}$, and the Root being extracted $x = \frac{-2eeb + d\sqrt{3eeaa - 3eebb + \frac{9}{4}ddaa}}{4ee + 3dd}$. But x being given, there is given $BC = a + x$, and $AC = a - x$.

PROBLEM XVII.

Having given the Sides of any Parallelogram AB, BD, DC, and AC, *and one of the Diagonals* BC, *to find the other Diagonal* AD. [*See* Figure 21.]

Let E be the Concourſe of the Diagonals, and to the Diagonal BC let fall the Perpendicular AF, and by the 13. 2 *Elem.* $\frac{ACq - ABq + BCq}{2BC} = CF$, and alſo $\frac{ACq - AEq + ECq}{2EC} = CF$. Wherefore ſince EC is $= \frac{1}{2}BC$, and $AE = \frac{1}{2}AD$ it will be $\frac{ACq - ABq + BCq}{2BC} = \frac{ACq - \frac{1}{4}ADq + \frac{1}{4}BCq}{BC}$, and having reduced, $AD = \sqrt{2ACq + 2ABq - BCq}$.

Whence, by the by, in any Parallelogram, the Sum of the Squares of the Sides is equal to the Sum of the Squares of the Diagonals.

PROBLEM XVIII.

Having given the Angles of the Trapezium ABCD, *alſo its Perimeter and Area, to determine the Sides.* [*See* Figure 22.]

Produce any two of the Sides AB and DC till they meet in E, and let AB be $= x$, and BC $= y$, and becauſe all the Angles are given, there are given the Ratio's of BC to CE and BE, which make d to e and f; and CE will be

be $= \frac{ey}{d}$ and BE $= \frac{fy}{d}$, and consequently AE $= x + \frac{fy}{d}$. There are also given the Ratio's of AE to AD and to DE; which make as g and as h to d; and AD will be $= \frac{dx+fy}{g}$ and ED $= \frac{dx+fy}{h}$, and consequently CD $= \frac{dx+fy}{h} - \frac{ey}{d}$, and the Sum of all the Sides $x + y + \frac{dx+fy}{g} + \frac{dx+fy}{h} - \frac{ey}{d}$; which, since it is given, call it a, and the Terms will be abbreviated by writing $\frac{p}{r}$ for the given Quantity $1 + \frac{d}{g} + \frac{d}{h}$, and $\frac{q}{r}$ for the given $1 + \frac{f}{g} + \frac{f}{h} - \frac{e}{d}$, and you will have the Equation $\frac{px+qy}{r} = a$.

Moreover, by reason of all the Angles being given, there is given the Ratio of BCq to the Triangle BCE, which make as m to n, and the Triangle BCE will be $= \frac{n}{m}yy$. There is also given the Ratio of AEq to the Triangle ADE; which make as m to d; and the Triangle ADE will be $= \frac{ddxx+2dfxy+ffyy}{dm}$. Wherefore, since the Area AC, which is the Difference of these Triangles, is given, let it be bb, and $\frac{ddxx+2dfxy+ffyy-dnyy}{dm}$ will be $= bb$. And so you have two Equations, from the Reduction whereof all is determined, *viz.* The former Equation gives $\frac{ra-qy}{p} = x$, and by writing $\frac{ra-qy}{p}$ for x in the last, there comes out

I $\qquad$ *drraa*

$\frac{drraa-2dqray+dqqyy}{ppm} + \frac{2afry-2fqyy}{pm} + \frac{ffyy-dnyy}{dm} = bb$. And the Terms being abbreviated by writing s for the given Quantity $\frac{dqq}{pp} - \frac{2fq}{p} + \frac{ff}{d} - n$, and st for the given $+\frac{adqr}{pp} - \frac{afr}{p}$, and stv for the given $bbm - \frac{drraa}{pp}$, there arises $yy = 2ty + tv$, or $y = t + \sqrt{st+tv}$.

PROBLEM XIX.

To surround the Fish-pond ABCD *with a Walk* ABCDEFGH *of a given Area, and of the same Breadth every where.* [*See* Figure 23.]

Let the Breadth of the Walk be x, and its Area aa. And, letting fall the Perpendiculars AK, BL, BM, CN, CO, DP, DQ, AI, from the Points A, B, C, D, to the Lines EF, FG, GH, and HE, to divide the Walk into the four Trapezia IK, LM, NO, PQ, and into the four Parallelograms AL, BN, CP, DI, of the Latitude x, and of the same Length with the Sides of the given Trapezium. Let therefore the Sum of the Sides (AB + BC + CD + DA) be $= b$, and the Sum of the Parallelograms will be $= bx$.

Moreover, having drawn AE, BF, CG, DH; since AI is $=$ AK, the Angle AEI will be $=$ Angle AEK $= \frac{1}{2}$ IEK, or $\frac{1}{2}$ DAB. Therefore the Angle AEI is given, and consequently the Ratio of AI to IE, which make as d to e, and IE will be $= \frac{ex}{d}$. Multiply this into $\frac{1}{2}$ AI, or $\frac{1}{2}x$, and the Area of the Triangle AEI will be $= \frac{exx}{2d}$. But by reason of equal Angles and Sides, the Triangles AEI and AEK are equal, and consequently the Trapezium IK ($= 2$ Triang. AEI) $= \frac{exx}{d}$. In like manner, by

putting

putting BL : LF :: $d:f$, and CN : NG :: $d:g$, and DP : PH :: $d:h$, (for thofe Ratio's are alfo given from the given Angles, B, C, and D) you will have the Trapezium LM $=\frac{fxx}{d}$, NO $=\frac{gxx}{d}$, and PQ $=\frac{hxx}{d}$. Wherefore $\frac{cxx}{d}+\frac{fxx}{d}+\frac{gxx}{d}+\frac{hxx}{d}$, or $\frac{pxx}{d}$, by writing p for $e+f+g+h$ will be equal to the four Trapeziums IK + LM + NO + PQ; and confequently $\frac{pxx}{d}+bx$ will be equal to the whole Walk aa. Which Equation, by dividing all the Terms by $\frac{p}{d}$, and extracting its Root, x will become $=\frac{-db+\sqrt{bbdd+4aapd}}{2p}$. And the Breadth of the Walk being thus found, it is eafy to defcribe it.

Problem XX.

From the given Point C, *to draw the right Line* CF, *which together with two other right Lines* AE and AF *given by Pofition, fhall comprehend or conftitute the Triangle* AEF *of a given Magnitude.* [*See* Figure 24.]

Draw CD parallel to AE, and CB and EG perpendicular to AF, and let AD $=a$, CB $=b$, and AF $=x$, and the Area of the Triangle AEF be cc, and by reafon of the proportional Quantities DF : AF (:: DC : AE) :: CB : EG; that is, $a+x:x::b:\frac{bx}{a+x}$ it will be $\frac{bx}{a+x}=$ EG. Multiply this into $\frac{1}{2}$ AF, and there will come out $\frac{bxx}{2a+2x}$, the Quantity of the Area AEF, which is $=cc$. And fo the Equation being ordered xx will be $=\frac{2ccx+2cca}{b}$ or $x=\frac{cc+\sqrt{c^4+2ccab}}{b}$.

After

After the fame manner a right Line may be drawn through a given Point, which fhall divide any Triangle or Trapezium in a given Ratio.

Problem XXI.

To determine the Point C *in the given right Line* DF, *from which the right Lines* AC *and* BC *drawn to two other Points* A *and* B *given by Pofition, fhall have a given Difference.* [*See* Figure 25.] [*See* Prob. xlv.]

From the given Points let fall the Perpendiculars AD and BF to the given right Line, and make AD $=a$, BF $=b$, DF $=c$, DC $=x$, and AC will be $=\sqrt{aa+xx}$, FC $=x-c$, and BC $=\sqrt{bb+xx-2cx+cc}$. Now let their given Difference be d, AC being greater than BC then $\sqrt{aa+xx}-d$ will be $=\sqrt{bb+xx-2cx+cc}$. And fquaring the Parts $aa+xx+dd-2d\sqrt{aa+xx}=bb+xx-2cx+cc$. And reducing, and for Abbreviation fake, writing $2ee$ inftead of the given Quantities $aa+dd-bb-cc$, there will come out $ee+cx=d\times\sqrt{aa+xx}$. And again, having fquared the Parts $e^4+2ceex+ccxx=ddaa+ddxx$. And the Equation being reduced $xx=\frac{2eecx+e^4-aadd}{dd-cc}$, or

$$x=\frac{eec+\sqrt{e^4dd-aad^4+aaddcc}}{dd-cc}.$$

The Problem will be refolved after the fame Way, if the Sum of the Lines AC and BC, or the Sum or the Difference of their Squares, or the Proportion or Rectangle, or the Angle comprehended by them be given: Or alfo, if inftead of the right Line DC, you make ufe of the Circumference of a Circle, or any other Curve Line, fo the Calculation (in this laft Cafe efpecially) relates to the Line that joyns the Points A and B.

R Pro-

PROBLEM XXII.

Having the three right Lines A D, A E, B F, *given by Position, to draw a fourth* D F, *whose Parts* D E *and* E F, *intercepted by the former, shall be of given Lengths.* [*See* Figure 49.]

Let fall E G perpendicular to B F, and draw E C parallel to A D, and the three right Lines given by Position meeting in A, B, and H, make A B $= a$, B H $= b$, A H $= c$ E D $= d$, E F $= e$, and H E $= x$. Now, by reason of the similar Triangles A B H, E C H, it is A H : A B :: H E : E C $= \frac{ax}{c}$, and A H : H B :: H E : C H $= \frac{bx}{c}$. Add H B, and there comes C B $= \frac{bx+bc}{c}$. Moreover, by reason of the similar Triangles F E C, F D B it is E D : C B : : E F : C F $= \frac{ebx+ebc}{dc}$. Lastly, by the 12 and 13. 2 *Elem.* you have $\frac{ECq - EFq}{2FC} + \frac{1}{2}FC = (CG) = \frac{HEq - ECq}{2CH} - \frac{1}{2}CH$; that is,

$$\frac{\frac{aaxx}{cc}-ee}{\frac{2ebx+2ebc}{dc}}+\frac{ebx+ebc}{2dc}=\frac{xx-\frac{aaxx}{cc}}{\frac{2bx}{c}}-\frac{bx}{2c}.$$ Or

$$\frac{aadxx-eedcc}{ebx+ebc}+\frac{ebx}{d}+\frac{ebc}{d}=\frac{ccx-aax-bbx}{b}.$$

Here, for Abbreviation sake, for $\frac{cc-aa-bb}{b}-\frac{eb}{d}$ write m, and you will have $\frac{aadxx-eedcc}{ebx+ebc}+\frac{ebc}{d}=mx$; and all the Terms being multiplied by $x+c$, there will come out $\frac{aadxx-eedcc}{eb}-\frac{ebcx}{d}+\frac{ebcc}{d}=mxx+mcx$. Again, for $\frac{aad}{eb}-m$ write p, and for $mc+\frac{ebc}{d}$ write $2pq$, and for $-\frac{ebcc}{d}+\frac{eedcc}{eb}$ write prr, and xx will become $= 2qx+rr$, and $x = q \pm \sqrt{qq+rr}$. Having found x or H E, draw E C parallel to A B, and take F C : B C :: e : d, and having drawn F E D, it will satisfy the Conditions of the Question.

PROBLEM XXIII.

To determine the Point Z, *from which if four right Lines* Z A, Z B, Z C, *and* Z D *are drawn at given Angles to four right Lines given by Position*, viz. F A, E B, F C, G D, *the Rectangle of two of the given Lines* Z A *and* Z B, *and the Sum of the other two* Z C *and* Z B *may be given.* [*See* Figure 26.]

From among the Lines chuse one, as F A, given by Position, as also another, Z A, not given by Position, and which is drawn to it, from the Lengths whereof the Point Z may be determined, and produce the other Lines given by Position until they meet these, or be produced farther out if there be Occasion, as you see here. And having made E A $= x$, and A Z $= y$, by reason of the given Angles of the Triangle A E H, there will be given the Ratio of A E to A H, which make as p to q, and A H will be $= \frac{qx}{p}$. Add A Z, and Z H will be $= y + \frac{qx}{p}$. And thence, since by reason of the given Angles of the Triangle H Z B, there is given the Ratio of H Z to B Z, if that be made as n to p you will have Z B $= \frac{py+qx}{n}$.

Moreover, if the given E F be called a, A F will be $= a - x$, and thence, if by reason of the given Angles of the Triangle A F I, A F be made to A I in the same Ratio as p to r, A I will become $= \frac{ra-rx}{p}$. Take this from A Z and there will remain I Z $= y - \frac{ra-rx}{p}$. And by reason of the

R 2 the

the given Angles of the Triangle ICZ, if you make IZ to ZC in the ſame Ratio as m to p, ZC will become $= \frac{py - ra + rx}{m}$.

After the ſame Way, if you make $EG = b$. $AG : AK :: l : s$, and $ZK : ZD :: p : l$, there will be obtained $ZD = \frac{sb - sx - ly}{p}$.

Now, from the State of the Queſtion, if the Sum of the two Lines ZC and ZD, *viz.* $\frac{py - ra + rx}{m} + \frac{sb - sx - ly}{p}$ be made equal to any given Quantity f; and the Rectangle of the other two $\frac{pyy + qxy}{n}$ be made $= gg$, you will have two Equations for determining x and y. By the latter there comes out $x = \frac{ngg - pyy}{qy}$, and by writing this Value of x in the room of that in the former Equation, there will come out $\frac{py - ra}{m} + \frac{rngg - rpyy}{mqy} + \frac{sb - ly}{p} - \frac{sngg - spyy}{pqy} = f$; and by Reduction $yy = \frac{apqry - bmqsy + fmpqy + ggmns - ggnpr}{ppq - ppr - mlq + mps}$; and for Abbreviation ſake, writing $2h$ for $\frac{apqr - bmqs + fmpq}{ppq - ppr - mlq + mps}$, and kk for $\frac{ggmns - ggpnr}{ppq - ppr - mlq + mps}$, you will have $yy = 2hy + kk$, or $y = h \pm \sqrt{hh + kk}$. And ſince y is known by means of this Equation, the Equation $\frac{ngg - pyy}{qy} = x$ will give x. Which is ſufficient to determine the Point Z.

After the ſame Way a Point may be determined from which other right Lines may be drawn to more or fewer right Lines given by Poſition, ſo that the Sum, or Difference, or Rectangle of ſome of them may be given, or may be made equal to the Sum, or Difference, or Rectangle of the reſt, or that they may have any other aſſigned Conditions.

PRO-

PROBLEM XXIV.

To ſubtend the right Angle EAF *with the right Line* EF *given in Magnitude, which ſhall paſs through the given Point* C, *equidiſtant from the Lines that comprehend the right Angle (when they are produced).* [*See* Figure 27.]

Complete the Square ABCD, and biſect the Line EF in G. Then call CB or CD, a; EG or FG, b; and CG, x; and CE will be $= x - b$, and $CF = x + b$. Then ſince $CFq - BCq = BFq$, BF will be $= \sqrt{xx + 2bx + bb - aa}$. Laſtly, by reaſon of the ſimilar Triangles CDE, FBC, $CE : CD :: CF : BF$, or $x - b : a :: x + b : \sqrt{xx + 2bx + bb - aa}$. Whence $ax + ab = \overline{x - b} \times \sqrt{xx + 2bx + bb - aa}$. Each Part of which Equation being ſquared, and the Terms that come out being reduced into Order, there comes out $x^4 = \begin{matrix} 2aa \\ +2bb \end{matrix} xx \begin{matrix} +2aabb \\ - b^4 \end{matrix}$. And extracting the Root as in Quadratick Equations, there comes out $xx = aa + bb + \sqrt{a^4 + 4aabb}$; and conſequently $x = \sqrt{aa + bb + \sqrt{a^4 + 4aabb}}$. And CG being thus found, gives CE or CF, which, by determining the Point E or F, ſatisfies the Problem.

The ſame otherwiſe.

Let CE be $= x$, $CD = a$, and $EF = b$; and CF will be $= x + b$, and $BF = \sqrt{xx + bb + 2bx - aa}$. And then ſince $CE : CD :: CF : BF$, or $x : a :: x + b : \sqrt{xx + 2bx + bb - aa}$, $ax + ab$ will be $= x \times \sqrt{xx + 2bx + bb - aa}$. The Parts of this Equation being ſquared, and the Terms reduced into Order, there will come out $x^4 + 2bx^3 \begin{matrix} + bb \\ - 2aa \end{matrix} xx - 2aabx - aabb = 0$, a Biquadratick Equation, the Inveſtigation of the Root of which is more difficult than in the former Caſe. But it may be thus inveſtigated; put $x^4 + 2bx^3 \begin{matrix} + bb \\ - 2aa \end{matrix} xx - 2aabx + a^4 = aabb + a^4$, and extracting the Root on both Sides $xx + bx - aa = \pm a\sqrt{aa + bb}$.

Hence

Hence I have an Opportunity of giving a Rule for the Election of Terms for the Calculus.

Viz. *When there happens to be ſuch an Affinity or Similitude of the Relation of two Terms to the other Terms of the Queſtion, that you ſhould be obliged in making Uſe of either of them to bring out Equations exactly alike; or that both, if they are made Uſe of together, ſhall bring out the ſame Dimenſions and the ſame Form (only excepting perhaps the Signs + and —) in the final Equation (which will be eaſily ſeen) then it will be the beſt Way to make Uſe of neither of them, but in their room to chuſe ſome third, which ſhall bear a like Relation to both, as ſuppoſe the half Sum, or half Difference, or perhaps a mean Proportional, or any other Quantity related to both indifferently and without a like.*

Thus, in the precedent Problem, when I ſee the Line EF alike related to both AB and AD, (which will be evident if you alſo draw EF in the Angle BAH) and therefore I can by no Reaſon be perſwaded why ED ſhould be rather made Uſe of than BF, or AE rather than AF, or CE rather than CF for the Quantity ſought: Wherefore, in the room of the Points E and F, from whence this Ambiguity comes, (in the former Solution) I made Uſe of the intermediate Point G, which has a like Relation to both the Lines AB and AD. Then from this Point G, I did not let fall a Perpendicular to AF for finding the Quantity ſought, becauſe I might by the ſame Reaſon have let one fall to AD. And therefore I let it fall upon neither CB nor CD, but propoſed CG for the Quantity ſought, which does not admit of a like; and ſo I obtained a Biquadratick Equation without the odd Terms.

I might alſo (taking Notice that the Point G lies in the Periphery of a Circle deſcribed from the Center A, by the Radius EG) have let fall the Perpendicular GK upon the Diagonal AC, and have ſought AK or CK, (as which bear alſo a like Relation to both AB and AD) and ſo I ſhould have fallen upon a Quadratick Equation, *viz.* $yy = -\frac{1}{2}ey + \frac{1}{2}bb$, making $AK = y$, $AC = e$, and $EG = b$. And AK being ſo found, there muſt have been erected the Perpendicular KG meeting the aforeſaid Circle in G, through which CF would paſs.

Taking particular Notice of this Rule in *Prob.* IX. and X. where the like Sides BC and AC of the Triangle were to be determined, I rather ſought the Semi-difference than either of them. But the Uſefulneſs of this Rule will be more evident from the XXVIIIth Problem.

PRO-

PROBLEM XXV.

To a Circle deſcribed from the Center C, *and with the Radius* CD, *to draw a Tangent* DB, *the Part whereof* PB *placed between the right Lines given by Poſition,* AP *and* AB *ſhall be of a given Length.* [*See* Figure 50.]

From the Center C to either of the right Lines given by Poſition, as ſuppoſe to AB, let fall the Perpendicular CE, and produce it till it meets the Tangent DB in H. To the ſame AB let fall alſo the Perpendicular PG, and making $EA = a$, $EC = b$, $CD = c$, $BP = d$, and $PG = x$, by reaſon of the ſimilar Triangles PGB, CDH, you will have $GB\ (\sqrt{dd - xx}) : PB :: CD : CH = \frac{cd}{\sqrt{dd - xx}}$. Add EC, and you will have $EH = b + \frac{cd}{\sqrt{dd - xx}}$. Moreover $PG : GB :: EH : EB = \frac{b}{x}\sqrt{dd - xx} + \frac{cd}{x}$. Farther becauſe of the given Angle PAG, there is given the Ratio of PG to AG, which being made as e to f, AG will be $= \frac{fx}{e}$. Add EA and BG, and you will have, laſtly, $EB = a + \frac{fx}{e} + \sqrt{dd - xx}$. Therefore it is $\frac{cd}{x} + \frac{b}{x}\sqrt{dd - xx} = a + \frac{fx}{e} + \sqrt{dd - xx}$, and by Tranſpoſition of the Terms, $a + \frac{fx}{e} - \frac{cd}{x} = \frac{b - x}{x}\sqrt{dd - xx}$. And the Parts of the Equation being ſquared, $aa + \frac{2afx}{e} - \frac{2acd}{x} + \frac{ffxx}{ee} - \frac{2cdf}{e} + \frac{ccdd}{xx} = \frac{bbdd}{xx} - bb - \frac{2bdd}{x} + 2bx + dd - xx$. And by a due Reduction

$$\frac{x^4 \begin{array}{l} +2aef \\ -2bee \end{array} x^3 \begin{array}{l} +aaee \\ +bbee \\ -ddee \\ -2cdef \end{array} xx \begin{array}{l} +2bddee \\ -2acdee \end{array} x \begin{array}{l} +ccddee \\ -bbddee \end{array}}{ee + ff} = 0.$$

PRO-

Problem XXVI.

To find the Point D, *from which three right Lines* DA, DB, DC, *let fall perpendicular to so many other right Lines* AE, BF, CF, *given in Position, shall obtain a given Ratio to one another.* [*See* Figure 44.]

Of the right Lines given in Position, let us suppose one as BF be produced, as also its Perpendicular BD, till they meet the rest AE and CF, *viz.* BF in E and F, and BD in H and G. Now let EB be $=x$, and EF $=a$; and BF will be $=a-x$. But since, by reason of the given Position of the right Lines EF, EA, and FC, the Angles E and F, and consequently the Proportions of the Sides of the Triangles EBH and FBG are given; let EB be to BH as d to e; and BH will be $=\frac{ex}{d}$, and EH ($=\sqrt{EBq+BHq}=\sqrt{xx+\frac{eexx}{dd}}$, that is, $\frac{x}{d}\times\sqrt{dd+ee}$. Let also BF be to BG as d to f; and BG will be $=\frac{fa-fx}{d}$, and FG ($=\sqrt{BFq+BGq}$) $=$

$$\sqrt{\frac{aadd-2axdd+xxdd+ffaa-2ffax+ffxx}{dd}},$$

that is, $=\frac{a-x}{d}\sqrt{dd+ff}$. Besides, make BD $=y$, and HD will be $=\frac{ex}{d}-y$, and GD $=\frac{fa-fx}{d}-y$; and so, since AD is : HD (:: EB : EH) :: $d:\sqrt{dd+ee}$, and DC : GD (:: BF : FG) :: $d:\sqrt{dd+ff}$, AD will be $=\frac{ex-dy}{\sqrt{dd+ee}}$, and DC $=\frac{fa-fx-dy}{\sqrt{dd+ff}}$. Lastly, by reason of the given Proportions of the Lines BD, AD, DC, let BD : AD :: $\sqrt{dd+ee}:h-d$, and $\frac{hy-dy}{\sqrt{dd+ee}}$ will be ($=$AD)$=\frac{ex-dy}{\sqrt{dd+ee}}$, or $hy=ex$. Let also BD : DC :: $\sqrt{dd+ff}:k-d$, and $\frac{ky-dy}{\sqrt{dd+ff}}$ will be ($=$DC)$=\frac{fa-fx-dy}{\sqrt{dd+ff}}$ or $ky=fa-fx$. Therefore $\frac{ex}{h}$ ($=y$) is $=\frac{fa-fx}{k}$; and by Reduction $\frac{fha}{ek+fh}=x$. Wherefore take EB : EF :: $h:\frac{ek}{f}+h$, then BD : EB :: $e:h$, and you will have the Point sought D.

Problem XXVII.

To find the Point D, *from which three right Lines* DA, DB, DC, *drawn to the three given Points,* A, B, C, *shall have a given Ratio among themselves.* [*See* Figure 45.]

Of the given three Points join any two of them, as suppose A and C, and let fall the Perpendicular BE from the third B, to the Line that conjoins A and C, as also the Perpendicular DF from the Point sought D; and making AE$=a$, AC$=b$, EB$=c$, AF$=x$, and FD$=y$; and ADq will be$=xx+yy$. FC$=b-x$, CDq ($=$FCq$+$FDq)$=bb-2bx+xx+yy$. EF$=x-a$, and BDq ($=$EFq$+$EB$+$FDq)$=xx-2ax+aa+cc+2cy+yy$. Now, since AD is to CD in a given Ratio, let it be as d to e; and CD will be $=\frac{e}{d}\sqrt{xx+yy}$. Since also AD is to BD in a given Ratio, let that be as d to f, and BD will be $=\frac{f}{d}\sqrt{xx+yy}$. And, consequently it is $\frac{eexx+eeyy}{dd}$ ($=$CDq) $=bb-2bx+xx+yy$, and $\frac{ffxx+ffyy}{dd}$ ($=$BDq)$=xx-2ax+aa+cc+2cy+yy$.

S In

In which if, for Abbreviation ſake, you write p for $\frac{dd-ee}{d}$, and q for $\frac{dd-ff}{d}$, there will come out $bb - 2bx + \frac{p}{d}xx + \frac{p}{d}yy = 0$, and $aa + cc - 2ax + 2cy + \frac{q}{d}xx + \frac{q}{d}yy = 0$. And by the former you have $\frac{2bqx - bbq}{p} = \frac{q}{d}xx + \frac{q}{d}yy$. Wherefore, in the latter, for $\frac{q}{d}xx + \frac{q}{d}yy$, write $\frac{2bqx - bbq}{p}$, and there will come out $\frac{2bqx - bbq}{p} + aa + cc - 2ax + 2cy = 0$. Again, for Abbreviation ſake, write m for $a - \frac{bq}{p}$, and $2cn$ for $\frac{bbq}{p} - aa - cc$, and you will have $2mx + 2cn = 2cy$, and the Terms being divided by $2c$, there ariſes $\frac{mx}{c} + n = y$. Wherefore, in the Equation $bb - 2bx + \frac{p}{d}xx + \frac{p}{d}yy = 0$, for yy write the Square of $\frac{mx}{c} + n$, and you will have $bb - 2bx + \frac{p}{d}xx + \frac{pmm}{dcc}xx + \frac{2pmn}{dc}x + \frac{pnn}{d} = 0$. Where, laſtly, if, for Abbreviation ſake, you write $\frac{b}{r}$ for $\frac{p}{d} + \frac{pmm}{dcc}$, and $\frac{sb}{r}$ for $b - \frac{pmn}{dc}$, and $\frac{tbb}{r}$ for $bb + \frac{pnn}{d}$, you will have $xx = 2sx - tb$. And having extracted the Root $x = s \pm \sqrt{ss - tb}$. Having found x, the Equation $\frac{mx}{c} + n = y$ will give y; and from x and y given, that is, AF and FD, the given Point D is determined.

PRO-

PROBLEM XXVIII.

So to inſcribe the right Line DC *of a given Length in the given Conick Section* DAC, *that it may paſs through the Point* G *given by Poſition.* [*See* Figure 28.]

Let AF be the Axis of the Curve, and from the Points D, G, and C, let fall to it the Perpendiculars DH, GE, and CB. Now to determine the Poſition of the right Line DC, it may be propoſed to find out the Point D or C; but ſince theſe are related, and ſo alike, that there would be the like Operation in determining either of them, whether I were to ſeek CG, CB, or AB; or their likes, DG, DH, or AH; therefore I look after a third Point, that regards D and C alike, and at the ſame time determines them. And I ſee F to be ſuch a Point.

Now let AE be $= a$, EG $= b$, DC $= c$, and EF $= z$; and beſides ſince the Relation between AB and BC is had in the Equation, I ſuppoſe, given for determining the Conick Section, let AB $= x$, BC $= y$, and FB will be $x - a + z$. And becauſe GE : EF :: CB : FB, FB will again be $= \frac{yz}{b}$. Therefore, $x - a + z = \frac{yz}{b}$.

Theſe Things being thus laid down, take away x, by the Equation that denotes the Curve. As if the Curve be a Parabola expreſſed by the Equation $rx = yy$, write $\frac{yy}{r}$ for x; and there will ariſe $\frac{yy}{r} - a + z = \frac{yz}{b}$, and extracting the Root $y = \frac{rz}{2b} \pm \sqrt{\frac{rrzz}{4bb} + ar - rz}$. Whence it is evident, that $\sqrt{\frac{rrzz}{bb} + 4ar - 4rz}$ is the Difference of the double Value of y, that is, of the Lines $+$ BC and $-$ DH, and conſequently (having let fall DK perpendicular upon CB) that Difference is equal to CK. But FG : GE :: DC : CK, that is, $\sqrt{bb + zz} : b :: c : \sqrt{\frac{rrzz}{bb} + 4ar - 4rz}$.

S 2 And

And by multiplying the Squares of the Means, and alſo the Squares of the Extreams into one another, and ordering the Products, there will ariſe $z^4 =$

$$\frac{4bbrz^3 \begin{matrix}-4abbr\\-bbrr\end{matrix} zz + 4b^4rz \begin{matrix}-4ab^4r\\+b^4cc\end{matrix}}{rr},$$ an Equation

of four Dimenſions, which would have riſen to one of eight Dimenſions if I had ſought either C G, or C B, or A B.

PROBLEM XXIX.

To multiply or divide a given Angle by a given Number. [*See* Figure 29.]

In any Angle F A G inſcribe the Lines A B, B C, C D, D E, &c. of any the ſame Length, and the Triangles A B C, B C D, C D E, D E F, &c. will be *Iſoſceles*, and conſequently by the 32. 1. *Eucl.* the Angle C B D will be = Angle A + A C B = 2 Angle A, and the Angle D C E = Angle A + A D C = 3 Angle A, and the Angle E D F = A + A E D = 4 Angle A, and the Angle F E G = 5 Angle A, and ſo onwards. Now, making A B, B C, C D, &c. the Radii of equal Circles, the Perpendiculars B K, C L, D M, &c. let fall upon A C, B D, C E, &c. will be the Sines of thoſe Angles, and A K, B L, C M, D N, &c. will be their Sines Complement to a right one; or making A B the Diameter, the Lines A K, B L, C M, &c. will be Chords. Let therefore A B = $2r$, and A K = x, then work thus:

$$AB : AK :: AC : AL.$$

$$2r : x :: 2x : \frac{xx}{r}.$$

And $\left\{\begin{matrix}AL - AB\\ \frac{xx}{r} - 2r\end{matrix}\right\}$ = B L, the Duplication.

$$AB : AK :: AD\,(2\,AL - AB) : AM.$$

$$2r : x :: \frac{2xx}{r} - 2r : \frac{x^3}{rr} - x.$$

And $\left\{\begin{matrix}AM - AC\\ \frac{x^3}{rr} - 3x\end{matrix}\right\}$ = C M, the Triplication.

$$AB : AK :: AE\,(2\,AM - AC) : AN.$$

$$2r : x :: \frac{2x^3}{rr} - 4x : \frac{x^4}{r^3} - \frac{2xx}{r}.$$

And $\left\{\begin{matrix}AN - AD\\ \frac{x^4}{r^3} - \frac{4xx}{r} + 2r\end{matrix}\right\}$ = D N, the Quadruplication;

$$AB : AK :: AF\,(2\,AN - AD) : AO.$$

$$2r : x :: \frac{2x^4}{r^3} - \frac{6xx}{r} + 2r : \frac{x^5}{r^4} - \frac{3x^3}{rr} + x.$$

And $\left\{\begin{matrix}AO - AE\\ \frac{x^5}{r^4} - \frac{5x^3}{rr} + 5x\end{matrix}\right\}$ = E O, the Quintuplication.

And ſo onwards. Now if you would divide an Angle into any Number of Parts, put q for B L, C M, D N, &c. and you will have $xx - 2rr = qr$ for the Biſection; $xxx - 3rrx = qr^2$ for the Triſection; $xxxx - 4rrxx + 2r^4 = qr^3$ for the Quadriſection; $xxxxx - 5r^2x^3 + 5r^4x = qr^4$ for the Quinquiſection, &c.

PROBLEM XXX.

To determine the Poſition of a Comet's Courſe that moves uniformly in a right Line, as B D, *from three Obſervations.* [*See* Figure 30.]

Suppoſe A to be the Eye of the Spectator, B the Place of the Comet in the firſt Obſervation, C in the ſecond, and D in the third; the Inclination of the Line B D to the Line A B is to be found. From the Obſervations therefore there are given the Angles B A C, B A D; and conſequently if B H be drawn Perpendicular to A B, and meeting A C and A D in E and F, aſſuming any how A B, there will be given B E and B F, *viz.* the Tangents of the Angles in reſpect of the Radius A B. Make therefore A B = a, B E = b, and B F = c. Moreover, from the given Intervals of

of the Obſervations, there will be given the Ratio of B C to B D, which, if it be made as b to e, and D G be drawn parallel to A C, ſince B E is to B G in the ſame Ratio, and B E was called b, B G will be $= e$, and conſequently G F $= e - c$. Farther, if you let fall D H perpendicular to B G, by reaſon of the Triangles A B F and D H F being like, and alike divided by the Lines A E and D G, F E will be : A B :: F G : H D, that is, $c - b : a :: e - c$: $\dfrac{ae - ac}{c - b} = $ H D. Moreover, F E will be : F B :: F G

: F H, that is, $c - b : c :: e - c : \dfrac{ce - cc}{c - b} = $ F H ; to

which add B F, or c, and B H will be $= \dfrac{ce - cb}{c - b}$. Where-

fore $\dfrac{ce - cb}{c - b}$ is to $\dfrac{ae - ac}{c - b}$ (or $ce - cb$ to $ae - ac$, or

$\dfrac{ce - cb}{e - c}$ to a) as B H to H D ; that is, as the Tangent of the Angle H D B, or A B K to the Radius. Wherefore ſince a is ſuppoſed to be the Radius, $\dfrac{ce - cb}{e - c}$ will be the Tangent of the Angle A B K, and therefore by reſolving them into an Analogy, it will be as $e - c$ to $e - b$, (or G F to G E) ſo c (or the Tangent of the Angle B A F) to the Tangent of the Angle A B K.

Say therefore, as the Time between the firſt and ſecond Obſervation to the Time between the firſt and third, ſo the Tangent of the Angle B A E to a fourth Proportional. Then as the Difference between that fourth Proportional and the Tangent of the Angle B A F, to the Difference between the ſame fourth Proportional and the Tangent of the Angle B A E, ſo the Tangent of the Angle B A F to the Tangent of the Angle A B K.

PRO-

PROBLEM XXXI.

Rays of Light from any ſhining or lucid Point diverging to a refracting Spherical Surface, to find the Concourſe of each of the refracted Rays with the Axis of the Sphere paſſing through that lucid Point. [*See* Figure 31.]

Let A be that lucid Point, and B V the Sphere, the Axis whereof is A D, the Center C, and the Vertex V ; and let A B be the incident Ray, and B D the refracted Ray ; and having let fall to thoſe Rays the Perpendiculars C E and C F, as alſo B G perpendicular to A D, and having drawn B C, make A C $= a$, V C or B C $= r$, C G $= x$, and C D $= z$, and A G will be $= a - x$, B G $= \sqrt{rr - xx}$, A B $= \sqrt{aa - 2ax + rr}$; and by reaſon of the ſimilar Triangles A B G and A C E, C E $= \dfrac{a\sqrt{rr - xx}}{\sqrt{aa - 2ax + rr}}$. Alſo G D $= z + x$, B D $= \sqrt{zz + 2zx + rr}$; and by reaſon of the ſimilar Triangles D B G and D C F, C F $= \dfrac{z\sqrt{rr - xx}}{\sqrt{zz + 2zx + rr}}$. Beſides ſince the Ratio of the Sines of Incidence and Refraction, and conſequently of C E to C F, is given, ſuppoſe that Ratio to be as a to f, and $\dfrac{fa\sqrt{rr - xx}}{\sqrt{aa - 2ax + rr}}$ will be $= \dfrac{az\sqrt{rr - xx}}{\sqrt{zz + 2zx + rr}}$; and multiplying croſs-ways, and dividing by $a\sqrt{rr - xx}$, it will be $f\sqrt{zz + 2zx + rr} = z\sqrt{aa - 2xa + rr}$, and by ſquaring and reducing the Terms into Order, $zz = \dfrac{2ffxz + ffrr}{aa - 2ax + rr - ff}$. Then for the given $\dfrac{ff}{a}$ write p, and q for the given $a + \dfrac{rr}{a} - p$, and zz will be $= \dfrac{2pxz + prr}{q - 2x}$, and $z = \dfrac{px + \sqrt{ppxx - 2prrx + pqrr}}{q - 2x}$. Therefore z is found ; that is, the Length of C D, and conſequently the Point ſought D, where the refracted Ray B D meets with the Axis. Q. E. F.

Here

Here I made the incident Rays to diverge, and fall upon a thicker Medium; but changing what is requisite to be changed, the Problem may be as easily resolved when the Rays converge, or fall from a thicker Medium into a thinner one.

PROBLEM XXXII.

If a Cone be cut by any Plane, to find the Figure of the Section. [*See* Figure 32 *and* 33.]

Let ABC be a Cone standing on a circular Base BC, and IEM its Section sought; and let KILM be any other Section parallel to the Base, and meeting the former Section in HI; and ABC a third Section, perpendicularly bisecting the two former in EH and KL, and the Cone in the Triangle ABC. And producing EH till it meet AK in D; and having drawn EF and DG, parallel to KL, and meeting AB and AC in F and G, call $EF=a$, $DG=b$, $ED=c$, $EH=x$, and $HI=y$; and by reason of the similar Triangles EHL, EDG, ED will be $:DG::EH:HL=\frac{bx}{c}$. Then by reason of the similar Triangles DEF, DHK, DE will be $:EF::DH:(c-x$ in the thirty second Figure, and $c+x$ in the thirty third Figure) $HK=\frac{ac\mp ax}{c}$. Lastly, since the Section KIL is parallel to the Base, and consequently circular, $HK\times HL$ will be $=HIq$, that is, $\frac{ab}{c}x\mp\frac{ab}{cc}xx-yy$, an Equation which expresses the Relation between EH (x) and HI (y), that is, between the Axis and the Ordinate of the Section EIM; which Equation, since it expresses an Ellipse in the thirty second Figure, and an Hyperbola in the thirty third Figure, it is evident, that that Section will be Elliptical or Hyperbolical.

Now if ED no where meets AK, being parallel to it, then HK will be $=EF$ (a), and thence $\frac{ab}{c}x$ $(HK\times HL)$ $=yy$, an Equation expressing a Parabola.

PRO-

3

PROBLEM XXXIII.

If the right Line XY *be turned about the Axis* AB, *at the Distance* CD, *with a given Inclination to the Plane* DCB, *and the Solid* PQRUTS, *generated by that Circumrotation, be cut by any Plane as* INQLK, *to find the Figure of the Section.* [*See* Figure 34.]

Let BHQ, or GHO be the Inclination of the Axis AB to the Plane of the Section; and let L be any Concourse of the right Line XY with that Plane. Draw DF parallel to AB, and let fall the Perpendiculars LG, LF, LM, to AB, DF, and HO, and join FG and MG. And having called $CD=a$, $CH=b$, $HM=x$, and $ML=y$, by reason of the given Angle GHO, making $MH:HG::d:e$, $\frac{ex}{d}$ will be $=GH$, and $b+\frac{ex}{d}=GC$ or FD. Moreover, by reason of the given Angle LDF (*viz.* the Inclination of the right Line XY to the Plane GCDF) putting $FD:FL::g:h$, it will be $\frac{hb}{g}+\frac{hex}{dg}=FL$, to whose Square add FGq (DCq, or aa) and there will come out $GLq=aa+\frac{hhbb}{gg}+\frac{2hhbex}{dgg}+\frac{hheexx}{ddgg}$. Hence subtract MGq ($HMq-HGq$, or $xx-\frac{ee}{dd}xx$) and there will remain $\frac{aagg+hhbb}{gg}+\frac{2hhbe}{dgg}x+\frac{hhee-ddgg+eegg}{ddgg}\times xx$ $(=MLq)=yy$: an Equation that expresses the Relation between x and y, that is, between HM the Axis of the Section, and ML its Ordinate. And therefore, since in this Equation x and y ascend only to two Dimensions, it is evident, that the Figure INQLK is a Conick Section. As for Example, if the Angle MHG is greater than the Angle LDF, this Figure will be an Ellipse; but if less, an Hyperbola; and if equal, either a Parabola, or (the Points C and H moreover coinciding) a Parallelogram.

T PRO-

PROBLEM XXXIV.

If you erect AD *of a given Length perpendicular to* AF, *and* ED, *one Leg of a Square* DEF, *paſs continually through the Point* D, *while the other Leg* EF *equal to* AD *ſlide upon* AF, *to find the Curve* HIC, *which the Leg* EF *deſcribes by its middle Point* C. [*See* Figure 35.]

Let EC or CF be $= a$, the Perpendicular CB $= y$, AB $= x$, and on account of the ſimilar Triangles FBC, FEG, it will be BF $(\sqrt{aa - yy})$: BC + CF $(y + a)$ :: EF $(2a)$: EG + GF (AG + GF) or AF. Wherefore $\frac{2ay + 2aa}{\sqrt{aa - yy}}$ (= AF = AB + BF) $= x + \sqrt{aa - yy}$. Now by multiplying by $\sqrt{aa - yy}$ there is made $2ay + 2aa = aa - yy + x\sqrt{aa - yy}$, or $2ay + aa + yy = x \times \sqrt{aa - yy}$, and by ſquaring the Parts, divided by $\sqrt{a + y}$, and ordering them, there comes out $y^3 + 3ayy \begin{matrix} +3aa \\ +xx \end{matrix} y \begin{matrix} +a^3 \\ -axx \end{matrix} = 0$.

The ſame otherwiſe. [*See* Figure 36.]

On BC take at each End BI, and CK equal to CF, and draw KF, HI, HC, and DF; whereof let HC and DF meet AF, and IK in M and N, and upon HC let fall the Perpendicular IL; and the Angle K will be $= \frac{1}{2}$BCF $= \frac{1}{2}$EGF = GFD = AMH = MHI = CIL; and conſequently the right-angled Triangles KBF, FBN, HLI, and ILC will be ſimilar. Make therefore FC $= a$, HI $= x$, and IC $= y$; and BN $(2a - y)$ will be : BK (y) :: LC : LH :: CIq (yy) : HIq (xx), and conſequently $2axx - yxx = y^3$. From which Equation it is eaſily inferred, that this Curve is the Ciſſoid of the Antients, belonging to a Circle, whoſe Center is A, and its Radius AH.

PRO-

PROBLEM XXXV.

If a right Line ED *of a given Length ſubtending the given Angle* EAD, *be ſo moved, that its Ends* D *and* E *always touch the Sides* AD *and* AE *of that Angle; let it be propoſed to determine the Curve* FCG, *which any given Point* C *in that right Line* ED *deſcribes.* [*See* Figure 37.]

From the given Point C draw CB parallel to EA; and make AB $= x$, BC $= y$, CE $= a$, and CD $= b$, and by reaſon of the ſimilar Triangles DCB, DEA, it will be EC : AB :: CD : BD; that is, $a : x :: b :$ BD $= \frac{bx}{a}$. Beſides, having let fall the Perpendicular CH, by reaſon of the given Angle DAE, or DBC, and conſequently of the given Ratio of the Sides of the right-angled Triangle BCH, you will have $a : e ::$ BC : BH, and BH will be $= \frac{ey}{a}$. Take away this from BD, and there will remain HD $= \frac{bx - ey}{a}$. Now in the Triangle BCH, becauſe of the right Angle BHC, it is BCq − BHq = CHq; that is $yy - \frac{eeyy}{aa}$ = CHq. In like manner, in the Triangle CDH, becauſe of the right Angle CHD, it is CDq − CHq = HDq; that is, $bb - yy + \frac{eeyy}{aa}$ (= HDq = $\frac{bx - ey}{a}$ q.) $= \frac{bbxx - 2bexy + eeyy}{aa}$; and by Reduction $yy = \frac{2be}{aa} \times xy + \frac{aabb - bbxx}{aa}$. Where, ſince the unknown Quantities riſe but to two Dimenſions, it is evident that the Curve is a Conick Section. Then extracting the Root, you will have $y = \frac{bex \pm b\sqrt{eexx - aaxx + a^4}}{aa}$. Where, in the Radical Term, the Coefficient of xx is $ee - aa$. But it was $a : e ::$ BC : BH; and BC is neceſſarily a greater Line than BH, *viz.* the Hypothenuſe of a right-angled Triangle is greater than the Side of it; therefore a is greater than e, and $ee - aa$ is a negative Quantity, and conſequently the Curve will be an Ellipſis.

T 2 PRO-

PROBLEM XXXVI.

If the Ruler EBD, *forming a right Angle, be so moved, that one Leg of it,* EB, *continually subtends the right Angle* EAB, *while the End of the other Leg,* BD, *describes some Curve Line, as* FD; *to find that Line* FD, *which the Point* D *describes.* [*See* Figure 38.]

From the Point D let fall the Perpendicular DC to the Side AC; and making $AC = x$, and $DC = y$, and $EB = a$, and $BD = b$. In the Triangle BDC, by reason of the right Angle at C, BCq is $= BDq - DCq = bb - yy$. Therefore $BC = \sqrt{bb - yy}$; and $AB = x - \sqrt{bb - yy}$. Besides, by reason of the similar Triangles BEA, DBC, it is BD : DC :: EB : AB; that is, $b : y :: a : x - \sqrt{bb - yy}$. Wherefore $bx - b\sqrt{bb - yy} = ay$, or $bx - ay = b\sqrt{bb - yy}$. And the Parts being squared and duly reduced $yy = \frac{2abxy + b^4 - bbxx}{aa + bb}$. And extracting the Root $y = \frac{abx + bb\sqrt{aa + bb - xx}}{aa + bb}$. Whence it is again evident, that the Curve is an Ellipsis.

This is so where the Angles EBD and EAB are right; but if those Angles are of any other Magnitude, as long as they are equal, you may proceed thus: [*See* Figure 39.] Let fall DC perpendicular to AC as before, and draw DH, making the Angle DHA equal to the Angle HAE, suppose Obtuse, and calling $EB = a$, $BD = b$, $AH = x$, and $HD = y$; by reason of the similar Triangles EAB, BHD, BD will be : DH :: EB : AB; that is, $b : y :: a : AB = \frac{ay}{b}$. Take this from AH and there will remain $BH = x - \frac{ay}{b}$. Besides, in the Triangle DHC, by reason of all the Angles given, and consequently the Ratio of the Sides given, assume DH to HC in any given Ratio, suppose as b to e; and since DH is y, HC will be $\frac{ey}{b}$, and $HB \times HC = \frac{exy}{b} - \frac{aeyy}{bb}$.

Lastly, by the 12, 2 *Elem.* in the Triangle BHD, it is $BDq = BHq + DHq + 2BH \times HC$; that is, $bb = xx - \frac{2axy}{b} + \frac{aayy}{bb} + yy + \frac{2exy}{b} - \frac{2aeyy}{bb}$. and extracting the Root $x = \frac{ay - ey \pm \sqrt{eeyy - bbyy + bbbb}}{b}$. Where when b is greater than e, that is, when $ee - bb$ is a negative Quantity, it is again evident, that the Curve is an Ellipse.

PROBLEM XXXVII.

In the given Angle PAB *having any how drawn the right Lines,* BD, PD, *in a given Ratio, on this Condition, that* BD *shall be parallel to* AP, *and* PD *terminated at the given Point* P *in the right Line* AP; *to find the Locus of the Point* D. [*See* Figure 41.]

Draw CD parallel to AB, and DE perpendicular to AP; and make $AP = a$, $CP = x$, and $CD = y$, and let BD be to PD in the same Ratio as d to e, and AC or BD will be $= a - x$, and $PD = \frac{ea - ex}{d}$. Moreover, by reason of the given Angle DCE, let the Ratio of CD to CE be as d to f, and CE will be $= \frac{fy}{d}$, and $EP = x - \frac{fy}{d}$. But by reason of the Angles at E being right ones, it is $CDq - CEq\ (= EDq) = PDq - EPq$; that is, $yy - \frac{ffyy}{dd} = \frac{eeaa - 2eeax + eexx}{dd} - xx + \frac{2fxy}{d} - \frac{ffyy}{dd}$; and blotting out on each Side $-\frac{ffyy}{dd}$, and the Terms being rightly disposed, $yy = \frac{2fxy}{d} + \frac{eeaa - 2eeax + eexx - ddxx}{dd}$, and extracting the Root $y =$

$$y = \frac{fx}{d} \pm \frac{\sqrt{eeaa - 2eeax \begin{array}{l}+ee\\-dd\\+ff\end{array} xx}}{d}.$$

Where, since x and y in the last Equation ascends only to two Dimensions, the Place of the Point D will be a Conick Section, and that either an Hyperbola, Parabola, or Ellipse, as $ee - dd + ff$, (the Co-efficient of xx in the last Equation) is greater, equal to, or less than nothing.

Problem XXXVIII.

The two right Lines V E and V C *being given in Position, and cut any how in* C *and* E *by another right Line*, P E *turning about the Pole*, P *given also in Position; if the intercepted Line* C E *be divided into the Parts* C D, D E, *that have a given Ratio to one another, it is proposed to find the Place of the Point* D. [*See* Figure 42.]

Draw V P, and parallel to it, D A, and E B meeting V C in A and B. Make $VP = a$, $VA = x$, and $AD = y$, and since the Ratio of C D to D E is given, or conversely of C D to C E, that is, the Ratio of D A to E B, let it be as d to e, and E B will be $= \frac{ey}{d}$. Besides, since the Angle E V B is given, and consequently the Ratio of E B to V B, let that Ratio be as e to f, and V B will be $= \frac{fy}{d}$. Lastly, by reason of the similar Triangles C E B, C D A, C P V, it is E B : C B :: D A : C A :: V P : V C, and by Composition E B + V P : C B + V C :: D A + V P : C A + V C; that is, $\frac{ey}{d} + a : \frac{fy}{d} :: y + a : x$, and multiplying together the Means and Extremes $eyx + dax = fyy + fay$. Where since the indefinite Quantities x and y ascend only to two Dimensions, it follows, that the Curve V D, in which the Point D is always found, is a Conick Section, and that an Hyperbola, because one of the indefinite Quantities, *viz.* x is only of one Dimension, and in the Term exy is multiplied by the other indefinite one y.

Pro-

Problem XXXIX.

If two right Lines, A C *and* B C, *in any given Ratio, are drawn from the two Points* A *and* B *given in Position, to a third Point* C, *to find the Place of* C, *the Point of Concourse.* [*See* Figure 43.]

Join A B, and let fall to it the Perpendicular C D; and making $AB = a$, $AD = x$, $DC = y$, A C will be $= \sqrt{xx + yy}$, $BD = x - a$, and $BC (= \sqrt{BDq + DCq}) = \sqrt{xx - 2ax + aa + yy}$. Now since there is given the Ratio of A C to B C, let that be as d to e; and the Means and Extremes being multiplied together, you will have $e\sqrt{xx + yy} = d\sqrt{xx - 2ax + aa + yy}$, and by Reduction $\sqrt{\frac{ddaa - 2ddax}{ee - dd} - xx} = y$. Where since xx is Negative, and affected only by Unity, and also the Angle A D C a right one, it is evident, that the Curve in which the Point C is placed is a Circle, *viz.* in the right Line A B take the Points E and F, so that $d : e ::$ A E : B E :: A F : B F, and E F will be the Diameter of this Circle.

And hence from the Converse this Theorem comes out, that in the Diameter of any Circle E F produced, having given any how the two Points A and B on this Condition, that A E : A F :: B E : B F, and having drawn from these Points the two right Lines A C and B C, meeting the Circumference in any Point C; A C will be to B C in the given Ratio of A E to B E.

Problem XL.

If a lucid Point, as A, *dart forth Rays towards a refracting plain Surface, as* C D; *to find the Ray* A C, *whose refracted Part* C B *will strike the given Point* B. [*See* Figure 51.]

From that lucid Point let fall the Perpendicular A D to the refracting Plane, and let the refracted Ray B C meet with it, being produced out on both Sides, in E; and a Perpendicular let fall from the Point B in F, and draw B D; and making $AD = a$, $DB = b$, $BF = c$, $DC = x$, make the Ratio of the Sines of Incidence and Refraction, that

2 is,

is, of the Sines of the Angles C A D, C E D, to be d to e, and since E C and A C (as is known) are in the same Ratio, and A C is $\sqrt{aa+xx}$, E C will be $= \frac{d}{e}\sqrt{aa+xx}$. Besides E D $(=\sqrt{ECq-CDq})$ is $=\sqrt{\frac{ddaa+ddxx}{ee}-xx}$, and D F $=\sqrt{bb-cc}$, and E F $=\sqrt{bb-cc}+\sqrt{\frac{ddaa+ddxx}{ee}-xx}$. Lastly, because of the similar Triangles E C D, E B F, it is E D : D C :: E F : F B, and multiplying the Values of the Means and Extremes into one another, $c\sqrt{\frac{ddaa+ddxx}{ee}-xx}=x\sqrt{bb-cc}+x\times\sqrt{\frac{ddaa+ddxx}{ee}-xx}$, or $c-x\sqrt{\frac{ddaa+ddxx}{ee}-xx}$ $=x\sqrt{bb-cc}$, and the Parts of the Equation being squared and duly disposed.

$$x^4-2cx^3 \begin{array}{l}+ddcc\\ +ddaaxx-2ddaacx+ddaacc\\ -eebb\end{array} \Big/ \, dd-ee \;=0.$$

PROBLEM XLI.

To find the Locus or Place of the Vertex of a Triangle D, *whose Base* A B *is given, and the Angles at the Base* D A B, D B A, *have a given Difference.* [*See* Figure 52.]

Where the Angle at the Vertex, or (which is the same Thing) where the Sum of the Angles at the Base is given, *Euclid* [in 29.3.] has taught us, that the Locus of the Vertex is in the Circumference of a Circle; but we have proposed the finding the Place when the Difference of the Angles at the Base is given. Let the Angle D B A be greater than the Angle D A B, and let A B F be their given Difference, the right Line B F meeting A D in F. Moreover, let fall the Perpendicular D E to B F, as also D C perpendicular to A B meeting B F in G. And making A B $=a$, A C $=x$, and C D $=y$, B C will be $=a-x$. Now since in the Triangle B C G there are given all the Angles, there will be given the Ratio of the Sides B C and G C, let that be as d to a, and C G will be $=\frac{aa-ax}{d}$; take away this from D C or y, and there will remain D G $=\frac{dy-aa+ax}{d}$. Besides because of the similar Triangles B G C, and D G E, it is B G : B C :: D G : D E. But in the Triangle B G C, it is $a:d$ :: C G : B C. And consequently $aa:dd$ :: C Gq : B Cq, and by compounding $aa+dd:dd$ :: B Gq : B Cq, and extracting the Roots $\sqrt{aa+dd}:d$ (:: B G : B C) :: D G : D E. Therefore D E $=\frac{dy-aa+ax}{\sqrt{aa+dd}}$. Moreover since the Angle A B F is the Difference of the Angles B A D and A B D, and consequently the Angles B A D and F B D are equal, the right-angled Triangles C A D and E B D will be similar, and therefore the Sides proportional or D A : D C :: D B : D E. But D C is $=y$. D A $(=\sqrt{ACq+DCq})=\sqrt{xx+yy}$. D B $(=\sqrt{BCq+DCq})=\sqrt{aa-2ax+xx+yy}$, and above D E was $=\frac{dy-aa+ax}{\sqrt{aa+dd}}$. Wherefore $\sqrt{xx+yy}:y$ :: $\sqrt{aa-2ax+xx+yy}:\frac{dy-aa+ax}{\sqrt{aa+dd}}$; and the Squares of the Means and Extremes being multiplied by each other

$$aayy-2axyy+xxyy+y^4=\frac{ddxxyy+ddy^4-2aadxxy-2aady^3+2adyx^3+2adxy^3+a^4x^2+a^4yy-2a^3x^3-2a^3xyy+aax^4+a^2x^2y^2}{aa+dd}.$$

Multiply all the

V

the Terms by $aa+dd$, and reduce those Terms that come out into due Order, and there will arise

$$x^4 \begin{matrix}-2a\\+\frac{2d}{a}y\end{matrix} x^3 \begin{matrix}-2dy\\+aa\end{matrix} xx \begin{matrix}+\frac{2d}{a}y^3\\+\frac{2dd}{a}yy\end{matrix} x \begin{matrix}-ddyy\\-2dy^3\\-y^4\end{matrix} = 0.$$

Divide this Equation by $xx - ax \begin{matrix}+dy\\+yy\end{matrix}$, and there will arise $xx \begin{matrix}-a\\+\frac{2d}{a}y\end{matrix} x \begin{matrix}-yy\\-dy\end{matrix} = 0$; there come out therefore two Equations in the Solution of this Problem: The first, $xx - ax \begin{matrix}+dy\\+yy\end{matrix} = 0$ is to a Circle, *viz.* the Place of the Point D, where the Angle F B D is taken on the other Side of the right Line B F than what is described in the Figure, the Angle A B F being the Sum of the Angles D A B and D B A at the Base, and so the Angle A D B at the Vertex being given. The last, *viz.* $xx \begin{matrix}-a\\+\frac{2d}{a}y\end{matrix} x \begin{matrix}-yy\\-dy\end{matrix} = 0$, is an Hyperbola, the Place of the Point D, where the Angle F B D obtains the Situation from the right Line B F, which we described in the Figure; that is, so that the Angle A B F may be the Difference of the Angles D A B, D B A, at the Base. And this is the Determination of the Hyperbola: Bisect A B in P; draw P Q, making the Angle B P Q equal to half the Angle A B F: To this draw the Perpendicular P R, and P Q and P R will be the Asymptotes of this Hyperbola, and B a Point through which the Hyperbola will pass.

Hence arises this *Theorem.* Any Diameter, as A B, of a right-angled Hyperbola, being drawn, and having drawn the right Lines A D, B D, A H, B H, from it's Ends to any two Points D and H of the Hyperbola; these right Lines will make equal Angles D A H, D B H at the Ends of the Diameter.

The same after a shorter Way.

At PROB. xxiv. I laid down a *Rule* about the most commodious Election of Terms to proceed with in the Calculus of

of Problems, where there happens any Ambiguity in the Election of such Terms. Here the Difference of the Angles at the Base is indifferent in respect to both Angles; and in the Construction of the Scheme, it might equally have been added to the lesser Angle D A B, by drawing from A a right Line parallel to B F, or subtracted from the greater Angle D B A, by drawing the right Line B F. Wherefore I neither add nor substract it, but add half of it to one of the Angles, and substract half of it from the other. Then since it is also doubtful whether A C or B C must be made Use of for the indefinite Term whereon the Ordinate D C stands, I use neither of them; but I bisect A B in P, and I make use of P C; or rather, having drawn M P Q [See *Figure* 53.] making, on both Sides, the Angles A P Q, B P M equal to half the Difference of the Angles at the Base, so that it, with the right Lines A D, B D, may make the Angles D Q P, D M P equal; I let fall to M Q the Perpendiculars A R, B N, D O, and I use D O for the Ordinate, and P O for the indefinite Line it stands on. I make therefore $PO = x$, $DO = y$, AR or $BN = b$, and PR or $PN = c$. And by reason of the similar Triangles B N M, D O M, B N will be: D O :: M N : M O. And by Division $DO - BN$ $(y-b)$: DO (y) :: $MO - MN$ (ON or $c-x$) : MO. Wherefore $MO = \frac{cy - xy}{y-b}$. In like Manner on the other Side, by reason of the similar Triangles A R Q, D O Q, A R will be: D O :: R Q : Q O, and by Composition $DO + AR$ $(y+b)$: DO (y) :: $QO + RQ$ (OR or $c+x$) : QO. Wherefore $QO = \frac{cy+xy}{y+b}$. Lastly by reason of the equal Angles D M Q, D Q M, M O and Q O are equal, that is, $\frac{cy-xy}{y-b} = \frac{cy+xy}{y+b}$. Divide all by y, and multiply by the Denominators, and there will arise $cy + cb - xy - xb = cy - cb + xy - xb$, or $cb = xy$, the most noted Equation that expresses the Hyperbola.

Moreover, the Locus or Place of the Point D might have been found without an Algebraick Calculus; for from what we have ſaid above, DO − BN : ON :: DO : MO (QO) :: DO + AR : OR. That is, DO − BN : DO + BN :: ON : OR. And mixtly, DO : BN :: $\frac{ON+OR}{2}$ (NP) : $\frac{OR-ON}{2}$ (OP). And conſequently, DO × OP = BN × NP.

PROBLEM XLII.

To find the Locus or Place of the Vertex of a Triangle whoſe Baſe is given, and one of the Angles at the Baſe differs by a given Angle from being double of the other.

In the laſt Scheme of the former Problem, let ABD be that Triangle, AB its Baſe biſected in P, APQ or BPM the third of the given Angle, by which DBA exceeds the double of the Angle DAB; and the Angle DMQ will be double of the Angle DQM.. To PM let fall the Perpendiculars AR, BN, DO, and biſect the Angle DMQ by the right Line MS meeting DO in S; and the Triangles DOQ, SOM will be ſimilar; and conſequently OQ : OM :: OD : OS, and by dividing OQ − OM : OM :: SD : OS :: (by the 3. of the 6th *Elem.*) DM : OM. Wherefore (by the 9. of the 5th *Elem.*) OQ − OM = DM. Now making PO = x, OD = y, AR or BN = b, and PR or PN = c, you will have, as in the former Problem, OM = $\frac{cy - xy}{y - b}$, and OQ = $\frac{cy + xy}{y + b}$, and conſequently OQ − OM = $\frac{-2bcy + 2xyy}{yy - bb}$. Make now DO$q$ + OMq = DMq, that is, $yy + \frac{cc - 2cx + xx}{yy - 2by + bb}yy = \frac{4bbcc - 8bcxy + 4xxyy}{y^4 - 2bbyy + b^4}yy$, and by due Reduction there will at length ariſe

$$y^4 * \begin{matrix} +cc \\ -2bb \\ -2cx \\ -3xx \end{matrix} yy \begin{matrix} +2bxx \\ +4bcx \\ +2bcc \end{matrix} y \begin{matrix} +b^4 \\ -3bbcc \\ -2bbcx \\ +bbxx \end{matrix} = 0.$$

Divide

Divide all by $y - b$, and it will become

$$y^3 + byy \begin{matrix} -bb \\ +cc \\ -2cx \\ -3xx \end{matrix} y \begin{matrix} -b^3 \\ +3bcc \\ +2bcx \\ -bxx \end{matrix} = 0.$$

Wherefore the Point D is in a Curve of three Dimenſions; which however becomes an Hyperbola when the Angle BPM vaniſhes or becomes nothing; or which is the ſame Thing, when one of the Angles at the Baſe DBA is double of the other DAB. For then BN or b vaniſhing, the Equation will become $yy = 3xx + 2cx - cc$.

And from the Conſtruction of this Equation there comes this *Theorem.* [See *Figure* 54.] If to the Center C, and Aſymptotes CS, CT, containing the Angle SCT of 120 Degrees, you deſcribe any Hyperbola, as DV, whoſe Semi-Axis's are CV, CA; produce CV to B, ſo that VB ſhall be = VC, and from A and B you draw any how the right Lines AD, BD, meeting at the Hyperbola; the Angle BAD will be half the Angle ABD, but a third Part of the Angle ADE, which the right Line AD comprehends with BD produced. This is to be underſtood of the Hyperbola that paſſes through the Point V. But if the two right Lines Ad and Bd, drawn from the ſame Points A and B, meet in the oppoſite Hyperbola that paſſes through A, then of thoſe two external Angles of the Triangle at the Baſe, that at B will be double of that at A.

PROBLEM XLIII.

To deſcribe a Circle through two given Points that ſhall touch a right Line given in Poſition. [*See* Figure 55.]

Let A and B be the two given Points, and EF the right Line given in Poſition, and let it be required to deſcribe a Circle ABE through thoſe Points which ſhall touch that right Line FE. Join AB and biſect it in D. Upon D erect the Perpendicular DF meeting the right Line FE in F, and the Center of the Circle will fall upon this laſt drawn Line DF, as ſuppoſe in C. Join therefore CB; and on FE let fall the Perpendicular CE, and E will be the Point of Contact, and CB and CE equal, as being Radii of the Circle ſought. Now ſince the Points A, B, D, and F, are given, let DB = a, and DF = b; and ſeek for DC to

to determine the Center of the Circle, which therefore call x. Now in the Triangle CDB, becauſe the Angle at D is a right one, you have $\sqrt{DBq + DCq}$, that is $\sqrt{aa+xx} = CB$. Alſo $DF - DC$, or $b - x = CF$. And ſince in the right-angled Triangle CFE the Angles are given, there will be given the Ratio of the Sides CF and CE. Let that be as d to e; and CE will be $= \frac{e}{d} \times CF$, that is, $= \frac{eb - ex}{d}$. Now put CB and CE (the Radii of the Circle ſought) equal to one another, and you will have the Equation $\sqrt{aa+xx} = \frac{eb-ex}{d}$. Whoſe Parts being ſquared and multiplied by dd, there ariſes $aadd + ddxx = eebb - 2eebx + eexx$; or $xx = \frac{-2eebx - aadd + eebb}{dd - ee}$. And extracting the Root $x = \frac{-eeb + d\sqrt{eebb + eeaa - ddaa}}{dd - ee}$. Therefore the Length of DC, and conſequently the Center C is found, from which a Circle is to be deſcribed through the Points A and B that ſhall touch the right Line FE.

Problem XLIV.

To deſcribe a Circle through a given Point that ſhall touch two right Lines given in Poſition. [*See* Figure 56.]

N. B. *This Propoſition is reſolved as* Prop. 43. *for the Point* A *being given, there is alſo given the other Point* B.

Suppoſe the given Point to be A; and let EF, FG, be the two right Lines given by Poſition, and AEG the Circle ſought touching the ſame, and paſſing through that Point A. Let the Angle EFG be biſected by the right Line CF, and the Center of the Circle will be found therein. Let that be C; and having let fall the Perpendiculars CE, CG to EF and FG, E and G will be the Points of Contact. Now in the Triangles CEF, CGF, ſince the Angles at E and G are right ones, and the Angles at F are halves of the Angle EFG, all the Angles are given, and conſequently the Ratio of the Sides CF and CE or CG. Let that be as d to e; and if for determining the Center of the Circle ſought C, there be aſſumed $CF = x$, CE or CG will be $= \frac{ex}{d}$. Beſides, let fall the Perpendicular AH to FC, and ſince the Point A is given, the right Lines AH and FH will be given. Let them be called a and b, and taking FC or x from FH or b, there will remain $CH = b - x$. To whoſe Square $bb - 2bx + xx$ add the Square of AH or aa, and the Sum $aa + bb - 2bx + xx$ will be ACq by the 47. 1. *Eucl.* becauſe the Angle AHC is, by Suppoſition, a right one. Now make the Radii of the Circle AC and CG equal to each other; that is, make an equality between their Values, or between their Squares, and you will have the Equation $aa + bb - 2bx + xx = \frac{eexx}{dd}$. Take away xx from both Sides, and changing all the Signs, you will have $-aa - bb + 2bx = xx - \frac{eexx}{dd}$. Multiply all by dd, and divide by $dd - ee$, and it will become $\frac{-aadd - bbdd + 2bddx}{dd - ee} = xx$. The Root of which Equation being extracted, is $x = \frac{bdd - d\sqrt{eebb + eeaa - ddaa}}{dd - ee}$. Therefore the Length FC is found, and conſequently the Point C, which is the Center of the Circle ſought.

If the found Value x or FC be taken from b or HF, there will remain $HC = \frac{-eeb + d\sqrt{eebb + eeaa - ddaa}}{dd - ee}$ the ſame Equation which came out in the former Problem, for determining the Length of DC.

Pro-

PROBLEM XLV.

To describe a Circle through two given Points, which shall touch another Circle given in Position. [*See* Problem 21, *and* Figure 57.]

Let A, B be the two Points given, EK the Circle given in Magnitude and Position, F its Center, ABE the Circle sought, passing through the Points A and B, and touching the other Circle in E, and let C be its Center. Let fall the Perpendiculars CD and FG to AB being produced, and draw CF cutting the Circles in the Point of Contact E, and draw also FH parallel to DG, and meeting CD in H. These being thus constructed, make AD or $DB = a$, DG or $HF = b$, $GF = c$, and EF (the Radius of the Circle given) $= d$, and $DC = x$; and CH will be $(= CD - FG) = x - c$, and $CFq\ (= CHq + HFq) = xx - 2cx + cc + bb$, and $CBq\ (= CDq + DBq) = xx + aa$, and consequently CB or $CE = \sqrt{xx + aa}$. To this add EF, and you will have $CF = d + \sqrt{xx + aa}$, whose Square $dd + aa + xx + 2d\sqrt{xx + aa}$, is equal to the Value of the same CFq found before, *viz.* $xx - 2cx + cc + bb$. Take away from both Sides xx, and there will remain $dd + aa + 2d\sqrt{xx + aa} = cc + bb - 2cx$. Take away moreover $dd + aa$, and there will come out $2d\sqrt{xx + aa} = cc + bb - dd - aa - 2cx$. Now, for Abbreviation sake, for $cc + bb - dd - aa$, write $2gg$, and you will have $2d\sqrt{xx + aa} = 2gg - 2cx$, or $d\sqrt{xx + aa} = gg - cx$. And the Parts of the Equation being squared, there will come out $ddxx + ddaa = g^4 - 2ggcx + ccxx$. Take from both Sides $ddaa$ and $ccxx$, and there will remain $ddxx - ccxx = g^4 - ddaa - 2ggcx$. And the Parts of the Equation being divided by $dd - cc$, you will have $xx = \frac{g^4 - ddaa - 2ggcx}{dd - cc}$. And by Extraction of the affected Root $x = \frac{-ggc + \sqrt{g^4dd - d^4aa + ddaacc}}{dd - cc}$.

Having

Having found therefore x, or the Length of DC, bisect AB in D, and at D erect the Perpendicular $DC = \frac{-ggc + d\sqrt{g^4 - aadd + aacc}}{dd - cc}$. Then from the Center C, through the Point A or B, describe the Circle ABE; for that will touch the other Circle EK, and pass through both the Points A, B. Q.E.F.

PROBLEM XLVI.

To describe a Circle through a given Point which shall touch a given Circle, and also a right Line, both given in Position. [*See* Figure 58.]

Let the Circle to be described be BD, its Center C, and B a Point through which it is to be described, and AD the right Line which it shall touch; the Point of Contact D, and the Circle which it shall touch GEM, its Center F, and its Point of Contact E. Join CB, CD, CF, and CD will be perpendicular to AD, and CF will cut the Circles in the Point of Contact E. Produce CD to Q, so that DQ shall be = EF, and through Q draw QN parallel to AD. Lastly, from B and F to AD and QN, let fall the Perpendiculars BA, FN; and from C to AB and FN let fall the Perpendiculars CK, CL. And since BC is = CD or AK, BK will be $(= AB - AK) = AB - BC$, and consequently $BKq = ABq - 2AB \times BC + BCq$. Subtract this from BCq, and there will remain $2AB \times BC - ABq$ for the Square of CK. Therefore $AB \times \overline{2BC - AB}$ is $= CKq$; and for the same Reason it will be $FN \times \overline{2FC - FN} = CLq$, and consequently $\frac{CKq}{AB} + AB = 2BC$, and $\frac{CLq}{FN} + FN = 2FC$. Wherefore, if for AB, CK, FN, KL, and CL, you write a, y, b, c, and $c - y$, you will have $\frac{yy}{2a} + \frac{1}{2}a = BC$, and $\frac{cc - 2cy + yy}{2b} + \frac{1}{2}b = FC$. From FC take away BC, and there will remain $EF = \frac{cc - 2cy + yy}{2b} + \frac{1}{2}b - \frac{yy}{2a} - \frac{1}{2}a$.

X Now,

Now, if the Points where F N being produced cuts the right Line A D, and the Circle G E M be marked with the Letters H, G, and M, and upon H G produced you take H R = A B, since H N (= D Q = E F) is = G F, by adding F H on both Sides, you will have F N = G H, and consequently A B — F N (= H R — G H) = G R, and A B — F N + 2 E F; that is, $a - b + 2EF = RM$, and $\frac{1}{2}a - \frac{1}{2}b + EF = \frac{1}{2}RM$. Wherefore, since above E F was $= \frac{cc - 2cy + yy}{2b} + \frac{1}{2}b - \frac{yy}{2a} - \frac{1}{2}a$, if this be written for E F you will have $\frac{1}{2}$ R M $= \frac{cc - 2cy + yy}{2b} - \frac{yy}{2a}$. Call therefore R M, d; and d will be $= \frac{cc - 2cy + yy}{b} - \frac{yy}{a}$. Multiply all the Terms by a and b, and there will arise $abd = acc - 2acy + ayy - byy$. Take away from both Sides $acc - 2acy$, and there will remain $abd - acc + 2acy = ayy - byy$. Divide by $a - b$, and there will arise $\frac{abd - acc + 2acy}{a - b} = yy$. And extracting the Root $y = \frac{ac}{a-b} \pm \sqrt{\frac{aabd - abbd + abcc}{aa - 2ab + bb}}$. Which Conclusions may be thus abbreviated; make $c : b :: d : e$, then $a - b : a :: c : f$; and $fe - fc + 2fy$ will be $= yy$, or $y = f \pm \sqrt{ff + fe - fc}$. Having found y or K C or A D, take $AD = f \pm \sqrt{ff + fe - fc}$, and at D erect the Perpendicular D C ($=$ B C) $= \frac{KCq}{2AB} + \frac{1}{2}AB$; and from the Center C, at the Interval C B or C D, describe the Circle B D E, for this passing through the given Point B, will touch the right Line A D in D, and the Circle G E M in E. Q. E. F.

Hence also a Circle may be described which shall touch two given Circles, and a right Line given in Position. [See *Figure* 59.] For let the given Circles be R T, S V, their Centers B, F, and the right Line given in Position P Q. From the Center F, with the Radius F S — B R, describe the Circle E M. From the Point B to the right Line P Q let fall the Perpendicular B P, and having produced it to A, so that P A shall be = B R, through A draw A H parallel to P Q, and describe a Circle which shall pass through the Point B, and touch the right Line A H and the Circle E M. Let its Center be C; join B C, cutting the Circle R T in R; and the Circle R S described from the same Center C, and the Radius C R will touch the Circles R T, S V, and the right Line P Q, as is manifest by the Construction.

PROBLEM XLVII.

To describe a Circle that shall pass through a given Point, and touch two other Circles given in Position and Magnitude. [*See* Figure 60.]

Let the given Point be A, and let the Circles given in Magnitude and Position be T I V, R H S, their Centers C and B; the Circle to be described A I H, its Center D, and the Points of Contact I and H. Join A B, A C, A D, D B, and let A B produced cut the Circle R H S in the Points R and S, and A C produced, cut the Circle T I V in T and V. And having from the Points D and C let fall the Perpendiculars D E to A B, and D F to A C meeting A B in G, and C K to A B; in the Triangle A D B, it will be $ADq - DBq + ABq = 2AE \times AB$, by the 13 of the 2 *Elem.* But D B = A D + B R, and consequently $DBq = ADq + 2AD \times BR + BRq$. Take away this from $ADq + ABq$, and there will remain $ABq - 2AD \times BR - BRq$ for $2AE \times AB$. Moreover $ABq - BRq$ is $= \overline{AB - BR} \times \overline{AB + BR} = AR \times AS$. Wherefore $AR \times AS - 2AD \times BR = 2AE \times AB$. And $\frac{AR \times AS - 2AB \times AE}{BR} = 2AD$.

And by a like Reasoning in the Triangle A D C, there will come out again $2AD = \frac{TAV - 2CAF}{CT}$. Wherefore $\frac{RAS - 2BAE}{BR} = \frac{TAV - 2CAF}{CT}$. And $\frac{TAV}{CT} - \frac{RAS}{BR} + \frac{2BAE}{BR} = \frac{2CAF}{CT}$. And

X 2 TAV

$\overline{\frac{TAV}{CT} - \frac{RAS}{BR} + \frac{2BAE}{BR}} \times \frac{CT}{2AC} = AF$. Whence since it is $AK : AC :: AF : AG$, AG will be $=$ $\overline{\frac{TAV}{CT} - \frac{RAS}{BR} + \frac{2BAE}{BR}} \times \frac{CT}{2AK}$. Take away this from AE, or $\frac{2KAE}{CT} \times \frac{CT}{2AK}$, and there will remain $GE =$ $\overline{\frac{RAS}{BR} - \frac{TAV}{CT} - \frac{2BAE}{BR} + \frac{2KAE}{CT}} \times \frac{CT}{2AK}$. Whence since it is $KC : AK :: GE : DE$; DE will be $=$ $\overline{\frac{RAS}{BR} - \frac{TAV}{CT} - \frac{2BAE}{BR} + \frac{2KAE}{CT}} \times \frac{CT}{2KC}$. Upon AB take AP, which let be to AB as CT to BR, and $\frac{2PAE}{CT}$ will be $= \frac{2BAE}{BR}$, and so $\frac{2PK \times AE}{CT} = \frac{2BAE}{BR} - \frac{2KAE}{CT}$, and so $DE = \overline{\frac{RAS}{BR} - \frac{TAV}{CT} - \frac{2PK \times AE}{CT}} \times \frac{CT}{2KC}$. Upon AB erect the Perpendicular $AQ = \overline{\frac{RAS}{BR} - \frac{TAV}{CT}} \times \frac{CT}{2KC}$, and in it take $QO = \frac{PK \times AE}{KC}$, and AO will be $=$ DE.

Join DO, DQ, and CP, and the Triangles DOQ, CKP will be similar, because their Angles at O and K are right ones, and the Sides ($KC : PK :: AE$, or $DO : QO$) proportional. Therefore the Angles OQD, KPC are equal, and consequently QD is perpendicular to CP. Wherefore if AN be drawn parallel to CP, and meeting QD in N, the Angle ANQ will be a right one, and the Triangles AQN, PCK similar; and consequently $PC : KC :: AQ : AN$. Whence since AQ is $\overline{\frac{RAS}{BR} - \frac{TAV}{CT}} \times \frac{CT}{2KC}$, AN will be $\overline{\frac{RAS}{BR} - \frac{TAV}{CT}} \times \frac{CT}{2PC}$. Produce AN to M, so that NM shall be $=$ AN, and AD will be $=$ DM, and consequently the Circle will pass through the Point M.

Since therefore the Point M is given, there follows this Resolution of the Problem, without any farther Analysis.

Upon AB take AP, which must be to AB as CT to BR; join CP, and draw parallel to it AM, which shall be to $\frac{RAS}{BR} - \frac{TAV}{CT}$, as CT to PC; and by the Help of the 45th *Problem*, describe through the Points A and M the Circle AIHM, which shall touch either of the Circles TIV, RHS, and the same Circle shall touch both. Q. E. F.

And hence also a Circle may be described, which shall touch three Circles given in Magnitude and Position. For let the Radii of the given Circles be A, B, C, and their Center D, E, F. From the Centers E and F, with the Radii $B + A$ and $C + A$ describe two Circles, and let a third Circle which touches these two be also described, and let it pass through the Point D; let its Radius be G, and its Center H, and a Circle described on the same Center H, with the Radius $G + A$, shall touch the three former Circles, as was required.

PROBLEM XLVIII.

If at the Ends of the Thread DAE, *moving upon the fixed Tack* A, *there are hanged two Weights,* D and E, *whereof the Weight* E *slides through the oblique Line* BG; *to find the Place of the Weight* E, *where these Weights are in Æquilibrio.* [*See* Figure 63.]

Suppose the Problem done, and parallel to AD draw EF, which let be to AE as the Weight E to the Weight D. And from the Points A and F to the Line BG let fall the Perpendiculars AB, FG. Now since the Weights are, by Supposition, as the Lines AE and EF, express those Weights by those Lines, the Weight D by the Line EA, and the Weight E by the Line EF. Therefore the Body E, directed by the Force of its own Weight EF, tends towards F, and by the oblique Force EG tends towards G. And the same Body E by the direct Force AE of the Weight D is drawn towards A, and by the oblique Force BE is drawn towards B. Since therefore the Weights sustain each other in Æquilibrio, the Force by which the Weight E is drawn towards B, ought to be equal to the contrary Force by which it tends towards G, that is, BE ought to be equal to EG. But now the Ratio of AE to EF

E F is given by the Hypothesis; and by reason of the given Angle F E G, there is also given the Ratio of F E to E G, to which B E is equal. Therefore there is given the Ratio of A E to B E. A B is also given in Length; and thence the Triangle A B E, and the Point E will easily be given, *Viz.* make $AB = a$, $BE = x$, and AE will be $= \sqrt{aa + xx}$; moreover, let A E be to B E in the given Ratio of d to e, and $e\sqrt{aa+xx}$ will be $= dx$. And the Parts of the Equation being squared and reduced, $eeaa = ddxx - eexx$, or $\frac{ea}{\sqrt{dd-ee}} = x$. Therefore the Length B E is found, which determines the Place of the Weight E. Q. E. F.

But if both Weights descend by oblique Lines, the Computation may be made thus [See *Figure* 64.] Let C D and B E be oblique Lines given in Position, through which those Weights D and E descend. From the fixed Tack A to these Lines let fall the Perpendiculars A C, A B, and let the Lines E G, D H, erected from the Weights perpendicularly to the Horizon, meet them in the Points G and H; and the Force by which the Weight E endeavours to descend in a perpendicular Line, that is the whole Gravity of E, will be to the Force by which the same Weight endeavours to descend in the oblique Line B E, as G E to B E; and the Force by which it endeavours to descend in the oblique Line B E, will be to the Force by which it endeavours to descend in the Line A E, that is, to the Force by which the Thread A E is distended or stretched as B E to A E. And consequently the Gravity of E will be to the Tension of the Thread A E as G E to A E. And by the same reason the Gravity of D will be to the Tension of the Thread A D as H D to A D. Let therefore the Length of the whole Thread $DA + AE$ be c, and let its Part A E be $= x$, and its other Part A D will be $= c - x$. And because $AEq - ABq$ is $= BEq$, and $ADq - ACq = CDq$; let, moreover, AB be $= a$, and $AC = b$, and BE will be $= \sqrt{xx - aa}$ and $CD = \sqrt{xx - 2cx + cc - bb}$. Farther, since the Triangles B E G, C D H are given in Specie, let $BE : EG :: f : E$ and $CD : DH :: f : g$, and E G will be $= \frac{E}{f}\sqrt{xx - aa}$, and

and $DH = \frac{g}{f}\sqrt{xx - 2cx + cc - bb}$. Wherefore since $GE : AE ::$ Weight $E :$ Tension of AE; and $HD : AD ::$ Weight $D :$ Tension of AD; and those Tensions are equal, you will have $\frac{Ex}{\frac{E}{f}\sqrt{xx - aa}} =$ Tension of $AE =$ the Tension $AD = \frac{Dc - Dx}{\frac{g}{f}\sqrt{xx - 2cx + cc - bb}}$; from the Reduction of which Equation there comes out $gxx\sqrt{xx - 2cx + cc - bb} = \overline{Dc - Dx}\sqrt{xx - aa}$, or

$$\begin{matrix} gg \\ -DD \end{matrix} x^4 \begin{matrix} -2ggc \\ +2DDc \end{matrix} x^3 \begin{matrix} +ggcc \\ -ggbb \\ -DDcc \\ +DDaa \end{matrix} xx - 2DDcaax + DDccaa = 0.$$

But if you desire a Case wherein this Problem may be constructed by a Rule and Compass, make the Weight D to the Weight E as the Ratio $\frac{BE}{EG}$ to the Ratio $\frac{CD}{DH}$, and g will become $= D$; and so in the Room of the precedent Equation you will have this, $\begin{matrix} aa \\ -bb \end{matrix} xx - 2acx + aaacc = 0$, or $x = \frac{ac}{a+b}$.

PROBLEM XLIX.

If on the String D A C B F, *that slides about the two Tacks* A *and* B, *there are hung three Weights*, D, E, F; D *and* F *at the Ends of the String, and* E *at its middle Point* C, *placed between the Tacks: From the given Weights and Position of the Tacks to find the Situation of the Point* C, *where the middle Weight hangs, and where they are in Æquilibrio.* [*See* Figure 65.]

Since the Tension of the Thread A C is equal to the Tension of the Thread A D, and the Tension of the Thread B C to the Tension of the Thread B F, the Tensions of the Strings or Threads A C, B C, E C will be as the Weights D, E, F. Then

Then take the Parts of the Thread CG, CH, CI, in the same Ratio as the Weights. Compleat the Triangle GHI. Produce IC till it meet GH in K, and GK will be $=$ KH, and CK $= \frac{1}{2}$ CI, and consequently C the Center of Gravity of the Triangle GHI. For, draw PQ through C, perpendicular to CE, and perpendicular to that, from the Points G and H, draw GP, HQ. And if the Force by which the Thread AC by the Force of the Weight D draws the Point C towards A, be expressed by the Line GC, the Force by which that Thread will draw the same Point towards P, will be expressed by the Line CP; and the Force by which it draws it towards K, will be expressed by the Line GP. And in like manner, the Forces by which the Thread BC, by means of the Weight F, draws the same Point C towards B, Q, and K, will be expressed by the Lines CH, CQ, and HQ; and the Force by which the Thread CE, by means of the Weight E, draws that Point C towards E, will be expressed by the Line CI. Now since the Point C is sustained in Æquilibrio by equal Forces, the Sum of the Forces by which the Threads AC and BC do together draw C towards K, will be equal to the contrary Force by which the Thread EC draws that Point towards E; that is, the Sum $GP + HQ$ will be equal to CI; and the Force by which the Thread AC draws the Point C towards P, will be equal to the contrary Force by which the Thread BC draws the same Point C towards Q; that is, the Line PC is equal to the Line CQ. Wherefore, since PG, CK, and QH are Parallel, GK will be also $=$ KH, and CK ($= \frac{GP+HQ}{2}$) $= \frac{1}{2}$ CI. Which was to be shewn. It remains therefore to determine the Triangle GCH, whose Sides GC and HC are given, together with the Line CK, which is drawn from the Vertex C to the middle of the Base. Let fall therefore from the Vertex C to the Base CH the Perpendicular CL, and $\frac{GCq - CHq}{2GH}$ will be $= KL = \frac{GCq - KCq - GKq}{2GK}$. For 2GK write GH, and having rejected the common Divisor GH, and ordered the Terms, you will have $GCq - 2KCq + CHq = 2GKq$, or $\sqrt{\frac{1}{2}GCq - KCq + \frac{1}{2}CHq} = GK$. Having found GK, or KH, there are given together the Angles GCK, KCH, or DAC, FBC. Wherefore, from the Points A and B in these given Angles DAC, FBC, draw the Lines AC, BC, meeting in the Point C; and C will be the Point sought.

But it is not always necessary to solve Questions that are of the same Kind, particularly by Algebra, but from the Solution of one of them you may most commonly infer the Solution of the other. As if now there should be proposed this Question.

The Thread ACDB *being divided into the given Parts* AC, CD, DB, *and its Ends being fastened to the two Tacks given in Position,* A *and* B; *and if at the Points of Division,* C *and* D, *there are hanged the two Weights* E *and* F; *from the given Weight* F, *and the Situation of the Points* C *and* D, *to know the Weight* E. [*See* Figure *66.*]

From the Solution of the former Problem the Solution of this may be easily enough found. Produce the Lines AC, BD, till they meet the Lines DF, CE in G and H; and the Weight E will be to the Weight F, as DG to CH.

And hence by the by may appear a Method of making a Balance of only Threads, by which the Weight of any Body E may be known, from only one given Weight F.

PROBLEM L.

A Stone falling down into a Well, from the Sound of the Stone striking the Bottom, to determine the Depth of the Well.

Let the Depth of the Well be x, and if the Stone descends with an uniformly accelerated Motion through any given Space a in any given Time b, and the Sound passes with an uniform Motion through the same given Space a in the given Time d, the Stone will descend through the Space x in the Time $b\sqrt{\frac{x}{a}}$; but the Sound which is caused by the Stone striking upon the Bottom of the Well, will ascend through the same Space x, in the Time $\frac{dx}{a}$. For the Spaces described by descending heavy Bodies, are as the Squares of the Times of Descent; or the Roots of the Spaces, that is, $\sqrt{x}$ and $\sqrt{a}$ are as the Times themselves. And the Spaces x and a, through which the Sound passes, are as the Times of Passage.

Y And

And the Sum of these Times $b\sqrt{\frac{x}{a}}$, and $\frac{dx}{a}$, is the Time of the Stone's falling to the Return of the Sound. This Time may be known by Observation. Let it be t, and you will have $b\sqrt{\frac{x}{a}}+\frac{dx}{a}=t$. And $b\sqrt{\frac{x}{a}}=t-\frac{dx}{a}$. And the Parts being squared, $\frac{bbx}{a}=tt-\frac{2tdx}{a}+\frac{ddxx}{aa}$. And by Reduction $xx=\frac{2adt+abb}{dd}x-\frac{aatt}{dd}$. And having extracted the Root $x=\frac{adt+\frac{1}{2}abb}{dd}-\frac{ab}{2dd}\times\sqrt{bb+4dt}$.

PROBLEM LI.

Having given the Globe A, *and the Position of the Wall* DE, *and* BD *the Distance of the Center of the Globe* B *from the Wall; to find the Bulk of the Globe* B, *on this Condition, that if the Globe* A, (*whose Center is in the Line* BD, *which is perpendicular to the Wall, and produced out beyond* B) *be moved in free absolute Space, and where Gravity cannot act, with an uniform Motion towards* D, *until it strikes against the other quiescent Globe* B; *and that Globe* B, *after it is reflected from the Wall, shall meet the Globe* A *in the given Point* C. [*See* Figure 81.]

Let the Velocity of the Globe A before Reflection be a, and by *Problem* XII. p. 80. the Velocity of the Globe A will be after Reflection $=\frac{aA-aB}{A+B}$, and the Velocity of the Globe B after Reflection will be $=\frac{2aA}{A+B}$. Therefore the Velocity of the Globe A to the Velocity of the Globe B is as A — B to 2 A. On GD take $gD=GH$, *viz.* to the Diameter of the Globe B, and those Velocities will be as GC to $Gg+gC$. For when the Globe A struck upon the Globe B, the Point G, which being on the Surface of the Globe B is moved in the Line AD, will go through the Space Gg before that Globe B shall strike against the Wall, and through the Space gC after it is reflected from the Wall; that is, through the whole Space $Gg+gC$, in the same Time wherein the Point F of the Globe A shall pass through the Space GC, so that both Globes may again meet and strike one another in the given Point C. Wherefore, since the Intervals BC and CD are given, make $BC=m$, $BD+CD=n$, and $BG=x$, and GC will be $=m+x$, and $Gg+gC=GD+DC-2gD=GB+BD+DC-2GH=x+n-4x$, or $=n-3x$. Above you had A — B to 2 A, as the Velocity of the Globe A to the Velocity of the Globe B, and the Velocity of the Globe A to the Velocity of the Globe B, as GC to $Gg+gC$, and consequently A — B to 2 A, as GC to $Gg+gC$; therefore since GC is $=m+x$, and $Gg+gC=n-3x$, A — B will be to 2 A as $m+x$ to $n-3x$. Moreover, the Globe A is to the Globe B as the Cube of its Radius AF to the Cube of the others Radius GB; that is, if you make the Radius AF to be s, as s^3 to x^3; therefore $s^3-x^3 : 2s^3$ (:: A — B : 2 A) :: $m+x : n-3x$. And multiplying the Means and Extreams by one another, you will have this Equation, $s^3n-3s^3x-nx^3+3x^4=2ms^3+2s^3x$. And by Reduction $3x^4-nx^3-5s^3x\begin{matrix}+s^3n\\-2s^3m\end{matrix}=0$. From the Construction of which Equation there will be given x, the Semi-Diameter of the Globe B; which being given, that Globe is also given. Q. E. F.

But note, when the Point C lies on contrary Sides of the Globe B, the Sign of the Quantity $2m$ must be changed, and written $3x^4-nx^3-5s^3x\begin{matrix}+s^3n\\+2s^3m\end{matrix}=0$.

If the Globe B were given, and the Globe A sought on this Condition, that the two Globes, after Reflection, should meet in C, the Question would be easier; *viz.* in the last Equation found, x would be supposed to be given, and s to be sought. Whereby, by a due Reduction of that Equation, the Terms $-5s^3x+s^3n-2s^3m$ being translated to the contrary Side of the Equation, and each Part divided by $5x-n+2m$, there would come out $\frac{3x^4-nx^3}{5x-n+2m}=s^3$. Where s will be obtained by the bare Extraction of the Cube Root.

Y 2 But

But if both Globes being given, you were to find the Point C, in which both would fall upon one another after Reflection: Since above it was $A - b$ to $2A$ as GC to $Gg + gC$, therefore by Inverſion and Compoſition $3A - B$ will be to $A - B$ as $2Gg$ to the ſought Diſtance GC.

Problem LII.

If two Globes, A *and* B, *are joined together by a ſmall Thread* P Q, *and the Globe* B *hanging on the Globe* A; *if you let fall the Globe* A, *ſo that both Globes may begin to fall together by the ſole Force of Gravity in the ſame perpendicular Line* P Q; *and then the lower Globe* B, *after it is reflected upwards from the Bottom or Horizontal Plane* F G, *it ſhall meet the upper Globe* A, *as falling, in a certain Point* D: *From the given Length of the Thread* P Q, *and the Diſtance* D F *of that Point* D *from the Bottom, to find the Height* P F, *from which the upper Globe* A *ought to be let fall to cauſe this Effect.* [*See* Figure 83.]

Let a be the Length of the Thread P Q. In the Perpendicular P Q R F from F upwards take F E equal to Q R the Diameter of the lower Globe, ſo that when the loweſt Point R of that Globe falls upon the Bottom in F, its upper Point Q ſhall poſſeſs the Place E; and let E D be the Diſtance through which that Globe, after it is reflected from the Bottom, ſhall, by aſcending, paſs, before it meets the upper falling Globe in the Point D. Therefore, by reaſon of the given Diſtance D F of the Point D from the Bottom, and the Diameter E F of the inferior Globe, there will be given their Difference D E. Let that be $= b$, and let the Height R F, or Q E, which that lower Globe deſcribes by falling through it before it touches the Bottom, be $= x$, by reaſon it is unknown. And having found x, if to it you add E F and P Q, there will be had the Height P F, from which the upper Globe ought to fall to have the deſired Effect.

Since therefore PQ is $= a$, and $QE = x$, PE will be $= a + x$. Take away DE or b, and there will remain $PD = a + x - b$. But the Time of the Deſcent of the Globe A is as the Root of the Space deſcribed in falling, or $\sqrt{a + x - b}$, and the Time of the Deſcent of the other Globe B as the Root of the Space deſcribed by its falling, or $\sqrt{x}$, and the Time of its Aſcent as the Difference of that

2 Root,

Root, and of the Root of the Space which it would deſcribe by falling only from Q to D. For this Difference is as the Time of Deſcent from D to E, which is equal to the Time of Aſcent from E to D. But that Difference is $\sqrt{x} - \sqrt{x - b}$. Whence the Time of Deſcent and Aſcent together will be as $2\sqrt{x} - \sqrt{x - b}$. Wherefore, ſince this Time is equal to the Time of Deſcent of the upper Globe, it will be $\sqrt{a + x - b} = 2\sqrt{x} - \sqrt{x - b}$. The Parts of which Equation being ſquared, you will have $a + x - b = 5x - b - 4\sqrt{xx - bx}$, or $a = 4x - 4\sqrt{xx - bx}$; and the Equation being ordered, $4x - a = 4\sqrt{xx - bx}$; and ſquaring the Parts of that Equation again, there ariſes $16xx - 8ax + aa = 16xx - 16bx$, or $aa = 8ax - 16bx$; and dividing all by $8a - 16b$, you will have $\frac{aa}{8a - 16b} = x$. Make therefore as $8a - 16b$ to a, ſo a to x, and you will have x or Q E. Q. E. I.

But if from the given Q E you are to find the Length of the Thread P Q or a; the ſame Equation $aa = 8ax - 16bx$, by extracting the affected Quadratick Root, would give $a = 4x - \sqrt{16xx - 16bx}$; that is, if you take Q Y a mean Proportional between Q D and Q E, P Q will be $= 4EY$. For that mean Proportional will be $\sqrt{x \times x - b}$, or $\sqrt{xx - bx}$; which ſubſtracted from x, or Q E, leaves E Y, the Quadruple whereof is $4x - 4\sqrt{xx - bx}$.

But if from the given Quantities Q E, or x, as alſo the Length of the Thread P Q, or a, there were ſought the Point D in which the upper Globe falls upon the under one; the Diſtance D E, or b, of that Point from the given Point E, will be had from the precedent Equation $aa = 8ax - 16bx$ by transferring aa and $16bx$ to the contrary Sides of the Equation with the Signs changed, and by dividing the whole by $16x$. For there will ariſe $\frac{8ax - aa}{16x} = b$. Make therefore as $16x$ to $8x - a$, ſo a to b, and you will have b or D E.

Hitherto I have ſuppoſed the Globes tied together by a ſmall Thread to be let fall together. Which, if they are let fall at different Times connected by no Thread, ſo that

the

the upper Globe A, for Example, being let fall firſt, ſhall deſcend through the Space PT before the other Globe begins to fall, and from the given Diſtances PT, PQ, and DE, you are to find the Height PF, from which the upper Globe ought to be let fall, ſo that it ſhall fall upon the inferior or lower one at the Point D. Make $PQ = a$, $DE = b$, $PT = c$, and $QE = x$, and PD will be $= a + x - b$, as above And the Times wherein the upper Globe, by falling, will deſcribe the Spaces PT and TD, and the lower Globe by falling before, and then by re-aſcending, will deſcribe the Sum of the Spaces $QE + ED$ will be as $\sqrt{PT}$, $\sqrt{PD} - \sqrt{PT}$, and $2\sqrt{QE} - \sqrt{QD}$; that is, as $\sqrt{c}$, $\sqrt{a+x-b} - \sqrt{c}$, and $2\sqrt{x} - \sqrt{x-b}$. But the two laſt Times, becauſe the Spaces TD and $QE + ED$ are deſcribed together, are equal. Therefore $\sqrt{a+x-b} - \sqrt{c} = 2\sqrt{x} - \sqrt{x-b}$. And the Parts being ſquared $a + c - 2\sqrt{ca + cx - cb} = 4x - 4\sqrt{xx - bx}$. Make $a + c = e$, and $a - b = f$, and by a due Reduction it will be $4x - e + 2\sqrt{cf + cx} = 4\sqrt{xx - bx}$, and the Parts being ſquared $ee - 8ex + 16xx + 4cf + 4cx + \overline{16x - 4e} \times \sqrt{cf + cx} = 16xx - 16bx$. And blotting out on both Sides $16xx$, and writing m for $ee + 4cf$, and alſo writing n for $8e - 16b - 4c$, you will have by due Reduction $\overline{16x - 4e} \times \sqrt{cf + cx} = nx - m$. And the Parts being ſquared you will have $256cfxx + 256cx^3 - 128cefx - 128cexx + 16ceef + 16ceex = nnxx - 2mnx + mm$. And having ordered the Equation

$$256cx^3 \begin{array}{l} +256cf \\ -128ce \\ -nn \end{array} xx \begin{array}{l} -128cef \\ +16cee \\ +2mn \end{array} x \begin{array}{l} +6ceef \\ -mm \end{array} = 0.$$

By the Conſtruction of which Equation x or QE will be given, to which if you add the given Diſtances PQ and EF, you will have the Height PF, which was to be found.

PRO-

PROBLEM LIII.

If two quieſcent Globes, the upper one A *and the under one* B, *are let fall at different Times; and the lower Globe begins to fall in the ſame Moment that the upper one, by falling, has deſcribed the Space* PT; *to find the Places* α, β, *which thoſe falling Globes ſhall occupy when their Interval or Diſtance* $\pi\chi$ *is given.* [*See* Figure 84.]

Since the Diſtances PT, PQ, and $\pi\chi$ are given, call the firſt a, the ſecond b, the third c, and for $P\pi$, or the Space that the ſuperior Globe deſcribes by falling before it comes to the Place ſought α, put x. Now the Times wherein the upper Globe deſcribes the Spaces PT, $P\pi$, $T\pi$, and the lower one the Space $Q\chi$, are as $\sqrt{PT}$, $\sqrt{P\pi}$, $\sqrt{P\pi} - \sqrt{PT}$, and $\sqrt{Q\chi}$. The latter two of which Times, becauſe the Globes by falling together deſcribe the Spaces $T\pi$ and $Q\chi$, are equal. Whence alſo $\sqrt{P\pi} - \sqrt{PT}$ will be equal to $\sqrt{Q\chi}$. $P\pi$ was $= x$, and $PT = a$, and by adding $\pi\chi$, or c, to $P\pi$, and ſubtracting PQ, or b, from the Sum, you will have $Q\chi = x + c - b$. Wherefore ſubſtituting theſe, you will have $\sqrt{x} - \sqrt{a} = \sqrt{x + c - b}$. And ſquaring both Sides of the Equation, there will ariſe $x + a - 2\sqrt{ax} = x + c - b$. And blotting out on both Sides x, and ordering the Equation, you will have $a + b - c = 2\sqrt{ax}$. And having ſquared the Parts, the Square of $a + b - c$ will be $= 4ax$, and that Square divided by $4a$ will be $= x$, or $4a$ will be to $a + b - c$ as $a + b - c$ is to x. But from x found, or $P\pi$, there is given the Place ſought, *viz.* α of the ſuperior Globe. And by the Diſtance of the Places, there is alſo given the Place of the lower one β.

And hence, if you were to find the Point where the upper Globe, by falling, will at length fall upon the lower one; by putting the Diſtance $\pi\chi = 0$, or by extirpating c, ſay $4a$ is to $a + b$ as $a + b$ is to x, or $P\pi$, and the Point π will be that ſought.

And reciprocally, if that Point π, or χ, in which the upper Globe falls upon the under one, be given, and you are to find the Place T which the lower Point P of the upper falling Globe poſſeſſed, or was then in, when the lower Globe began to fall; becauſe $4a$ is to $a + b$ as $a + b$ is to x; or multiplying the Means and Extremes together, $4ax$

$= aa$

$=aa+2ab+bb$, and by due ordering of the Equation $aa=4ax-2ab-bb$; extract the Square Root and you will have $a=2x-b-2\sqrt{xx-bx}$. Take therefore $V\pi$, a mean Proportional between $P\pi$ and $Q\pi$, and towards V take $VT=VQ$, and T will be the Point you ſeek. For $V\pi$ will be $=\sqrt{P\pi\times Q\pi}$, that is $=\sqrt{x\times\overline{x-b}}$, or $=\sqrt{xx-bx}$; the double whereof ſubtracted from $2x-b$, or from $2P\pi-PQ$, that is, from $PQ+2Q\pi$, leaves $PQ-2VQ$, or $PV-VQ$, that is, PT.

If, laſtly, the lower of the Globes, after the upper has fallen upon the lower, and the lower, by their Shock upon one another, is accelerated, and the ſuperior one retarded, the Places are required where, in falling, they ſhall acquire a Diſtance equal to a given right Line. In the firſt Place you muſt ſeek the Place where the upper one falls upon the lower one; then from the known Magnitudes of the Globes, as alſo from their Celerities where they fall on each other, you muſt find the Celerities they ſhall have immediately after Reflection, after the ſame Way as in *Probl.* XII. *p.* 80. Afterwards you muſt find the higheſt Places to which the Globes with theſe Celerities, if they were carried upwards, would aſcend, and thence the Spaces will be known, which the Globes will deſcribe by falling in any given Times after Reflection, as alſo the Difference of the Spaces; and reciprocally from that Difference aſſumed, you may go back Analytically to the Spaces deſcribed in falling.

As if the upper Globe falls upon the lower one at the Point π, [See *Figure* 85.] and after Reflection, the Celerity of the upper one downwards be ſo great, as if it were upwards, it would cauſe that Globe to aſcend through the Space πN; and the Celerity of the lower one downwards was ſo great, as that, if it were upwards, it would cauſe the lower one to aſcend through the Space πM; then the Times wherein the upper Globe would reciprocally deſcend through the Spaces $N\pi$, NG, and the inferior one through the Spaces $M\pi$, MH, would be as $\sqrt{N\pi}$, $\sqrt{NG}$, $\sqrt{M\pi}$, $\sqrt{MH}$; and conſequently the Times wherein the upper Globe would run the Space πG, and the lower one πH, would be as $\sqrt{NG}-\sqrt{N\pi}$, to $\sqrt{MH}-\sqrt{M\pi}$. Make thoſe Times equal, and $\sqrt{NG}-\sqrt{N\pi}$ will be $=\sqrt{MH}-\sqrt{M\pi}$. And, moreover, ſince there is given the Diſtance GH, put $\pi G+GH=\pi H$. And by the Reduction of theſe two Equations, the Problem will be ſolved. As if $M\pi$ is $=a$,

$N\pi$·

$N\pi=b$, $GH=c$, $\pi G=x$, you will have, according to the latter Equation, $x+c=\pi H$. Add $M\pi$, you will have $MH=a+c+x$. To πG add $N\pi$, and you will have $NG=b+x$. Which being found, according to the former Equation, $\sqrt{b+x}-\sqrt{b}$ will be $=\sqrt{a+c+x}-\sqrt{a}$. Write e for $a+c$, and $\sqrt{f}$ for $\sqrt{a}+\sqrt{b}$, and the Equation will become $\sqrt{b+x}=\sqrt{e+x}-\sqrt{f}$. And the Parts being ſquared $b+x=e+x+f-2\sqrt{ef+fx}$, or $e+f-b=2\sqrt{ef+fx}$. For $e+f-b$ write g, and you will have $g=2\sqrt{ef+fx}$, and the Parts being ſquared, $gg=4ef+4fx$, and by Reduction $\frac{gg}{4f}-e=x$.

Problem LIV.

If there are two Globes, A, B, *whereof the upper one* A *falling from the Height* G, *ſtrikes upon another lower one* B *rebounding from the Ground* H *upwards; and theſe Globes ſo part from one another by Reflection, that the Globe* A *returns by Force of that Reflection to its former Altitude* G, *and that in the ſame Time that the lower Globe* B *returns to the Ground* H; *then the Globe* A *falls again, and ſtrikes again upon the Globe* B, *rebounding again back from the Ground; and after this rate the Globes always rebound from one another and return to the ſame Place: From the given Magnitude of the Globes, the Poſition of the Ground, and the Place* G *from whence the upper Globe falls, to find the Place where the Globes ſhall ſtrike upon each other.* [*See* Figure 86.]

Let e be the Center of the Globe A, and f the Center of the Globe B, d the Center of the Place G wherein the upper Globe is in its greateſt Height, g the Center of the Place of the lower Globe where it falls on the Ground, a the Semi-Diameter of the Globe A, b the Semi-Diameter of the Globe B, c the Point of Contact of the Globes falling upon one another, and H the Point of Contact of the lower Globe and the Ground. And the Celerity of the Globe A, where it falls on the Globe B, will be the ſame which is generated by the Fall of the Globe from the Height de, and conſequently is as $\sqrt{de}$. With this ſame Celerity the Globe A ought to be reflected upwards, that it may return to its former Place G. And the Globe B ought to be

Z reflected

reflected with the same Celerity downwards wherewith it ascended, that it may return in the same Time to the Ground it took up in mounting from it. And that both these may come to pass, the Motion of the Globes in reflecting ought to be equal. But the Motions are compounded of the Celerities and Magnitudes together, and consequently the Product of the Bulk and Celerity of one Globe will be equal to the Product of the Bulk and Celerity of the other. Whence, if the Product of the Bulk and Celerity of one Globe be divided by the Bulk of the other Globe, you will have the Celerity of the other just before and after Reflection, or at the End of the Ascent, and at the Beginning of the Descent. Therefore this Celerity will be as $\frac{A\sqrt{de}}{B}$, or since the Globes are as the Cubes of the Radii as $\frac{a^3\sqrt{de}}{b^3}$. But as the Square of this Celerity to the Square of the Celerity of the Globe A just before Reflection, so is the Height to which the Globe B would ascend with this Celerity, if it was not hindered by meeting the Globe A falling upon it, to the Height ed from which the Globe B descends. That is, as $\frac{Aq}{Bq}de$ to de, or as Aq to Bq, or a^6 to b^6, so that first Height to x, if you put x for the latter Height cd. Therefore this Height, *viz.* to which B would ascend, if it was not hindered, is $\frac{a^6}{b^6}x$. Let that be fK. To fK add fg, or $dH - de - ef - gH$; that is, $p - x$, if for the given $dH - ef - gh$ you write p, and x for the unknown de; and you will have $Kg = \frac{a^6}{b^6}x + p - x$. Whence the Celerity of the Globe B, when it falls from K to the Ground, that is when it falls through the Space Kg, which its Center would describe in falling, will be as $\sqrt{\frac{a^6}{b^6}x + p - x}$. But that Globe falls from the Place Bcf to the Ground in the same Time that the upper Globe A ascends from the Place Ace to its greatest Height d, or on the other Hand falls from d to the Place Ace; and therefore since the Celerities of falling Bodies are

are equally augmented in equal Times, the Celerity of the Globe B, by falling to the Ground, will be augmented as much as is the whole Celerity which the Globe A acquires by falling in the same Time from d to e, or loses by ascending from e to d. Therefore, to the Celerity which the Globe B has in the Place Bcf, add the Celerity which the Globe A has in the Place Ace, and the Sum, which is as $\sqrt{de} + \frac{a^3\sqrt{de}}{b^3}$, or $\sqrt{x} + \frac{a^3}{b^3}\sqrt{x}$, will be the Celerity of the Globe B when it falls on the Ground. Therefore $\sqrt{x} + \frac{a^3}{b^3}\sqrt{x}$ will be equal to $\sqrt{\frac{a^6}{b^6}x + p - x}$. For $\frac{a^3 + b^3}{b^3}$ write $\frac{r}{s}$, and for $\frac{a^6 - b^6}{b^6}$, $\frac{rt}{ss}$, and that Equation will become $\frac{r}{s} \times \sqrt{x} = \sqrt{\frac{rt}{ss}x + p}$, and the Parts being squared, $\frac{rr}{ss}x = \frac{rt}{ss}x + p$. Subtract from both Sides $\frac{rt}{ss}x$, multiply all into ss, and divide by $rr - rt$, and there will arise $x = \frac{ssp}{rr - rt}$. Which Equation would have come out more simple, if I had taken $\frac{p}{s}$ for $\frac{a^3 + b^3}{b^3}$, for there would have come out $\frac{ss}{p - t} = x$. Whence making that $p - t$ shall be to s as s to x, you will have x, or ed; to which if you add ec, you will have dc, and the Point c, in which the Globes shall fall upon one another. Q. E. F.

Z 2 PRO-

PROBLEM LV.

Three Staves being erected, or set up an End, in some certain Part of the Earth perpendicular to the Plane of the Horizon, in the Points A, B, *and* C, *whereof that which is in* A *is six Foot long, that in* B *eighteen, and that in* C *eight, the Line* A B *being thirty Foot long; it happens on a certain Day in the Year that the End of the Shadow of the Staff* A *passes through the Points* B *and* C, *and of the Staff* B *through* A *and* C, *and of the Staff* C *through the Point* A. *To find the Sun's Declination, and the Elevation of the Pole, or the Day and Place where this shall happen.* [*See* Figure 61.]

Because the Shadow of each Staff describes a Conick Section, or the Section of a luminous Cone, whose Vertex is the Top of the Staff; I will feign B C D E F to be such a Curve, (whether it be an Hyperbola, Parabola, or Ellipse) as the Shadow of the Staff A describes that Day, by putting A D, A E, A F, to have been its Shadows, when B C, B A, C A, were respectively the Shadows of the Staves B and C. And besides I will suppose P A Q to be the Meridional Line, or the Axis of this Curve, to which the Perpendiculars BM, CH, DK, EN, and FL, being let fall, are Ordinates. And I will denote these Ordinates indefinitely by the Letter y, and the intercepted Parts of the Axis AM, AH, AK, AN, and AL by the Letter x. I will suppose, lastly, the Equation $aa \perp bx \perp cxx = yy$, to express the Relation of x and y, (*i. e.* the Nature of the Curve) assuming aa, b and c, as known Quantities, as they will be found to be from the Analysis. Where I made the unknown Quantities of two Dimensions only because the Equation is to express a Conick Section: and I omitted the odd Dimensions of y, because it is an Ordinate to the Axis. And I denoted the Signs of b and c, as being indeterminate by the Note $\perp$, which I use indifferently for $+$ or $-$, and its opposite $\top$ for the contrary. But I made the Sign of the Square aa Affirmative, because the concave Part of the Curve necessarily contains the Staff A, projecting its Shadows to the opposite Parts (C and F, D and E); and therefore if at the Point A you erect the Perpendicular

Aβ, this will some where meet the Curve, suppose in β, that is, the Ordinate y, where x is nothing, will still be real. From thence it follows that its Square, which in that Case is aa, will be Affirmative.

It is manifest therefore, that this fictitious Equation $aa \perp bx \perp cxx = yy$, as it is not filled with superfluous Terms, so neither is it more restrained than what is capable of satisfying all the Conditions of this Problem, and will denote the Hyperbola, Ellipse, or Parabola, according as the Values of aa, b, c, shall be determined, or perhaps found to be nothing. But what may be their Values, and with what Signs b and c are to be affected, and thence what Sort of a Curve this may be, will be manifest from the following Analysis.

The former Part of the Analysis.

Since the Shadows are as the Altitudes of the Staves, you will have B C : A D :: A B : A E (:: 18 : 6) :: 3 : 1. Also C A : A F (:: 8 : 6) :: 4 : 3. Wherefore naming A M $= r$, M B $= s$, A H $= t$, and H C $= \perp v$. From the Similitude of the Triangles A M B, A N E, and A H C, A L F, A N will be $= -\frac{r}{3}$. N E $= -\frac{s}{3}$. A L $= -\frac{3t}{4}$, and L F $= \top \frac{3v}{4}$; whose Signs I put contrary to the Signs of A M, M B, A H, H C, because they tend contrary Ways with respect to the Point A from which they are drawn, or to the Axis P Q on which they stand. Now these being respectively written for x and y in the fictitious Equation $aa \perp bx \perp cxx = yy$.

r and s will give $aa \perp br \perp crr = ss$.

$-\frac{r}{3}$ and $-\frac{s}{3}$ will give $aa \top \frac{br}{3} \perp \frac{1}{9}crr = \frac{1}{9}ss$.

t and $\perp v$ will give $aa \perp bt \perp ctt = vv$.

$-\frac{3}{4}t$ and $\top \frac{3}{4}v$ will give $aa \top \frac{3}{4}bt \perp \frac{9}{16}ctt = \frac{9}{16}vv$.

Now, by exterminating ss from the first and second Equations, in order to obtain r, there comes out $\frac{2aa}{\perp b} = r$. Whence it is manifest, that $\perp b$ is Affirmative. Also by exterminating vv from the third and fourth, to obtain t, there comes

comes out $\frac{aa}{3b} = t$. And having writ $\frac{2aa}{b}$ for r in the first, and $\frac{aa}{3b}$ for t in the third, there arise $3aa \perp \frac{4a^4c}{bb} = ss$, and $\frac{4}{3}aa \perp \frac{a^4c}{9bb} = vv$.

Moreover, having let fall Bλ perpendicular upon CH, BC will be : AD (:: 3 : 1) :: Bλ : AK :: Cλ : DK. Wherefore, since Bλ is $(= AM - AH = r - t) = \frac{5aa}{3b}$, AK will be $= \frac{5aa}{9b}$, or rather $= -\frac{5aa}{9b}$. Also since Cλ is $(= CH \perp BM = v \perp s) = \sqrt{\frac{4aa}{3} \perp \frac{a^4c}{9bb}} \perp \sqrt{3aa \perp \frac{4a^4c}{bb}}$, it will be DK $(= \frac{1}{3}C\lambda) = \sqrt{\frac{4aa}{27} \perp \frac{a^4c}{81bb}} \perp \sqrt{\frac{1}{3}aa \perp \frac{4a^4c}{9bb}}$. Which being respectively written in the Equation $aa + bx \perp cxx = yy$, for AK and DK, or x and y, there comes out $\frac{4aa}{9} \perp \frac{25a^4c}{81bb} = \frac{13}{27}aa \perp \frac{37a^4c}{81bb} \perp 2\sqrt{\frac{4aa}{27} \perp \frac{a^4c}{81bb}} \times \sqrt{\frac{aa}{3} \perp \frac{4a^4c}{9bb}}$. And by Reduction $-bb \top 4aac = \perp 2\sqrt{36b \perp 51aabbc + 4a^4cc}$; and the Parts being squared, and again reduced, there comes out $o = 143b^4 \perp 196aabbc$, or $\frac{-143bb}{196aa} = \perp c$. Whence it is manifest, that $\perp c$ is Negative, and consequently the fictitious Equation $aa \perp bx \perp cxx = yy$ will be of this Form, $aa + bx - cxx = yy$. And therefore the Curve, which it denotes, is an Ellipsis; whose Center and two Axes are thus found.

Making $y = o$, as happens in the Vertex's of the Figure P and Q, you will have $aa + bx = cxx$, and having extracted the Root $x = \frac{b}{2c} \pm \sqrt{\frac{bb}{4cc} + \frac{aa}{c}} = \begin{cases} AQ \\ AP \end{cases}$.

And consequently, taking $AV = \frac{b}{2c}$, V will be the Center of the Ellipse, and VQ, or VP $\left(\sqrt{\frac{bb}{4cc} + \frac{aa}{c}}\right)$ the greatest Semi-Axis. If, moreover, the Value of AV, or $\frac{b}{2c}$, be put for x in the Equation $aa + bx - cxx = yy$, there will come out $aa + \frac{bb}{4c} = yy$. Wherefore $aa + \frac{bb}{4c}$ will be $= VZq$, that is, to the Square of the least Semi-Axis. Lastly, in the Values of AV, VQ, and VZ already found, writing $\frac{143bb}{196aa}$ for c, there come out $\frac{98aa}{143b} = AV$, $\frac{112aa\sqrt{3}}{143b} = VQ$, and $\frac{8a\sqrt{3}}{\sqrt{143}} = VZ$.

The other Part of the Analysis. [*See* Figure 62.]

Suppose now the Staff AR standing on the Point A, and RPQ will be the Meridional Plane, and RPZQ the luminous Cone whose Vertex is R. Let moreover TXZ be a Plane cutting the Horizon in VZ, and the Meridional Plane in TVX, which Section let be perpendicular to the Axis of the World, or of the Cone, and the Plane TXZ will be perpendicular to the same Axis, and will cut the Cone in the Periphery of the Circle TZX, which will be every where at an equal Distance, as RX, RZ, RT, from its Vertex. Wherefore, if PS be drawn parallel to TX, you will have RS = RP, by reason of the equal Quantities RX, RT; and also SX = XQ, by reason of the equal Quantities PV, VQ; whence RX or RZ $= \left(\frac{RS + RQ}{2}\right)$ is $= \frac{RP + RQ}{2}$. Lastly, draw RV, and since VZ perpendicularly stands on the Plane RPQ, (as being the Section of the Planes perpendicularly standing on the same Plane) the Triangle RVZ will be right-angled at V.

2 Now

Now making RA $=d$, AV $=e$, VP or VQ $=f$, and VZ $=g$, you will have AP $=f-e$, and RP $=\sqrt{ff-2ef+ee+dd}$. Alſo AQ $=f+e$, and RQ $=\sqrt{ff+2ef+ee+dd}$; and conſequently RZ $\left(=\frac{RP+RQ}{2}\right)=\frac{\sqrt{ff-2ef+ee+dd}+\sqrt{ff+2ef+ee+dd}}{2}$.

Whoſe Square $\frac{dd+ee+ff}{2}+\frac{1}{2}\sqrt{f^4-2eeff+e^4+2ddff+2ddee+d^4}$ is equal (RVq + VZq = RAq + AVq + VZq =) $dd+ee+gg$. Now having reduced, it is $\sqrt{f^4-2eeff+e^4+2ddff+2ddee+d^4}=dd+ee-ff+2gg$, and the Parts being ſquared and reduced into Order, $ddff=ddgg+eegg-ffgg+g^4$, or $\frac{ddff}{gg}=dd+ee-ff+gg$. Laſtly, 6, $\frac{98aa}{143b}$, $\frac{112aa\sqrt{3}}{143b}$, and $\frac{8a\sqrt{3}}{\sqrt{143}}$ (the Values of AR, AV, VQ, and VZ) being reſtored for d, e, f, and g, there ariſes $36-\frac{196a^4}{143bb}+\frac{192aa}{143}=\frac{36\times14\times14aa}{143bb}$, and thence by Reduction $\frac{49a^4+36\times49aa}{48aa+1287}=bb$.

In the firſt Scheme AMq + MBq is = ABq, that is, $rr+ss=33\times33$. But r was $=\frac{2aa}{b}$, and $ss=3aa-\frac{4a^4c}{bb}$, whence $rr=\frac{4a^4}{bb}$, and (ſubſtituting $\frac{143bb}{196aa}$ for c) $ss=\frac{4aa}{49}$. Wherefore $\frac{4a^4}{bb}+\frac{4aa}{49}=33\times33$, and thence by Reduction there again reſults $\frac{4\times49a^4}{53361-4aa}=bb$. Putting therefore an Equality between the two Values of bb, and dividing each Part of the Equation by 49, you will have

$\frac{a^4+36aa}{48aa+1287}=\frac{4a^4}{53361-4aa}$; whoſe Parts being multiplied croſs-ways, ordered and divided by 49, there comes out $4a^4=981aa+39204$, whoſe Root aa is $\frac{981+\sqrt{1589625}}{8}=280{,}2254144$.

Above was found $\frac{4\times49a^4}{53361-4aa}=bb$, or $\frac{14aa}{\sqrt{53361-4aa}}=b$. Whence AV $\left(\frac{98aa}{143b}\right)$ is $\frac{7\sqrt{53361-4aa}}{143}$, and VP or VQ $\left(\frac{112aa\sqrt{3}}{143b}\right)$ is $\frac{8}{143}\sqrt{160083-12aa}$. That is, by ſubſtituting 280,2254144 for aa, and reducing the Terms into Decimals, AV = 11,188297, and VP or VQ = 22,147085; and conſequently AP (PV − AV) = 10,958788, and AQ (AV + VQ) 33,335382.

Laſtly, if $\frac{1}{6}$ AR or 1 be made Radius, $\frac{1}{6}$ AQ or 5,555897 will be the Tangent of the Angle ARQ of 79 *gr.* 47′. 48″. and $\frac{1}{6}$ AP or 1,826465 the Tangent of the Angle ARP of 61 *gr.* 17′. 57 . half the Sum of which Angles 70 *gr.* 32′. 52″. is the Complement of the Sun's Declination; and the Semi-difference 9 *gr.* 14′. 56″. the Complement of the Latitude of the Place. Therefore, the Sun's Declination was 19 *gr.* 27′. 10″. and the Latitude of the Place 80 *gr.* 45′. 4″. which were to be found.

PROBLEM LVI.

From the Obſervation of four Places of a Comet, moving with an uniform right-lined Motion through the Heaven, to determine its Diſtance from the Earth, and Direction and Velocity of its Motion, according to the Copernican *Hypotheſis.* [*See* Figure 73.]

If from the Center of the Comet in the four Places obſerved, you let fall ſo many Perpendiculars to the Plane of the Eclipticks; and A, B, C, D, be the Points in that Plane on which the Perpendiculars fall; through thoſe Points draw the right Line AD, and this will be cut by the Perpendiculars in the ſame Ratio with the Line which the Comet deſcribes

A a

ſcribes by its Motion; that is, ſo that AB ſhall be to AC as the Time between the firſt and ſecond Obſervation to the Time between the firſt and third; and AB to AD as the Time between the firſt and ſecond to the Time between the firſt and fourth. From the Obſervations therefore there are given the Proportions of the Lines AB, AC, AD, to one another.

Moreover, let the Sun S be in the ſame Plane of the Ecliptick, and EH an Arch of the Ecliptical Line in which the Earth moves; E, F, G, H, four Places of the Earth at the Times of the Obſervations, E the firſt Place, F the ſecond, G the third, H the fourth. Join AE, BF, CG, DH, and let them be produced until the three latter cut the former in I, K, and L, *viz.* BF in I, CG in K, DH in L. And the Angles AIB, AKC, ALD will be the Differences of the obſerved Longitudes of the Comet; AIB the Difference of the Longitudes of the firſt and ſecond Place of the Comet; AKC the Difference of the Longitudes of the firſt and third Place, and ALD the Difference of the Longitudes of the firſt and fourth Place. There are given therefore from the Obſervations the Angles AIB, AKC, ALD.

Join SE, SF, EF; and by reaſon of the given Points S, E, F, and the given Angle ESF, there will be given the Angle SEF. There is given alſo the Angle SEA, as being the Difference of Longitude of the Comet and Sun in the Time of the firſt Obſervation. Wherefore, if you add its Complement to two right Angles, *viz.* the Angle SEI to the Angle SEF, there will be given the Angle IEF. Therefore there are given the Angles of the Triangle IEF, together with the Side EF, and conſequently there is given the Side IE. And by a like Argument there are given KE and LE. There are given therefore in Poſition the four Lines AI, BI, CK, DL, and conſequently the Problem comes to this, that four Lines being given in Poſition, we may find a fifth, which ſhall be cut by theſe four in a given Ratio.

Having let fall to AI the Perpendiculars BM, CN, DO, by reaſon of the given Angle AIB there is given the Ratio of BM to MI. But BM to CN is in the given Ratio of BA and CA, and by reaſon of the given Angle CKN there is given the Ratio of CN to KN. Wherefore, there is alſo given the Ratio of BM to KN; and thence alſo the Ratio of BM to $MI - KN$, that is, to $MN + IK$. Take P to IK as is AB to BC, and ſince MA is to MN in the ſame Ratio, $P + MA$ will be to $IK + MN$ in the ſame Ratio, that is, in a given Ratio. Wherefore, there is given the Ratio of BM to $P + MA$. And by a like Argument, if Q be taken to IL in the Ratio of AB to BD, there will be given the Ratio of BM to $Q + MA$. And therefore the Ratio of BM to the Difference of $P + MA$ and $Q + MA$ will be alſo given. But that Difference, *viz.* $P - Q$, or $Q - P$ is given, and therefore there will be given BM. But BM being given, there are alſo given $P + MA$ and MI, and thence, MA, ME, AE, and the Angle EAB.

Theſe being found, erect at A a Line perpendicular to the Plane of the Ecliptick, which ſhall be to the Line EA as the Tangent of the Comet's Latitude in the firſt Obſervation to Radius, and the End of that Perpendicular will be the Place of the Comet's Center in the firſt Obſervation. Whence the Diſtance of the Comet from the Earth is given in the Time of that Obſervation. And after the ſame Manner, if from the Point B you erect a Perpendicular which ſhall be to the Line BF as the Tangent of the Comet's Latitude in the ſecond Obſervation to Radius, you will have the Place of the Comet's Center in that ſecond Obſervation. And a Line drawn from the firſt Place to the ſecond, is that in which the Comet moves through the Heaven.

PROBLEM LVII.

If the given Angle CAD *move about the angular Point* A *given in Poſition, and the given Angle* CBD *about the angular Point* B *given alſo in Poſition, on this Condition, that the Legs* AD, BD, *ſhall always cut one another in the right Line* EF *given likewiſe in Poſition; to find the Curve, which the Interſection* C *of the other Legs* AC, BC, *deſcribes.* [*See* Figure 74.]

Produce CA to *d*, ſo that A*d* ſhall be = AD, and produce CB to *δ*, ſo that B*δ* ſhall be = to BD. Make the Angle A*de* equal to the Angle ADE, and the Angle B*δf* equal to the Angle BDF, and produce AB on both Sides until it meet *de* and *δf* in *e* and *f*. Produce alſo *ed* to G, that *d*G ſhall be = *δf*, and from the Point C to the

Aa 2

the Line AB draw CH parallel to ed, and CK parallel to $f\delta$. And conceiving the Lines eG, $f\delta$ to remain immoveable while the Angles CAD, CBD, move by the aforesaid Law about the Poles A and B, Gd will always be equal to $f\delta$, and the Triangle CHK will be given in Specie. Make therefore A$e = a$, eG$= b$, B$f = c$, AB$= m$, BK$= x$, and CK$= y$. And BK will be : CK :: Bf : $f\delta$. Therefore $f\delta = \frac{cy}{x} = $ Gd. Take this from Ge, and there will remain $ed = b - \frac{cy}{x}$. Since the Triangle CKH is given in Specie, make CK : CH :: $d : e$, and CH : HK :: $e : f$, and CH will be $= \frac{ey}{d}$, and HK $= \frac{fy}{d}$. And consequently AH$= m - x - \frac{fy}{d}$. But AH : HC :: Ae : ed, that is, $m - x - \frac{f}{d}y : \frac{ey}{d} :: a : b - \frac{cy}{x}$. Therefore, by multiplying the Means and Extreams together, there will be made $mb - \frac{mcy}{x} - bx + cy - \frac{bf}{d}y + \frac{cfyy}{dx} = \frac{aey}{d}$. Multiply all the Terms by dx, and reduce them into Order, and there will come out $fcyy \begin{matrix} +dc \\ -ae \\ -fb \end{matrix} xy - dcmy - bdxx + bdmx = 0$. Where, since the unknown Quantities x and y ascend only to two Dimensions, it is evident, that the Curve Line that the Point C describes is a Conick Section. Make $\frac{ae + fb - dc}{c} = 2p$, and there will come out $yy = \frac{2p}{f}xy + \frac{dm}{f}y + \frac{bd}{fc}xx - \frac{bdm}{fc}x$. And the Square Root being extracted, $y = \frac{p}{f}x + \frac{dm}{2f} \pm$

$\sqrt{pp}$

$\sqrt{\frac{pp}{ff}xx + \frac{bd}{fc}xx + \frac{pdm}{ff}x - \frac{bdm}{fc}x + \frac{ddmm}{4ff}}$.

Whence we infer, that the Curve is an Hyperbola, if $\frac{bd}{fc}$ be Affirmative, or Negative and less than $\frac{pp}{ff}$; and a Parabola, if $\frac{bd}{fc}$ be Negative and equal to $\frac{pp}{ff}$; an Ellipse or a Circle, if $\frac{bd}{fc}$ be both Negative and greater than $\frac{pp}{ff}$. Q. E. I.

PROBLEM LVIII.

To describe a Parabola which shall pass through four Points given. [*See* Figure 75.]

Let those given Points be A, B, C, D. Join AB, and bisect it in E. And through E draw VE a right Line, which conceive to be the Diameter of a Parabola, the Point V being its Vertex. Join AC, and draw DG parallel to AB, and meeting AC in G. Make AB$= a$, AC$= b$, AG$= c$, GD$= d$. Upon AC take AP of any Length, and from P draw PQ parallel to AB, and conceiving Q to be a Point of the Parabola; make AP$= x$, PQ$= y$. And take any Equation expressive of a Parabola, which may determine the Relation between AP and PQ. As that y is $= e + fx \pm \sqrt{gg + hx}$.

Now if AP or x be put $= 0$, the Point P falling upon A, PQ or y will be $= 0$, as also $= -$AB. And by writing in the assumed Equation 0 for x, you will have $y = e + \sqrt{gg}$, that is $= e + g$. The greater of which Values of y, $e + g$ is $= 0$, the lesser $e - g = -$AB, or to $-a$. Therefore $e = -g$, and $e - g$, that is, $-2g = -a$, or $g = \frac{1}{2}a$. And so in room of the assumed Equation you will have this $y = -\frac{1}{2}a + fx \pm \sqrt{\frac{1}{4}aa + hx}$.

Moreover, if AP or x be made $=$ AC, so that the Point P falls upon C, you will have again PQ$= 0$. For x therefore in the last Equation write AC or b, and for y write 0; and you will have $0 = -\frac{1}{2}a + fb + \sqrt{\frac{1}{4}aa + hb}$, or $\frac{1}{2}a$ $-fb$

$-fb=\sqrt{\tfrac{1}{4}aa+bb}$; and the Parts being squared $-afb+ffbb=bb$, or $ffb-fa=b$. And so, in room of the assumed Equation, there will be had this, $y=-\tfrac{1}{2}a+fx\pm\sqrt{\tfrac{1}{4}aa+ffbx-fax}$.

Moreover, if A P or x be made $=$ A G or c, P Q or y will be $=-$G D or $-d$. Wherefore, for x and y in the last Equation write c and $-d$, and you will have $-d=-\tfrac{1}{2}a+fc-\sqrt{\tfrac{1}{4}aa+ffbc-fac}$, or $\tfrac{1}{2}a-d-fc=\sqrt{\tfrac{1}{4}aa+ffbc-fac}$. And the Parts being squared, $-ad-fac+dd+2dcf+ccff=ffbc-fac$. And the Equation being ordered and reduced, $ff=\frac{2d}{b-c}f+\frac{dd-ad}{bc-cc}$. For $b-c$, that is, for G C write k, and that Equation will become $ff=\frac{2d}{k}f+\frac{dd-ad}{kc}$. And the Root being extracted, $f=\frac{d}{k}\pm\sqrt{\frac{ddc+ddk-adk}{kkc}}$. But f being found, the Parabolick Equation, *viz.* $y=-\tfrac{1}{2}a+fx\pm\sqrt{\tfrac{1}{4}aa+ffbx-fax}$ will be fully determined; by whose Construction therefore the Parabola will also be determined. The Construction is thus: Draw C H parallel to B D meeting D G in H. Between D G and D H take a mean Proportional D K, and draw E I parallel to C K, bisecting A B in E, and meeting D G in I. Then produce I E to V, so that E V shall be to E I :: E Bq : D Iq — E Bq, and V will be the Vertex, V E the Diameter, and $\frac{\text{BE}q}{\text{VE}}$ the *Latus Rectum* of the Parabola sought.

Problem LIX.

To describe a Conick Section through five Points given. [*See* Figure 76.]

Let those Points be A, B, C, D, E. Join A C, B E, cutting one another in H. Draw D I parallel to B E, and meeting A C in I. As also E K parallel to A C, and meeting D I produced in K. Produce I D to F, and E K to G; so that A H C shall be : B H E : : A I C : F I D : : E K G : F K D, and the Points F and G will be in a Conick Section, as is known.

But you ought to observe this, if the Point H falls between all the Points A, C, and B E, or without them all, the Point I must either fall between all the Points A, C, and F, D, or without them all; and the Point K between all the Points D, F, and E, G, or without them all. But if the Point H falls between the two Points A, C, and without the other two B, E, or between those two B, E, and without the other two A, C, the Point I ought to fall between two of the Points A, C and F, D, and without the other two of them; and in like Manner, the Point K ought to fall between two of the Points D, F, and E, G, and without Side of the two other of them; which will be done by taking I F, K G, on this or that Side of the Points I, K, according to the Exigency of the Problem. Having found the Points F and G, bisect A C and E G in N and O; also B E, F D in L and M. Join N O, L M, cutting one another in R; and L M and N O will be the Diameters of the Conick Section, R its Center, and B L, F M, Ordinates to the Diameter L M. Produce L M on both Sides, if there be Occasion, to P and Q, so that B Lq shall be to F Mq : : P L Q : P M Q, and P and Q will be the Vertex's of the Conick Section, and P Q the *Latus Transversum*. Make P L Q : L Bq : : P Q : T, and T will be the *Latus Rectum*. Which being known, the Figure is known.

It remains only that we may shew how L M is to be produced each Way to P and Q, so that B Lq may be : F Mq : : P L Q : P M Q, *viz.* P L Q, or P L × L Q, is $\overline{\text{PR}-\text{LR}}\times\overline{\text{PR}+\text{LR}}$; for P L is P R — L R, and L Q is R Q + L R, or P R + L R. Moreover, $\overline{\text{PR}-\text{LR}}\times\overline{\text{PR}+\text{LR}}$, by multiplying, becomes P Rq — L Rq. And after the same Manner, P M Q is $\overline{\text{PR}+\text{RM}}\times\overline{\text{PR}-\text{RM}}$, or P R$q$ — R Mq. Therefore B Lq : F Mq : : P Rq — L Rq : P Rq — R Mq; and by dividing, B Lq — F Mq : F Mq : : R Mq — L Rq : P Rq — R Mq. Wherefore since there are given B Lq — F Mq, F Mq and R Mq — L Rq, there will be given P Rq — R Mq. Add the given Quantity R Mq, and there will be given the Sum P Rq, and consequently its Root P R, to which Q R is equal.

PROBLEM LX.

To describe a Conick Section which shall pass through four given Points, and in one of those Points shall touch a right Line given in Position. [*See* Figure 77.]

Let the four given Points be A, B, C, D, and the right Line given in Position be A E, which let the Conick Section touch in the Point A. Join any two Points D, C, and let D C produced, if there be Occasion for it, meet the Tangent in E. Through the fourth Point B draw B F parallel to D C, which may meet the same Tangent in F. Also draw D I parallel to the Tangent, and which may meet B F in I. Upon F B, D I, produced if there be Occasion, take F G, H I, of such Length as that it may be $AEq : CED :: AFq : BFG :: DIH : BIG$. And the Points G and H will be in a Conick Section as is known; provided you take F G, I H, on the proper Sides of the Points F and I, according to the Rule delivered in the foregoing Problem. Bisect B G, D C, D H, in K, L, and M. Join K L, A M, cutting one another in O, and O will be the Center, A the Vertex, and H M an Ordinate to the Semi-Diameter A O; which being known, the Figure is known.

PROBLEM LXI.

To describe a Conick Section which shall pass through three given Points, and touch right Lines given in Position in two of those Points. [*See* Figure 78.]

Let those given Points be A, B, C, the Tangents A D, B D, to the Points A and B, and let D be the common Intersection of those Tangents. Bisect A B in E. Draw D E, and produce it till in F it meets C F drawn parallel to A B; and D F will be the Diameter, and A E and C F the Ordinates to that Diameter. Produce D F to O, and on D O take O V a mean Proportional between D O and E O, on this Condition, that also $AEq : CFq :: VE \times \overline{VO+OE} : VF \times \overline{VO+OF}$; and V will be the Vertex, and O the Center of the Figure. Which being known, the Figure will also be known. But V E is $= VO - OE$, and consequently $VE \times \overline{VO+OE} = \overline{VO-OE} \times \overline{VO+OE} = VOq - OEq$. Besides, Because V O is a mean Proportional between D O and E O, VOq will be $= DOE$, and consequently $VOq - OEq = DOE - OEq = DEO$. And by a like Argument you will have $VF \times \overline{VO+OF} = VOq - OFq = DOE - OFq$. Therefore $AEq : CFq :: DEO : DOE - OFq$. OFq is $= EOq - 2FEO + FEq$. And consequently $DOE - OFq = DOE - OEq + 2FEO - FEq = DEO + 2FEO - FEq$. And $AEq : CFq :: DEO : DEO + 2FEO - FEq :: DE : DE + 2FE - \frac{FEq}{EO}$. Therefore there is given $DE + 2FE - \frac{FEq}{EO}$. Take away from this given Quantity $DE + 2FE$, and there will remain $\frac{FEq}{EO}$ given. Call that N; and $\frac{FEq}{N}$ will be $= EO$, and consequently E O will be given. But E O being given, there is also given V O, the mean Proportional between D O and E O.

After this Way, by some of *Apollonius*'s Theorems, these Problems are expeditiously enough solved; which yet may be solved by Algebra alone without those Theorems. As if the first of the last three Problems be proposed: [See *Figure* 78.] Let the five given Points be A, B, C, D, E, through which the Conick Section is to pass. Join any two of them, A, C, and any other two, B, E, by right Lines intersecting one another in H. Draw D I parallel to B E meeting A C in I; as also any other right Line K L meeting A C in K, and the Conick Section in L. And imagine the Conick Section to be given, so that the Point K being known, there will at the same Time be known the Point L; and making $AK = x$, and $KL = y$, to express the Relation between x and y, assume any Equation which generally expresses the Conick Sections; suppose this, $a + bx + cxx + dy + exy + yy = 0$. Wherein a, b, c, d, e, denote determinate Quantities with their Signs, but x and y indeterminate Quantities. Now if we can find the determinate Quantities a, b, c, d, e, the Conick Section will be known. Let us therefore feign the Point L to fall successively upon the Points A, C, B, E, D, and let us see what will follow thence. If therefore the Point L falls upon the Point A, in that Case A K and K L, that is, x and y, will be 0. Then all the Terms of the Equation besides a will vanish, and there will remain $a = 0$. Wherefore a is to be blotted out in that Equation, and the other Terms $bx + cxx + dy + exy + yy$ will be $= 0$.

B b Moreover

Moreover if L falls upon C, A K, or x, will be $=$ A C, and L K or $y = 0$. Put therefore A C $= f$, and by substituting f for x and 0 for y, the Equation for the Curve $bx + cxx + dy + exy + yy = 0$, will become $bf + cff = 0$, or $b = -cf$. And having writ in that Equation $-cf$ for b, it will become $-cfx + cxx + dy + exy + yy = 0$. Farther, if the Point L falls upon the Point B, A K or x will be A H, and K L or $y =$ B H. Put therefore A H $= g$, and B H $= h$, and then write g for x and h for y, and the Equation $-cfx + cxx$, &c. will become $-cfg + cgg + dh + egh + hh = 0$. But if the Point L falls upon E, A K will be $=$ A H, or $x = g$, and K L or $y =$ H E. For H E therefore write $-k$, with a Negative Sign, because H E lies on the contrary Side of the Line A C, and by substituting g for x and $-k$ for y, the Equation $-cfx + cxx$, &c. will become $-cfg + cgg - dk - egk + kk = 0$. Take away this from the former Equation $-cfg + cgg + dh + egh + hh$, and there will remain $dh + egh + hh + dk + egk - kk = 0$. Divide this by $h + k$, and there will come out $d + eg + h - k = 0$. Take away this multiplied by h from $-cfg + cgg + dh + egh + hh = 0$, and there will remain $-cfg + cgg + hk = 0$, or $\frac{hk}{-gg + fg} = c$. Lastly, if the Point L falls upon the Point D, A K or x will be $=$ A I, and K L or y will be $=$ I D. Wherefore, for A I write m, and for I D, n, and likewise for x and y substitute m and n, and the Equation $-cfx + cxx$, &c will become $-cfm + cmm + dn + emn + nn = 0$. Divide this by n, and there will come out $\frac{-cfm + cmm}{n} + d + em + n = 0$. Take away $d + eg + h - k = 0$, and there will remain $\frac{-cfm + cmm}{n} + em - eg + n - h + k = 0$, or $\frac{cmm - cfm}{n} + n - h + k$ $eg - em$. But now by reason of the given Points A, B, C, D, E, there are given A C, A H, A I, B H, E H, D I, that is, f, g, m, h, k, n. And consequently by the Equation $\frac{hk}{fg - gg} = c$ there is given c. But c being given by the Equation $\frac{cmm - cfm}{n} + n - h + k = eg - em$ there is given $eg - em$. Divide this given Quantity by the given one $g - m$, and there will come out the given e. Which being found, the Equation $d + eg + h - k = 0$, or $d = k - h - eg$, will give d. And these being known, there will at the same Time be determined the Equation expressive of the Conick Section sought, *viz.* $cfx = cxx + dy + exy + yy$. And from that Equation, by the Method of *Des Cartes*, the Conick Section will be determined.

Now if the four Points A, B, C, E, and the Position of the right Line A F, which touches the Conick Section in one of those Points A were given, the Conick Section may be thus more easily determined. Having found, as above, the Equations $cfx \quad cxx + dy + exy + yy$, $d = k - h - eg$, and $c = \frac{hk}{fg - gg}$, conceive the Tangent A F to meet the right Line E H in F, and then the Point L to be moved along the Perimeter of the Figure C D E till it fall upon the Point A; and the ultimate Ratio of L K to A K will be the Ratio of F H to A H, as will be evident to any one that contemplates the Figure. Make F H $= p$, and in this Case where L K, A K, are in a vanishing State, you will have $p : g :: y : x$, or $\frac{gy}{p} = x$. Wherefore for x, in the Equation $cfx = cxx + dy + exy + yy$, write $\frac{gy}{p}$, and there will arise $\frac{cfgy}{p} = \frac{cggyy}{pp} + dy + \frac{egyy}{p} + yy$. Divide all by y, and there will come out $\frac{cfg}{p} = \frac{cggy}{pp} + d + \frac{cgy}{p} + y$. Now because the Point L is supposed to fall upon the Point A, and consequently K L, or y, to be infinitely small or nothing, blot out the Terms which are multiplied by y, and there will remain $\frac{cfg}{p} = d$. Wherefore make $\frac{hk}{fg - gg} = c$, then $\frac{cfg}{p} = d$. Lastly, $\frac{k - h - d}{g} = e$, and having found c, d, and e, the Equation $cfx = cxx + dy + exy + yy$ will determine the Conick Section.

Bb 2 If,

If, lastly, there are only given the three Points A, B, C, together with the Position of the two right Lines A T, C T, which touch the Conick Section in two of those Points, A and C, there will be obtained, as above, this Equation expressive of a Conick Section, $cfx = cxx + dy + exy + yy$. [See *Figure* 80.] Then if you suppose the Ordinate K L to be parallel to the Tangent A T, and it be conceived to be produced, till it again meets the Conick Section in M, and that Line L M to approach to the Tangent A T till it coincides with it at A; the ultimate Ratio of the Lines K L and K M to one another, will be a Ratio of Equality, as will appear to any one that contemplates the Figure. Wherefore in that Case K L and K M being equal to each other, that is, the two Values of y, (*viz.* the Affirmative one K L, and the Negative one K M) being equal, those Terms of the Equation $cfx = cxx + dy + exy + yy$ in which y is of an odd Dimension, that is, the Terms $dy + exy$ in respect of the Term yy, wherein y is of an even Dimension, will vanish. For otherwise the two Values of y, *viz.* the Affirmative and the Negative, cannot be equal; and in that Case A K is infinitely less than L K, that is x than y, and consequently the Term exy than the Term yy. And consequently being infinitely less, may be reckoned for nothing. But the Term dy, in respect of the Term yy, will not vanish as it ought to do, but will grow so much the greater, unless d be supposed to be nothing. Therefore the Term dy is to be blotted out, and so there will remain $cfx = cxx + exy + yy$, an Equation expressive of a Conick Section. Conceive now the Tangents A T, C T, to meet one another in T, and the Point L to come to approach to the Point C, till it coincides with it. And the ultimate Ratio of K L to K C will be that of A T to A C. K L was y; A K, x; and A C, f; and consequently K C, $f - x$; make A T $= g$, and the ultimate Ratio of y to $f - x$, will be the same as of g to f. The Equation $cfx = cxx + exy + yy$, subtracting on both Sides cxx, becomes $cfx - cxx = exy + yy$, that is, $\overline{f-x}$ into $cx = y$ into $\overline{ex+y}$. Therefore it is $y : f - x :: cx : ex + y$, and consequently $g : f :: cx : ex + y$. But the Point L falling upon C, y becomes nothing. Therefore $g : f :: cx : ex$. Divide the latter Ratio by x, and it will become $g : f :: c : e$, and $\frac{cf}{g} = e$. Wherefore, if in the Equation $cfx = cxx + exy + yy$, you write $\frac{cf}{g}$ for e, it will become $cfx = cxx + \frac{cf}{g}xy + yy$, an Equation expressive of a Conick Section. Lastly, draw B H parallel to K L, or A T, from the given Point B, through which the Conick Section ought to pass, and which shall meet A C in H, and conceiving K L to come towards B H, until it coincides with it, in that Case A H will be $= x$, and B H $= y$. Call therefore the given quantity A H $= m$, and the given B H $= n$, and then for x and y, in the Equation $cfx = cxx + \frac{cf}{g}xy + yy$, write m and n, and there will arise $cfm = cmm + \frac{cf}{g}mn + nn$. Take away on both Sides $cmm + \frac{cf}{g}mn$, and there will come out $cfm - cmm - \frac{cf}{g}mn = nn$. Put $f - m - \frac{fn}{g} = s$, and csm will be $= nn$. Divide each Part of the Equation by sm, and there will arise $c = \frac{nn}{sm}$. But having found c, the Equation for the Conick Section is determined $cfx = cxx + \frac{cf}{g}xy + yy$. And then, by the Method of *Des Cartes*, the Conick Section is given, and may be described.

Hitherto I have been solving several Problems. For in learning the Sciences, Examples are of more Use than Precepts. Wherefore I have been the larger on this Head. And some which occurred as I was putting down the rest, I have given their Solutions without using Algebra, that I might shew that in some Problems that at first Sight appear difficult, there is not always Occasion for Algebra. But now it is Time to shew the Solution of Equations. For after a Problem is brought to an Equation, you must extract the Roots of that Equation, which are the Quantities that satisfy the Problem.

How

How EQUATIONS *are to be solved.*

AFTER therefore in the Solution of a Question you are come to an Equation, and that Equation is duly reduced and ordered ; when the Quantities which are denoted by Species, and which are supposed given, are really given in Numbers, those Numbers are to be substituted in their room in the Equation, and you will have a Numeral Equation, whose Root being extracted will satisfy the Question. As if in the Division of an Angle into five equal Parts, by putting r for the Radius of the Circle, q for the Chord of the Complement of the proposed Angle to two right ones, and x for the Chord of the Complement of the fifth Part of that Angle, I had come to this Equation, $x^5 - 5 r r x^3 + 5 r^4 x - r^4 q = 0$. Where in any particular Case the Radius r is given in Numbers, and the Line q subtending the Complement of the given Angle ; as if the Radius were 10, and the Chord 3 ; I substitute those Numbers in the Equation for r and q, and there comes out the Numeral Equation $x^5 - 500 x^3 + 50000 x - 30000 = 0$, whereof the Root being extracted will be x, or the Line subtending the Complement of the fifth Part of that given Angle.

Of the Nature of the Roots of an EQUATION.

But the Root is a Number which being substituted in the Equation for the Letter or Species signifying the Root, will make all the Terms vanish.

Thus Unity is the Root of the Equation $x^4 - x^3 - 19 x x + 49 x - 30 = 0$, because being writ for x it produces $1 - 1 - 19 + 49 - 30$, that is, nothing. But there may be more Roots of the same Equation. As if in this same Equation $x^4 - x^3 - 19 x x + 49 x - 30 = 0$, for x you write the Number 2, and for the Powers of x the like Powers of the Number 2, there will be produced $16 - 8 - 76 + 98 - 30$, that is nothing. And so if for x you write the Number 3, or the Negative Number $- 5$, in both Cases there will be produced nothing, the Affirmative and Negative Terms in these four Cases destroying one another. Therefore since any of the Numbers written in the Equation fulfils the Condition of x, by making all the Terms of the Equation together equal to nothing, any of them will be the Root of the Equation.
And

And that you may not wonder that the same Equation may have *several Roots*, you must know *that there may be more Solutions than one of the same Problem.*

As if there was sought the *Intersection* of two given Circles ; there are *two* Intersections, and consequently the Question admits *two Answers* ; and therefore the Equation determining the Intersection will have *two Roots*, whereby it determines both the Intersections, *provided there be nothing in the Data whereby the Answer is determined to only one Intersection.* [See Figure 87.]

And thus, if of the Arch A P B its fifth Part A P were to be found, though perhaps you might apply your Thoughts only to the Arch A P B, yet the Equation, whereby the Question will be solved, will determine the fifth Part of all the Arches which are terminated at the Points A and B ; *viz.* the fifth Part of the Arches A S B, A P B S A P B, A S B P A S B, and A P B S A P B S A P B, as well as the fifth Part of the Arch A P B ; which fifth Parts, if you divide the whole Circumference into five equal Parts P Q, Q R, R S, S T, T P, will be A T, A Q, A T S, A Q R. Wherefore, by seeking the fifth Parts of the Arches which the right Line A B subtends, to determine all the Cases the whole Circumference ought to be divided in the five Points P, Q, R, S, T, therefore the Equation that will determine all the Cases will have five Roots. For the fifth Parts of all these Arches depend on the same Data, and are found by the same kind of Calculus ; so that you will always fall upon the same Equation, whether you seek the fifth Part of the Arch A P B, or the fifth Part of the Arch A S B, or the fifth Part of any other of the Arches. Whence, if the Equation by which the fifth Part of the Arch A P B is determined, should not have more than one Root, while by seeking the fifth Part of the Arch A S B we fall upon that same Equation ; it would follow, that this greater Arch would have the same fifth Part with the former, which is less, because its Subtense or Chord is expressed by the same Root of the Equation. *In every Problem therefore it is necessary, that the Equation which answers should have as many Roots as there are different Cases of the Quantity sought depending on the same Data, and to be determined by the same Method of Reasoning.*

But an Equation may have as many Roots as it has Dimensions, and not more.

Thus the Equation $x^4 - x^3 - 19 x x + 49 x - 30 = 0$, has four Roots, 1, 2, 3, $- 5$; but not more. For any

any of these Numbers writ in the Equation for x will cause all the Terms to destroy one another as we have said; but besides these, there is no Number by whose Substitution this will happen.

But the Number and Nature of the Roots will be best understood from the Generation of the Equation.

As if we would know how an Equation is generated, whose Roots are 1, 2, 3, and -5; we are to suppose x to signify ambiguously those Numbers, or x to be $=1$, $x=2$, $x=3$, and $x=-5$, or which is the same Thing, $x-1=0$, $x-2=0$, $x-3=0$, and $x+5=0$; and multiplying these together, there will come out by the Multiplication of $x-1$ by $x-2$ this Equation $xx-3x+2=0$, which is of two Dimensions, and has two Roots 1 and 2. And by the Multiplication of this by $x-3$, there will come out $x^3-6xx+11x-6=0$, an Equation of three Dimensions and as many Roots; which again multiplied by $x+5$ becomes $x^4-x^3-19xx+49x-30=0$, as above. Since therefore this Equation is generated by four Factors, $x-1$, $x-2$, $x-3$, and $x+5$, continually multiplied by one another, where any of the Factors is nothing, that which is made by all will be nothing; but where none of them is nothing, that which is contained under them all cannot be nothing. That is, $x^4-x^3-19xx+49x-30$ cannot be $=0$, as ought to be, except in these four Cases, where $x-1$ is $=0$, or $x-2=0$, or $x-3=0$, or, lastly, $x+5=0$, therefore only the Numbers 1, 2, 3, and -5 can exhibit x, or be the Roots of the Equation. And you are to reason alike of all Equations. For we may imagine all to be generated by such a Multiplication, although it is usually very difficult to separate the Factors from one another, and is the same Thing as to resolve the Equation and extract its Roots. For the Roots being had, the Factors are had also.

But the Roots are of two Sorts, Affirmative, *as in the Example brought,* 1, 2, *and* 3, *and* Negative, *as* -5. *And of these some are often* impossible.

Thus, the two Roots of the Equation $xx-2ax+bb=0$, which are $a+\sqrt{aa-b}$ and $a-\sqrt{aa-bb}$, are real when aa is greater than bb; but when aa is less than bb, they become impossible, because then $aa-bb$ will be a Negative Quantity, and the Square Root of a Negative Quantity is impossible. For every possible Root, whether it be Affirmative or Negative, if it be multiplied by it self, produces an Affirmative Square; therefore that will be an impossible one which is to produce a Negative Square. By the same Argument you may conclude, that the Equation $x^3-4xx+7x-6=0$, has one real Root, which is 2, and two impossible ones $1+\sqrt{-2}$ and $1-\sqrt{-2}$. For any of these, 2, $1+\sqrt{-2}$, $1-\sqrt{-2}$ being writ in the Equation for x, will make all its Terms destroy one another; but $1+\sqrt{-2}$, and $1-\sqrt{-2}$, are impossible Numbers, because they suppose the Extraction of the Square Root out of the Negative Number -2.

But it is just, that the Roots of Equations should be often impossible, lest they should exhibit the Cases of Problems that are often impossible as if they were possible.

As if you were to determine the Intersection of a right Line and a Circle, and you should put two Letters for the Radius of the Circle and the Distance of the right Line from its Center; and when you have the Equation defining the Intersection, if for the Letter denoting the Distance of the right Line from the Center, you put a Number less than the Radius, the Intersection will be possible; but if it be greater, impossible; and the two Roots of the Equation, which determine the two Intersections, ought to be either possible or impossible, that they may truly express the Matter. [See *Figure* 88.] And thus, if the Circle C D E F, and the Ellipsis A C B F, cut one another in the Points C, D, E, F, and to any right Line given in Position, as A B, you let fall the Perpendiculars C G, D H, E I, F K, and by seeking the Length of any one of the Perpendiculars, you come at length to an Equation; that Equation, when the Circle cuts the Ellipsis in four Points, will have four real Roots, which will be those four Perpendiculars. But if the Radius of the Circle, its Center remaining, be diminished until the Points E and F meeting, the Circle at length touches the Ellipse, those two of the Roots which express the Perpendiculars E I and F K now coinciding, will become equal. And if the Circle be yet diminished, so that it does not touch the Ellipse in the Point E F, but only cuts it in the other two Points C, D, then out of the four Roots those two which expressed the Perpendiculars E I, F K, which are now become impossible, will become, together with those Perpendiculars, also impossible. And after this Way in all Equations, by augmenting or diminishing their Terms, of the unequal Roots, two will become first equal and then impossible.

C c

possible. And thence it is, that the Number of the impossible Roots is always even.

But sometimes the Roots of Equations are possible, when the Schemes exhibit them as impossible. But this happens by reason of some Limitation in the Scheme, which does not belong to the Equation. [*See* Figure 89.]

As if in the Semi-Circle A D B, having given the Diameter A B, and the Chord A D, and having let fall the Perpendicular D C, I was to find the Segment of the Diameter A C, you will have $\frac{ADq}{AB} = AC$. And, by this Equation, A C is exhibited a real Quantity, where the inscribed Line A D is greater than the Diameter A B; but by the Scheme, A C then becomes impossible, *viz.* in the Scheme the Line A D is supposed to be inscribed in the Circle, and therefore cannot be greater than the Diameter of the Circle; but in the Equation there is nothing that depends upon that Condition. From this Condition alone of the Lines the Equation comes out, that A B, A D, and A C are continually proportional. And because the Equation does not contain all the Conditions of the Scheme, it is not necessary that it should be bound to the Limits of all Conditions. Whatever is more in the Scheme than in the Equation may constrain that to Limits, but not this. For which reason, when Equations are of odd Dimensions, and consequently cannot have all their Roots impossible, the Schemes often set Limits to the Quantities on which all the Roots depend, which Limits it is impossible they can exceed, keeping the same Conditions of the Schemes.

Of those Roots that are real ones, the Affirmative and Negative ones lie on contrary Sides, or tend contrary Ways.

Thus, in the last Scheme but one, by seeking the Perpendicular C G, you will light upon an Equation that has two Affirmative Roots C G and D H, tending from the Points C and D the same Way; and two Negative ones, E I and F K, tending from the Points E and F the opposite Way. Or if in the Line A B to which the Perpendiculars are let fall, there be given any Point P, and the Part of it P G extending from that given Point to some of the Perpendiculars, as C G, be sought, we shall light on an Equation of four Roots, P G, P H, P I, and P K, whereof the Quantity sought P G, and those that tend from the Point P the same Way with P G, (as

2 P K)

P K) will be Affirmative, but those which tend the contrary Way (as P H, P I) Negative.

Where there are none of the Roots of the Equation impossible, the Number *of the Affirmative and Negative* Roots *may be known from the* Signs *of the Terms of the Equation. For there are* so many *Affirmative Roots as there are* Changes *of the Signs in a continual Series from* + *to* —, *and from* — *to* +; *the rest are* Negative.

As in the Equation $x^4 - x^3 - 19xx + 49x - 30 = 0$, where the Signs of the Terms follow one another in this Order, $+ - - + -$, the Variations of the second — from the first +, of the fourth + from the third —, and of the fifth — from the fourth +, shew, that there are three Affirmative Roots, and consequently, that the fourth is a Negative one. But where some of the Roots are *impossible*, the Rule is of no Force, unless as far as those impossible Roots, which are neither Negative nor Affirmative, may be taken for *ambiguous ones*. Thus in the Equation $x^3 + pxx + 3ppx - q = 0$, the Signs shew that there is one Affirmative Root and two Negative ones. Suppose $x = 2p$, or $x - 2p = 0$, and multiply the former Equation by this, $x - 2p = 0$, that one Affirmative Root more may be added to the former, and you will have this Equation, $x^4 - px^3 + ppxx \begin{matrix} -bp^3 \\ -q \end{matrix} x + 2pq = 0$, which ought to have two Affirmative and two Negative Roots; yet it has, if you regard the Change of the Signs, four Affirmative ones. There are therefore *two impossible ones*, which for their Ambiguity in the former Case seem to be Negative ones, in the latter, Affirmative ones.

But you may know almost by this Rule how many Roots are impossible.

Make a Series of Fractions, whose Denominators are Numbers in this Progression 1, 2, 3, 4, 5, &c. *going on to the Number which shall be the same as that of the Dimensions of the Equation; and the Numerators the same Series of Numbers in a contrary Order. Divide each of the latter Fractions by each of the former. Place the Fractions that come out over the middle Terms of the Equation. And under any of the middle Terms, if its Square, multiplied into the Fraction standing over its Head, is greater than the Rectangle of the Terms on both Sides, place the Sign* +; *but if it be less, the Sign* —. *But under the first and last Term place the Sign* +. *And there will be as many impossible Roots as there*

C c 2 *are*

are Changes in the Series of the under-written Signs from + *to* —, *and* — *to* +.

As if you have the Equation $x^3 + pxx + 3ppx - q = 0$; I divide the second of the Fractions of this Series $\frac{3}{1}.\ \frac{2}{2}.\ \frac{1}{3}$, *viz.* $\frac{2}{2}$ by the first $\frac{3}{1}$, and the third $\frac{1}{3}$ by the second $\frac{2}{2}$, and I place the Fractions that come out, *viz.* $\frac{1}{3}$ and $\frac{1}{3}$ over the middle Terms of the Equation, as follows;

$$x^3 + p\overset{\frac{1}{3}}{x}x + 3p\overset{\frac{1}{3}}{p}x - q = 0.$$
$$+ \qquad - \qquad + \qquad +$$

Then, because the Square of the second Term pxx multiplied into the Fraction over its Head $\frac{1}{3}$, *viz.* $\frac{ppx^4}{3}$ is less than $3ppx^4$, the Rectangle of the first Term x^3 and third $3ppx$, I place the Sign — under the Term pxx. But because $9p^4xx$ (the Square of the third Term $3ppx$) multiplied into the Fraction over its Head $\frac{1}{3}$, is greater than nothing, and therefore much greater than the Negative Rectangle of the second Term pxx, and the fourth $-q$, I place the Sign + under that third Term. Then, under the first Term x^3 and the last $-q$, I place the Sign +. And the two Changes of the underwritten Signs; which are in this Series + — + +, the one from + into —, and the other from — into +, shew that there are two impossible Roots. And thus the Equation $x^3 - 4xx + 4x - 6 = 0$ has two impossible Roots, $x^3 - 4\overset{\frac{1}{3}}{x}x + 4\overset{\frac{1}{3}}{x} - 6 = 0.$

$$+ \qquad + \qquad - \qquad +$$

Also the Equation $x^4 - 6xx - 3x - 2 = 0$ has two.

$$x^4 \overset{\frac{3}{8}}{*} - 6\overset{\frac{4}{9}}{x}x - \overset{\frac{3}{8}}{3}x - 2 = 0.$$
$$+ \; + \qquad + \qquad - \qquad +$$

For this Series of Fractions $\frac{4}{1}.\ \frac{3}{2}.\ \frac{2}{3}.\ \frac{1}{4}$, by dividing the second by the first, and the third by the second, and the fourth by the third, gives this Series $\frac{3}{8}.\ \frac{4}{9}.\ \frac{3}{8}$, to be placed over the middle Terms of the Equation. Then the Square of the second Term, which is here nothing, multiplied into the Fraction over Head, *viz.* $\frac{3}{8}$, produces nothing, which is yet greater than the Negative Rectanlge $-6x^6$ contained under the Terms on each side x and $-6xx$. Wherefore, under the Term that is wanting I write +. In the rest I go on as in the former Example; and there comes out this Series of the underwritten Signs + + + — +, where two Changes shew there are two impossible Roots. And after the same Way in the Equation $x^5 - 4x^4 + 4x^3 - 2xx - 5x - 4 = 0$, are discovered two impossible Roots, as follows;

$$x^5 - 4\overset{\frac{2}{5}}{x^4} + 4\overset{\frac{1}{2}}{x^3} - 2\overset{\frac{1}{2}}{x}x - 5\overset{\frac{2}{5}}{x} - 4 = 0.$$
$$+ \qquad + \qquad - \qquad + \qquad + \quad +$$

Where two or more Terms are wanting together, under the first of the deficient Terms you must write the Sign —, under the second Sign +, under the third the Sign —, and so on, always varying the Signs, except that under the last of such deficient Terms you must always place +, when the Terms next on both Sides the deficient Terms have contrary Signs. As in the Equations

$$x^5 + ax^4 * * * + a^5 = 0,$$
$$+ \quad + \; - + - +$$

and

$$x^5 + ax^4 * * * - a^5 = 0;$$
$$+ \quad + \; - + + \quad +$$

the first whereof has four, and the latter two impossible Roots. Thus also the Equation,

$$x^7 - 2\overset{\frac{3}{7}}{x^6} + 3\overset{\frac{5}{9}}{x^5} - 2\overset{\frac{3}{5}}{x^4} + \overset{\frac{3}{5}}{x^3} \overset{\frac{5}{9}}{*} \overset{\frac{3}{7}}{*} - 3 = 0$$
$$+ \quad - \quad + \quad - \quad + - + \quad +$$

has six impossible Roots.

Hence also may be known whether the impossible Roots are among the Affirmative or Negative ones. For the Signs of the Terms over Head of the subscribed changing Terms shew, that there are as many impossible Affirmative Roots as there are Variations of them, and as many Negative ones as there are Successions without Variations. Thus, in the Equation

$$x^5 - 4x^4 + 4x^3 - 2xx - 5x - 4 = 0,$$
$$+ \quad + \quad - \quad + \quad + \quad +$$

because by the Signs that are writ underneath that are changeable, *viz.* + — +, by which it is shewn there are two impossible Roots, the Terms over Head $-4x^4 + 4x^3 - 2xx$ have the Signs — + —, which by two Variations shew there are two Affirmative Roots; therefore there will be two impossible Roots among the Affirmative ones. Since therefore the Signs of all the Terms of the Equation + — + — — — by three Variations shew that there are three Affirmative Roots, and that the other two are Negative, and that among the Affirmative ones there are two impossible ones; it follows that the Equation has one true affirmative Root, two negative ones, and two impossible ones.

ones. But if the Equation had been $\underset{+}{x^5} - \underset{+}{4x^4} - \underset{-}{4x^3} - \underset{-}{2xx} - \underset{+}{5x} - \underset{+}{4} = 0$, then the Terms over Head of the subscribed former varying Terms $+-$, *viz.* $-4x^4 - 4x^3$, by their Signs that do not change $-$ and $-$, shew, that one of the Negative Roots is impossible; and the Terms over the latter underwritten varying Terms $-+$, *viz.* $-2xx - 5x$, by their Terms not varying, $-$ and $-$, shew that another of the Negative Roots is impossible. Wherefore, since the Signs of the Equation $+-----$ by one Variation shew there is one Affirmative Root, and that the other four are Negative; it follows, there is one Affirmative, two Negative, and two Impossible ones. And this is so where there are not more impossible Roots than what are discovered by the Rule preceding. For there may be more, although it seldom happens.

Of the Transmutations *of* Equations.

Moreover all the Affirmative *Roots of any Equation may be changed into* Negative *ones, and the* Negative *into* Affirmative *ones, and that only by changing the Signs of the alternate Terms.*

Thus in the Equation $x^5 - 4x^4 + 4x^3 - 2xx - 5x - 4 = 0$, the three Affirmative Roots will be changed into Negative ones, and the two Negative ones into Affirmatives, by changing only the Signs of the second, fourth, and sixth Terms, as is done here, $x^5 + 4x^4 + 4x^3 + 2xx - 5x + 4 = 0$. This Equation has the same Roots with the former, unless that in this, those Roots are Affirmative that were there Negative, and Negative here that there were Affirmative; and the two impossible Roots, which lay hid there among the Affirmative ones, lie hid here among the Negative ones; so that these being deducted, there remains only one Root truly Negative.

There are also other Transmutations of Equations which are of Use in divers Cases. *For we may suppose the Root of an Equation to be composed any how out of a known and unknown Quantity, and then substitute what we suppose equivalent to it.* As if we suppose the Root to be equal to the Sum or Difference of any known and unknown Quantity. For after this Rate we may augment or diminish the Roots of the Equation by that known Quantity, or subtract them from it; and thereby cause that some of them that were before Negative shall now become Affirmative, or some of the Affirmative ones become Negative, or also that all shall become Affirmative or all Negative. Thus in the Equation $x^4 - x^3 - 19xx + 49x - 30 = 0$, if I have a mind to augment the Roots by Unity, I suppose $x + 1 = y$, or $x = y - 1$; and then for x I write $y - 1$ in the Equation, and for the Square, Cube, or Biquadrate of x, I write the like Power of $y - 1$, as follows.

x^4	$y^4 - 4y^3 + 6yy - 4y + 1$
$-x^3$	$- y^3 + 3yy - 3y + 1$
$-19xx$	$-19yy + 38y - 19$
$+49x$	$+49y - 49$
-30	-30
Sum	$y^4 - 5y^3 - 10yy + 80y - 96 = 0.$

And the Roots of the Equation that is produced, (*viz.*) $y^4 - 5y^3 - 10yy + 80y - 96 = 0$, will be 2, 3, 4, -4, which before were 1, 2, 3, -5, *i.e.* bigger by Unity. Now, if for x I had writ $y + 1\frac{1}{2}$, there would have come out the Equation $y^4 + 5y^3 - 10yy - \frac{5}{4}y + \frac{39}{16} = 0$, whereof there be two Affirmative Roots, $\frac{1}{2}$ and $1\frac{1}{2}$, and two Negative ones, $-\frac{1}{2}$ and $-6\frac{1}{2}$. But by writing $y - 6$ for x, there would have come out an Equation whose Roots would have been 7, 8, 9, 1, *viz.* all Affirmative; and writing for the same [x] $y + 4$, there would have come out those Roots diminished by 4, *viz.* $-3 -2 -1 -9$, all of them Negative.

After this Manner, by augmenting or diminishing the Roots, if any of them are impossible, they will sometimes be more easily detected than before. Thus in the Equation $x^3 - 3aax - 3a^3 = 0$, there are no Roots that appear impossible by the preceding Rule; but if you augment the Roots by the Quantity a, writing $y - a$ for x, you may now by that Rule discover two impossible Roots in the Equation resulting, $y^3 - 3ayy - a^3 = 0$.

By the same Operation you may also take away the second Terms of Equations. This will be done, if you subduct the known Quantity of the second Term of the Equation proposed, divided by the Number of Dimensions of the highest Term

Term of the Equation, from the Quantity which you aſſume to ſignify the Root of the new Equation, and ſubſtitute the Remainder for the Root of the Equation propoſed. As if there was propoſed the Equation $x^3 - 4xx + 4x - 6 = 0$, I ſubtract the known Quantity of the ſecond Term, which is -4, divided by the Number of the Dimenſions of the Equation, *viz.* 3, from the Species or Letter which is aſſumed to ſignify the new Root, ſuppoſe from y, and the Remainder $y + \frac{4}{3}$ I ſubſtitute for x, and there comes out

$$\begin{array}{rrrr} y^3 & +4yy & +\frac{16}{3}y & +\frac{64}{27} \\ & -4yy & -\frac{32}{3}y & -\frac{64}{9} \\ & & +4y & +\frac{16}{3} \\ & & & -6 \\ \hline y^3 & * & -\frac{4}{3}y & -{}^{146} = 0. \end{array}$$

By the ſame Method, the third Term of an Equation may be alſo taken away. Let there be propoſed the Equation $x^4 - 3x^3 + 3xx - 5x - 2 = 0$, and make $x = y - e$, and ſubſtituting $y - e$ in the room of x, there will ariſe this Equation;

$$y^4 \begin{array}{l} -4e \\ -3 \end{array} y^3 \begin{array}{l} +6ee \\ +9e \\ +3 \end{array} yy \begin{array}{l} -4e^3 \\ -9ee \\ -6e \\ -5 \end{array} y \begin{array}{l} +e^4 \\ +3e^3 \\ +3ee \\ +5e \\ -2 \end{array} \Bigg\} = 0.$$

The third Term of this Equation is $6ee + 9e + 3$ multiplied by yy. Where, if $6ee + 9e + 3$ were nothing, you would have what you deſired. Let us ſuppoſe it therefore to be nothing, that we may thence find what Number ought to be ſubſtituted in this Caſe for e, and we ſhall have the Quadratick Equation $6ee + 9e + 3 \quad 0$; which divided by 6 will become $ee + \frac{3}{2}e + \frac{1}{2} = 0$, or $ee = -\frac{3}{2}e - \frac{1}{2}$, and extracting the Root $e = -\frac{3}{4} \pm \sqrt{\frac{9}{16} - \frac{1}{2}}$, or $= -\frac{3}{4} \pm \sqrt{\frac{1}{16}}$, that is, $= -\frac{3}{4} \pm \frac{1}{4}$, and conſequently either $= -\frac{1}{2}$ or $= -1$. Whence $y - e$ will be either $y + \frac{1}{2}$, or $y + 1$. Wherefore, ſince $y - e$ was writ for x; in the room of $y - e$ there ought to be writ $y + \frac{1}{2}$, or $y + 1$ for x, that the third Term of the Equation that reſults may be taken away. And that will happen in both Caſes. For if for x you write $y + \frac{1}{2}$, there will ariſe this Equation, $y^4 - y^3 - \frac{5}{4}y - \frac{65}{16} = 0$; but if you write $y + 1$, there will ariſe this Equation, $y^4 + y^3 - 4y - 6 = 0$.

Moreover, the Roots of Equations may be multiplied or divided by given Numbers; and after this Rate, the Terms of Equations be diminiſhed, and Fractions and Radical Quantities ſometimes be taken away.

As if the Equation were $y^3 - \frac{4}{3}y - \frac{146}{27} = 0$; in order to take away the Fractions, I ſuppoſe y to be $= \frac{1}{3}z$, and then by ſubſtituting $\frac{1}{3}z$ for y, there comes out this new Equation, $\frac{z^3}{27} - \frac{12z}{27} - \frac{146}{27} = 0$, and having rejected the common Denominator of the Terms, $z^3 - 12z - 146 = 0$, the Roots of which Equation are thrice greater than before. And again to diminiſh the Terms of this Equation, if you write $2v$ for z, there will come out $8v^3 - 24v - 146 = 0$, and dividing all by 8, you will have $v^3 - 3v - 18\frac{1}{4} = 0$; the Roots of which Equation are half of the Roots of the former. And here, if at laſt you find v make $2v = z$, $\frac{1}{3}z = y$, and $y + \frac{4}{3} = x$, and you will have x the Root of the Equation $x^3 - 4xx + 4x - 6 = 0$, as firſt propoſed.

And thus, in the Equation $x^3 - 2x + \sqrt{3} = 0$, to take away the Radical Quantity $\sqrt{3}$; for x I write $y\sqrt{3}$, and there comes out the Equation $3y^3\sqrt{3} - 2y\sqrt{3} + \sqrt{3} = 0$, which, dividing all the Terms by $\sqrt{3}$, becomes $3y^3 - 2y + 1 = 0$.

Again, the Roots of an Equation may be changed into their Reciprocals, and after this Way the Equation may be ſometimes reduced to a more commodious Form.

Thus, the laſt Equation $3y^3 - 2y + 1 = 0$, by writing $\frac{1}{z}$ for y, becomes $\frac{3}{z^3} - \frac{2}{z} + 1 = 0$, and all the Terms being multiplied by z^3, and the Order of the Terms changed, $z^3 - 2zz + 3 = 0$. The laſt Term but one of an Equation may alſo by this Method be taken away, provided the ſecond was taken away before, as you ſee done in the precedent Example. Or if you would take away the laſt but two, it may be done, provided you have taken away the third before. Moreover, the leaſt Root may be thus converted into the greateſt, and the greateſt into the leaſt, which may be of ſome Uſe in what follows. Thus, in the Equation $x^4 - x^3 - 19xx + 49x - 30 = 0$, whoſe Roots are 3, 2, 1, − 5, if you write $\frac{1}{y}$ for x, there will come out the

Dd

the Equation $\frac{1}{y^4} - \frac{1}{y^3} - \frac{19}{yy} + \frac{49}{y} - 30 = 0$, which, multiplying all the Terms by y^4, and dividing them by 30, the Signs being changed, becomes $y^4 - \frac{49}{30}y^3 + \frac{19}{30}y^2 + \frac{1}{30}y - \frac{1}{30} = 0$, the Roots whereof are $\frac{1}{3}, \frac{1}{2}, 1, -\frac{1}{5}$; the greatest of the Affirmative Roots 3 being now changed into the least $\frac{1}{3}$, and the least 1 being now made greatest, and the Negative Root -5, which of all was the most remote from 0, now coming nearest to it.

There are also other Transmutations of Equations, but which may all be performed after that Way of transmutating we have shewn, when we took away the third Term of the Equation.

From the Generation of Equations it is evident, that the known Quantity of the second *Term of the Equation, if its Sign be changed, is equal to the Aggregate of all the Roots under their proper Signs; and that of the* third *Term equal to the Aggregate of the Rectangles of each two of the Roots; that of the* fourth, *if its Sign be changed, is equal to the Aggregate of the Contents under each three of the Roots; that of the* fifth *is equal to the Aggregate of the Contents under each four, and so on* ad infinitum.

Let us assume $x = a$, $x = b$, $x = -c$, $x = d$, &c. or $x - a = 0$, $x - b = 0$, $x + c = 0$, $x - d = 0$, and by the continual Multiplication of these we may generate Equations, as above. Now, by multiplying $x - a$ by $x - b$ there will be produced the Equation $xx \begin{matrix}-a\\-b\end{matrix} x + ab = 0$; where the known Quantity of the second Term, if its Signs are changed, *viz.* $a + b$, is the Sum of the two Roots a and b, and the known Quantity of the third Term is the only Rectangle contained under both. Again, by multiplying this Equation by $x + c$, there will be produced the Cubick Equation

$$x^3 \begin{matrix}-a\\-b\\+c\end{matrix} xx \begin{matrix}+ab\\-ac\\-bc\end{matrix} x + abc = 0,$$

where the known Quantity of the second Term having its Signs changed, *viz.* $a + b - c$, is the Sum of the Roots a, and b, and $-c$; the known Quantity of the third Term $ab - ac - bc$ is the Sum of the Rectangles under each two of the Roots a and b, a and $-c$, b and $-c$; and the known Quantity of the fourth Term under its Sign changed, $-abc$, is the only Content generated by the continual Multiplication of all the Roots, a by b into $-c$. Moreover, by multiplying that Cubick Equation by $x - d$, there will be produced this Biquadratick one;

$$x^4 \begin{matrix}-a\\-b\\+c\\-d\end{matrix} x^3 \begin{matrix}+ab\\-ac\\-bc\\+ad\\+bd\\-cd\end{matrix} xx \begin{matrix}+abc\\-abd\\+bcd\\+acd\end{matrix} x - abcd = 0.$$

Where the known Quantity of the second Term under its Signs changed, *viz.* $a + b - c + d$, is the Sum of all the Roots; that of the third, $ab - ac - bc + ad + bd - cd$, is the Sum of the Rectangles under every two Roots; that of the fourth, its Signs being changed, $-abc + abd - bcd - acd$, is the Sum of the Contents under each Ternary; that of the fifth, $-abcd$, is the only Content under them all. And hence we first infer, that of any Equation that involves neither Surds nor Fractions all the rational Roots, and the Rectangles of any two of the Roots, or the Contents of any three or more of them, or some of the Integral Divisors of the last Term; and therefore when it is evident that no Divisor of the last Term is either a Root of the Equation, or Rectangle, or Content of two or more Roots, it will also be evident that there is no Root, or Rectangle, or Content of Roots, except what is Surd.

Let us suppose now, that the known Quantities of the Terms of any Equation under their Signs changed, are p, q, r, s, t, v, &c. *viz.* that of the second p, that of the third q, of the fourth r, of the fifth s, and so on. And the Signs of the Terms being rightly observed, make $p = a$, $pa + 2q = b$, $pb + qa + 3r = c$, $pc + qb + ra + 4s = d$, $pd + qc + rb + sa + 5t = e$, $pe + qd + rc + sb + ta + 6v = f$, and so on *in infinitum*, observing the Series of the Progression. And a will be the Sum of the Roots, b the Sum of the Squares of each of the Roots, c the Sum of the Cubes, d the Sum of the Biquadrates, e the Sum of the Quadrato-Cubes, f the Sum of the Cubo-Cubes, and so on. As in the Equation $x^4 - x^3 - 19xx + 49x - 30 = 0$, where the known Quantity of the second Term is -1, of the third -19, of the fourth $+49$, of the fifth -30; you must make $1 = p$,

$1 = p$, $19 = q$, $-49 = r$, $30 = s$. And there will thence arise $a = (p =)\ 1$, $b = (pa + 2q = 1 + 38 =)\ 39$, $c = (pb + qa + 3r = 39 + 19 - 147 =) - 89$, $d = (pc + qb + ra + 4s = -89 + 741 - 49 + 120 =)\ 723$. Wherefore the Sum of the Roots will be 1, the Sum of the Squares of the Roots 39, the Sum of the Cubes -89, and the Sum of the Biquadrates 723, *viz.* the Roots of that Equation are 1, 2, 3, and -5, and the Sum of these $1 + 2 + 3 - 5$ is 1; the Sum of the Squares, $1 + 4 + 9 + 25$, is 39; the Sum of the Cubes, $1 + 8 + 27 - 125$, is -89; and the Sum of the Biquadrates, $1 + 16 + 81 + 625$, is 723.

Of the LIMITS *of* EQUATIONS.

AND hence are collected the *Limits* between which the Roots of the Equation shall consist, if none of them is impossible. For when the Squares of all the Roots are Affirmative, the Sum of the Squares will be Affirmative, and therefore greater than the Square of the greatest Root. And by the same Argument, the Sum of the Biquadrates of all the Roots will be greater than the Biquadrate of the greatest Root, and the Sum of the Cubo-Cubes greater than the Cubo-Cube of the greatest Root.

Wherefore, if you desire the Limit which no Roots can pass, seek the Sum of the Squares of the Roots, and extract its Square Root. For this Root will be greater *than the greatest Root of the Equation.* But you will come nearer the greatest Root if you seek *the Sum of the Biquadrates, and extract its Biquadradick Root*; *and yet* nearer, *if you seek the Sum of the Cubo-Cubes, and extract its Cubo-Cubical Root*; *and so on* in infinitum.

Thus, in the precedent Equation, the Square Root of the Sum of the Squares of the Roots, or $\sqrt{39}$, is $6\frac{1}{2}$ nearly, and $6\frac{1}{2}$ is farther distant from 0 than any of the Roots 1, 2, 3, -5. But the Biquadratick Root of the Sum of the Biquadrates of the Roots, *viz.* $\sqrt[4]{723}$, which is $5\frac{1}{4}$ nearly, comes nearer to the Root that is most remote from nothing, *viz.* -5.

If, between the Sum of the Squares and the Sum of the Biquadrates of the Roots you find a mean Proportional, that will be a little greater than the Sum of the Cubes of the Roots connected under Affirmative Signs. And hence, the half Sum of this mean Proportional, and of the Sum of the Cubes collected under their proper Signs, found as before, will be greater than the Sum of the Cubes of the Affirmative Roots, and the half Difference greater than the Sum of the Cubes of the Negative Roots.

And consequently, the greatest of the Affirmative Roots will be less than the Cube Root of that half Sum, and the greatest of the Negative Roots less than the Cube Root of that Semi-difference.

Thus, in the precedent Equation, a mean Proportional between the Sum of the Squares of the Roots 39, and the Sum of the Biquadrates 723, is nearly 168. The Sum of the Cubes under their proper Signs was, as above, -89, the half Sum of this and 168 is $39\frac{1}{2}$, the Semi-difference $128\frac{1}{2}$. The Cube Root of the former, which is about $3\frac{1}{2}$, is greater than the greatest of the Affirmative Roots 3. The Cube Root of the latter, which is $5\frac{1}{11}$ nearly, is greater than the Negative Root -5. By which Example it may be seen how near you may come this Way to the Root, where there is only one Negative Root or one Affirmative one. *And yet you might come nearer still*, if you found a mean Proportional between the Sum of the Biquadrates of the Roots and the Sum of the Cubo-Cubes, and if from the Semi-Sum and Semi-Difference of this, and of the Sum of the Quadrato-Cube of the Roots, you extracted the Quadrato-Cubical Roots. For the Quadrato-Cubical Root of the Semi-Sum would be greater than the greatest Affirmative Root, and the Quadrato-Cubick Root of the Semi-Difference would be greater than the greatest Negative Root, but by a less Excess than before. Since therefore any Root, by augmenting or diminishing all the Roots, may be made the least, and then the least converted into the greatest, and afterwards all besides the greatest be made Negative, it is manifest how any Root desired may be found nearly.

If all the Roots except two are Negative, those two may be both together found this Way.

The Sum of the Cubes of those two Roots being found according to the precedent Method, as also the Sum of the Quadrato-Cubes, and the Sum of the Quadrato-Quadrato-Cubes of all the Roots: between the two latter Sums seek a mean Proportional, and that will be the Difference between the Sum of the Cubo-Cubes of the Affirmative Roots, and the Sum of the Cubo-Cubes of the Negative Roots nearly; and consequently,

quently, the half Sum of this mean Proportional, and of the Sum of the Cubo-Cubes of all the Roots, will be the Sum of the Cubo-Cubes of the Affirmative Roots, and the Semi-Difference will be the Sum of the Cubo-Cubes of the Negative Roots. Having therefore both the Sum of the Cubes, and alſo the Sum of the Cubo-Cubes of the two Affirmative Roots, from the double of the latter Sum ſubtract the Square of the former Sum, and the Square Root of the Remainder will be the Difference of the Cubes of the two Roots. And having both the Sum and Difference of the Cubes, you will have the Cubes themſelves. Extract their Cube Roots, and you will nearly have the two Affirmative Roots of the Equation. And if in higher Powers you ſhould do the like, you will have the Roots yet more nearly. But theſe Limitations, by reaſon of the Difficulty of the Calculus, are of leſs Uſe, and extend only to thoſe Equations that have no imaginary Roots. Wherefore I will now ſhew how to find the Limits another Way, which is more eaſy, and extends to all Equations.

Multiply every Term of the Equation by the Number of its Dimenſions, and divide the Product by the Root of the Equation. Then again multiply every one of the Terms that come out by a Number leſs by Unity than before, and divide the Product by the Root of the Equation. And ſo go on, by always multiplying by Numbers leſs by Unity than before, and dividing the Product by the Root, till at length all the Terms are deſtroyed, whoſe Signs are different from the Sign of the firſt or higheſt Term, except the laſt. And that Number will be greater than any Affirmative Root; which being writ in the Terms that come out for the Root, makes the Aggregate of thoſe which were each Time produced by Multiplication to have always the ſame Sign with the firſt or higheſt Term of the Equation.

As if there was propoſed the Equation $x^5 - 2x^4 - 10x^3 + 30xx + 63x - 120 = 0$. I firſt multiply this thus;

$$\overset{5}{x^5} - \overset{4}{2x^4} - \overset{3}{10x^3} + \overset{2}{30xx} + \overset{1}{63x} - \overset{0}{120}.$$

Then I again multiply the Terms that come out divided by x, thus;

$$\overset{4}{5x^4} - \overset{3}{8x^3} - \overset{2}{30xx} + \overset{1}{60x} + \overset{0}{63},$$

and dividing the Terms that come out again by x, there comes out $20x^3 - 24xx - 60x + 60$; which, to leſſen them, I divide by the greateſt common Diviſor 4, and you have $5x^3 - 6xx - 15x + 15$. Theſe being again multiplied by the Progreſſion 3, 2, 1, 0, and divided by x, become $15xx - 12x - 15$, and again divided by 3 become $5xx - 4x - 5$. And theſe multiplied by the Progreſſion 2, 1, 0, and divided by $2x$ become $5x - 2$. Now, ſince the higheſt Term of the Equation x^5 is Affirmative, I try what Number writ in theſe Products for x will cauſe them all to be Affirmative. And by trying 1, you have $5x - 2 = 3$ Affirmative; but $5xx - 4x - 5$, you have -4 Negative. Wherefore the Limit will be greater than 1. I therefore try ſome greater Number, as 2. And ſubſtituting 2 in each for x, they become.

$$\begin{array}{l} 5x - 2 = 8 \\ 5xx - 4x - 5 = 7 \\ 5x^3 - 6xx - 15x + 15 = 1 \\ 5x^4 - 8x^3 - 30xx + 60x + 63 = 79 \\ x^5 - 2x^4 - 10x^3 + 30xx + 63x - 120 = 46. \end{array}$$

Wherefore, ſince the Numbers that come out 8. 7. 1. 79. 46. are all Affirmative, the Number 2 will be greater than the greateſt of the Affirmative Roots. In like manner, if I would find the Limit of the Negative Roots, I try Negative Numbers. Or that which is all one, I change the Signs of every other Term, and try Affirmative ones. But having changed the Signs of every other Term, the Quantities in which the Numbers are to be ſubſtituted, will become

$$\begin{array}{l} 5x + 2 \\ 5xx + 4x - 5 \\ 5x^3 + 6xx - 15x - 15 \\ 5x^4 + 8x^3 - 30xx - 60x + 63 \\ x^5 + 2x^4 - 10x^3 - 30xx + 63x + 120 \end{array}$$

Out of theſe I chuſe ſome Quantity wherein the Negative Terms ſeem moſt prevalent; ſuppoſe $5x^4 + 8x^3 - 30xx - 60x + 63$, and here ſubſtituting for x the Numbers 1 and 2, there come out the Negative Numbers -14 and -33. Whence the Limit will be greater than -2. But ſubſtituting the Number 3, there comes out the Affirmative Number 234. And in like manner in the other Quantities, by ſubſtituting the Number 3 for x, there comes out always an Affirmative Number, which may be ſeen by bare Inſpection. Wherefore the Number -3 is greater than all the Negative Roots. And ſo you have the Limits 2 and -3, between which are all the Roots.

But

But the Invention of theſe Limits is of Uſe both in the Reduction of Equations by Rational Roots, and in the Extraction of Surd Roots out of them; leſt we might ſometimes go about to look for the Root beyond theſe Limits. Thus, in the laſt Equation, if I would find the Rational Roots, if perhaps it has any; from what we have ſaid, it is certain they can be no other than the Diviſors of the laſt Term of the Equation, which here is 120. Then trying all its Diviſors, if none of them writ in the Equation for x would make all the Terms vaniſh, it is certain that the Equation will admit of no Root but what is Surd. But there are many Diviſors of the laſt Term 120, *viz.* 1. — 1. 2. — 2. 3. — 3. 4. — 4. 5. — 5. 6. — 6. 8. — 8. 10. — 10. 12. — 12. 15. — 15. 20. — 20. 24. — 24. 30. — 30. 40. — 40. 60. — 60. 120. and — 120. To try all theſe Diviſors would be tedious. But it being known that the Roots are between 2 and — 3, we are freed from that Labour. For now there will be no need to try the Diviſors, unleſs thoſe only that are within theſe Limits, *viz.* the Diviſors 1, and — 1. and — 2. For if none of theſe are the Root, it is certain that the Equation has no Root but what is Surd.

The Reduction of EQUATIONS *by Surd Diviſors.*

Hitherto I have treated of the Reduction of Equations which admit of Rational Diviſors. But before we can conclude, that an Equation of four, ſix, or more Dimenſions is irreducible, we muſt firſt try whether or not it may be reduced by any Surd Diviſor; or, which is the ſame Thing, you muſt try whether the Equation can be ſo divided into two equal Parts, that you can extract the Root out of both. But that may be done by the following Method.

Diſpoſe the Equation according to the Dimenſions of ſome certain Letter, ſo that all its Terms jointly under their proper Signs, may be equal to nothing, and let the higheſt Term be adfected with an Affirmative Sign. Then, if the Equation be a Quadratick, (*for we may add this Caſe for the Analogy of the Matter*) *take from both Sides the loweſt Term, and add one fourth Part of the Square of the known Quantity of the middle Term.*

As if the Equation be $xx - ax - b = 0$, ſubtract from both Sides $-b$, and add $\frac{1}{4}aa$, and there will come out

xx —

$xx - ax + \frac{1}{4}aa = b + \frac{1}{4}aa$, *and extracting on both Sides the Root, you will have* $x - \frac{1}{2}a = \pm\sqrt{b + \frac{1}{4}aa}$, or $x = \frac{1}{2}a \pm \sqrt{b + \frac{1}{4}aa}$.

But if the Equation be of four Dimenſions, *ſuppoſe* $x^4 + px^3 + qxx + rx + s = 0$, where p, q, r, and s *denote the known Quantities of the Terms of the Equation adfected by their proper Signs, make*

$$q - \tfrac{1}{4}pp = \alpha. \quad r - \tfrac{1}{2}\alpha p = \beta.$$
$$s - \tfrac{1}{4}\alpha\alpha = \zeta.$$

Then put for n ſome common Integral Diviſor of the Terms β *and* 2ζ, *that is not a Square, and which ought to be odd, and divided by* 4 *to leave Unity, if either of the Terms p and r be odd. Put alſo for k ſome Diviſor of the Quantity* $\frac{\beta}{n}$ *if p be even; or half of the odd Diviſor, if p be odd; or nothing, if the Dividual β be nothing. Take the Quotient from* $\frac{1}{2}pk$, *and call the half of the Remainder l. Then for Q put* $\frac{\alpha + nkk}{2}$, *and try if n divides* $QQ - s$, *and the Root of the Quotient be rational and equal to l; which if it happen, add to each Part of the Equation* $nkkxx + 2nklx + nll$, *and extract the Rooot on both Sides, there coming out* $xx + \frac{1}{2}px + Q = \sqrt{n}$ *into* $\overline{kx + l}$.

For Example, let there be propoſed the Equation $x^4 + 12x - 17 = 0$, and becauſe p and q are both here wanting, and r is 12, and s is -17, having ſubſtituted theſe Numbers, you will have $\alpha = 0$, $\beta = 12$, and $\zeta = -17$, and the only common Diviſor of β and 2ζ, or 12 and -34, *viz.* 2, will be n. Moreover, $\frac{\beta}{n}$ is 6, and its Diviſors 1, 2, 3, and 6, are ſucceſſively to be tried for k, and -3, $-\frac{3}{2}$, -1, $-\frac{1}{2}$, for l reſpectively. But $\frac{\alpha + nkk}{2}$, that is, kk is equal to Q. Moreover, $\sqrt{\frac{QQ - s}{n}}$, that is, $\sqrt{\frac{QQ + 17}{2}}$ is $= l$.

E e Where

Where the even Numbers 2 and 6 are writ for k, Q becomes 4 and 36, and $QQ - s$ will be an odd Number, and consequently cannot be divided by n or 2. Wherefore those Numbers 2 and 6 are to be rejected. But when 1 and 3 are writ for k, Q becomes 1 and 9, and $QQ - s$ is 18 and 98, which Numbers may be divided by n, and the Roots of the Quotients extracted. For they are ± 3 and ± 7; whereof however only -3 agrees with l. I put therefore $k = 1$, $l = -3$, and $Q = 1$, and I add the Quantity $nkkxx + 2nklx + nll$, that is, $2xx - 12x + 18$ to each Part of the Equation, and there comes out $x^4 + 2xx + 1 = 2xx - 12x + 18$, and extracting on both Sides the Root $xx + 1 = x\sqrt{2} - 3\sqrt{2}$. But if you had rather avoid the Extraction of the Root, make $xx + \frac{1}{2}px + Q = \sqrt{n} \times \overline{kx + l}$, and you will find, as before, $xx + 1 = \pm\sqrt{2} \times \overline{x - 3}$. And if again you extract the Root of this Equation, there will come out $x = \pm\frac{1}{2}\sqrt{2} \pm \sqrt{\frac{-1}{2} \mp 3\sqrt{2}}$, that is, according to the Variations of the Signs, $x = -\frac{1}{2}\sqrt{2} + \sqrt{3\sqrt{2} - \frac{1}{2}}$, and $x = -\frac{1}{2}\sqrt{2} - \sqrt{3\sqrt{2} - \frac{1}{2}}$. Also $x = \frac{1}{2}\sqrt{2} + \sqrt{-3\sqrt{2} - \frac{1}{2}}$, and $x = \frac{1}{2}\sqrt{2} - \sqrt{-3\sqrt{2} - \frac{1}{2}}$. Which are four Roots of the Equation at first proposed, $x^4 + 12x - 17 = 0$. But the two last of them are impossible.

Let us now propose the Equation $x^4 - 6x^3 - 58xx - 114x - 11 = 0$, and by writing -6, -58, -114, and -11, for p, q, r, and s respectively, there will arise $-67 = \alpha$, $-315 = \beta$, and $-1133\frac{1}{4} = \zeta$. The only common Divisor of the Numbers β and 2ζ, or of -315 and $-\frac{4533}{2}$ is 3, and consequently will be here n, and the Divisors of $\frac{\beta}{n}$ or -105, are 3, 5, 7, 15, 21, 35, and 105, which are therefore to be tried for k. Wherefore, I try first 3, and the Quotient -35, which comes out by dividing $\frac{\beta}{n}$ by k, or -105 by 3, I subtract from $\frac{1}{2}pk$, or -3×3, and there remains 26; the half whereof, 13 ought to be l. But $\frac{\alpha + nkk}{2}$, or $\frac{-67 + 27}{2}$, that is, -20, will be Q, and $QQ - s$ will be 411, which may be divided by n, or 3, but the Root of the Quotient 137 cannot be extracted. Wherefore I reject 3, and try 5 for k. The Quotient that now comes out by dividing $\frac{\beta}{n}$ by k, or -105 by 5, is -21, and subtracting this from $\frac{1}{2}pk$, or -3×5, there remains 6, the half whereof 3 will be l. Also Q or $\frac{\alpha + nkk}{2}$, that is, $\frac{-67 + 75}{2}$, is the Number 4. And $QQ - s$, or $16 + 11$ may be divided by n; and the Root of the Quotient, which is 9, being extracted, *i. e.* 3 agrees with l. Wherefore I conclude, that l is $= 3$, $k = 5$, $Q = 4$, and $n = 3$; and if $nkkxx + 2nklx + nll$, that is, $75xx + 90x + 27$ be added to each Part of the Equation, the Root may be extracted on both Sides, and there will come out $xx + \frac{1}{2}px + Q = \sqrt{n} \times \overline{kx + l}$, or $xx - 3x + 4 = \pm\sqrt{3} \times \overline{5x + 3}$; and the Root being again extracted, $x = \frac{3 \pm 5\sqrt{3}}{2} \pm \sqrt{17 \pm \frac{21 \times \sqrt{3}}{2}}$.

Thus, if there was proposed this Equation $x^4 - 9x^3 + 15xx - 27x + 9 = 0$, by writing -9, $+15$, -27, and $+9$ for p, q, r, and s respectively, there will come out $-5\frac{1}{4} = \alpha$, $-50\frac{5}{8} = \beta$, and $2\frac{7}{64} = \zeta$. The common Divisors of β and 2ζ, or $-\frac{405}{8}$ and $\frac{135}{32}$ are 3, 5, 9, 15, 27, 45, and 135; but 9 is a Square Number, and 3, 15, 27, 135, divided by the Number 4, do not leave Unity, as, by reason of the odd Term p, they ought to do. These therefore being rejected, there remain only 5 and 45 to be tried for n. Let us put therefore, first $n = 5$, and the odd Divisors of $\frac{\beta}{n}$ or $-\frac{81}{8}$ being halved, *viz.* $\frac{1}{2}$, $\frac{3}{2}$, $\frac{9}{2}$, $\frac{27}{2}$, $\frac{81}{2}$, are to be tried for k. If k be made $\frac{1}{2}$, the Quotient $-\frac{81}{4}$, which comes out by dividing $\frac{\beta}{n}$ by k, subtracted from $\frac{1}{2}pk$, or

E e 2 $-\frac{9}{4}$

$-\frac{9}{4}$, leaves 18 for $2l$, and $\frac{\alpha + nkk}{2}$ or -2 is Q, and $QQ - s$, or -5 may be divided indeed by n or 5, but the Root of the Negative Quotient -1 is impoſſible, which yet ought to be 9. Wherefore I conclude k not to be $\frac{1}{2}$, and then I try if it be $\frac{3}{2}$. The Quotient which ariſes by dividing $\frac{\beta}{n}$ by k, or $-\frac{81}{8}$ by $\frac{3}{2}$, *viz.* the Quotient $-\frac{27}{4}$ I ſubtract from $\frac{1}{2}pk$ or $-\frac{27}{4}$, and there remains 0. Whence now l will be nothing. But $\frac{\alpha + nkk}{2}$ or 3 is equal to Q, and $QQ - s$ is nothing; whence again l, which is the Root of $QQ - s$, divided by n, is found to be nothing. Wherefore theſe Things thus agreeing, I conclude n to be $= 5$, $k = \frac{3}{2}$, $l = 0$, and $Q = 3$, and therefore by adding to each Part of the Equation propoſed the Terms $nkkxx + 2nlkx + nll$, that is, $\frac{45}{4}xx$, and by extracting on both Sides the Square Root, there comes out $xx + \frac{1}{2}px + Q = \sqrt{n} \times \overline{kx + l}$, that is, $xx - 4\frac{1}{2}x + 3 = \sqrt{5} \times \frac{3}{2}x$.

By the ſame Method Literal Equations are alſo reduced. As if there was $x^4 - 2ax^3 \begin{matrix} +2aa \\ -cc \end{matrix} xx - 2a^3 x + a^4 = 0$, by ſubſtituting $-2a$, $2aa - cc$, $-2a^3$, and $+a^4$ for p, q, r, and s reſpectively, you will obtain $aa - cc = \alpha$, $-acc - a^3 = \beta$, and $\frac{3}{4}a^4 + \frac{1}{2}aacc - \frac{1}{4}c^4 = \zeta$. The common Diviſor of the Quantities β and 2ζ is $aa + cc$, which therefore will be n; and $\frac{\beta}{n}$ or $-a$, has the Diviſors 1 and a. But becauſe n is of two Dimenſions, and $k\sqrt{n}$ ought to be of no more than one, therefore k will be of none, and conſequently cannot be a. Let therefore k be 1, and $\frac{\beta}{n}$ being divided by k, take the Quotient $-a$ from $\frac{1}{2}pk$ or $-a$ and there will remain nothing for l. Moreover, $\frac{\alpha + nkk}{2}$ or aa is Q, and $QQ - s$ or $a^4 - a^4$ is 0; and thence again there comes out nothing for l. Which ſhews the Quantities n, k, l, and Q to be rightly found; and adding to each Part of the Equation propoſed, the Terms $nkkxx + 2nklx + nll$, that is, $aaxx + ccxx$, the Root may be extracted on both Sides; and by that Extraction there will come out $xx + \frac{1}{2}px + Q = \sqrt{n} \times \overline{kx + l}$, that is, $xx - ax + aa = \pm x\sqrt{aa + cc}$. And the Root being again extracted, you will have $x = \frac{1}{2}a \pm \frac{1}{2}\sqrt{aa + cc} \pm \sqrt{\frac{1}{4}cc - \frac{1}{2}aa \pm \frac{1}{2}a\sqrt{aa + cc}}$.

Hitherto I have applied the Rule to the Extraction of *ſurd Roots*; the ſame may alſo be applied to the Extraction of *Rational Roots*, if for the Quantity n you make Uſe of Unity; and after that Manner we may examine, whether an Equation that wants Fracted or Surd Terms can admit of any Diviſor, either Rational or Surd, of two Dimenſions. As if the Equation $x^4 - x^3 - 5xx + 12x - 6 = 0$ was propoſed, by ſubſtituting -1, -5, $+12$, and -6 for p, q, r, and s reſpectively, you will find $-5\frac{1}{4} = \alpha$, $9\frac{3}{8} = \beta$, and putting $n = 1$. The Diviſors of the Quantity $\frac{\beta}{n}$, or $\frac{75}{8}$, are 1, 3, 5, 15, 25, 75; the Halves whereof (if p be odd) are to be tried for k. And if for k we try $\frac{5}{2}$, you will have $\frac{1}{2}pk - \frac{\beta}{nk} = -5$, and its half $-\frac{5}{2} = l$. Alſo $\frac{\alpha + nkk}{2} = \frac{1}{2} = Q$, and $\frac{QQ - s}{n} = 6\frac{1}{4}$, the Root whereof agrees with l.

I therefore conclude, that the Quantities n, k, l, Q, are rightly found; and having added to each Part of the Equation the Terms $nkkxx + 2nklx + nll$, that is, $6\frac{1}{4}xx - 12\frac{1}{2}x + 6\frac{1}{4}$, the Root may be extracted on both Sides; and by that Extraction there will come out $xx + \frac{1}{2}px + Q = \pm\sqrt{n} \times \overline{kx + l}$, that is, $xx - \frac{1}{2}x + \frac{1}{2} = \pm 1 \times \overline{2\frac{1}{2}x - 2\frac{1}{2}}$, or $xx - 3x + 3 = 0$, and $xx + 2x - 2 = 0$, and ſo by theſe two Quadratick Equations the Biquadratick one propoſed may be divided. But Rational Diviſors of this Sort may more expeditiouſly be found by another Method delivered above.

If at any Time there are many Diviſors of the Quantity $\frac{\beta}{n}$, ſo that it may be too difficult to try all of them for k, their Number may be ſoon diminiſhed, by ſeeking all the Diviſors of

of the Quantity, $\alpha s - \frac{1}{4}rr$. For the Quantity Q ought to be equal to fome of thefe, or to the half of fome odd one. Thus, in the laft Example, $\alpha s - \frac{1}{4}rr$ is $-\frac{9}{2}$, fome one of whofe Divifors, 1, 3, 9, or of them halved $\frac{1}{2}$, $\frac{3}{2}$, $\frac{9}{2}$, ought to be Q. Wherefore, by trying fingly the halved Divifors of the Quantity $\frac{\beta}{n}$, *viz.* $\frac{1}{2}$, $\frac{3}{2}$, $\frac{5}{2}$, $\frac{15}{2}$, $\frac{25}{2}$, and $\frac{75}{2}$ for k, I reject all that do not make $\frac{1}{2}\alpha + \frac{1}{2}nkk$, or $-\frac{21}{8} + \frac{1}{2}kk$; that is, Q to be one of the Numbers 1, 3, 9, $\frac{1}{2}$, $\frac{3}{2}$, $\frac{9}{2}$. But by writing $\frac{1}{2}$, $\frac{3}{2}$, $\frac{5}{2}$, $\frac{15}{2}$, &c. for k, there come out refpectively $-\frac{5}{2}$, $-\frac{3}{2}$, $+\frac{1}{2}$, $+\frac{51}{2}$, &c. for Q; out of which only $-\frac{3}{2}$ and $\frac{1}{2}$ are found among the aforefaid Numbers 1, 3, 9, $\frac{1}{2}$, $\frac{3}{2}$, $\frac{9}{2}$, and confequently the reft being rejected, either k will be $= \frac{1}{2}$ and $Q = -\frac{3}{2}$, or $k = \frac{5}{2}$ and $Q = \frac{1}{2}$. Which two Cafes let be examined. And fo much of Equations of *four Dimenfions*.

If an Equation of fix Dimenfions is to be reduced, let it be $x^6 + px^5 + qx^4 + rx^3 + sxx + tx + v = 0$, and make

$$q - \tfrac{1}{4}pp = \alpha. \quad r - \tfrac{1}{2}p\alpha = \beta. \quad s - \tfrac{1}{2}p\beta = \gamma.$$
$$\gamma - \tfrac{1}{4}\alpha\alpha = \zeta. \quad t - \tfrac{1}{2}\alpha\beta = \eta. \quad v - \tfrac{1}{4}\beta\beta = \theta.$$
$$\zeta\theta - \tfrac{1}{4}\eta\eta = \lambda.$$

Then for n take of the Terms 2ζ, η, 2θ, fome common Integer Divifor, that is not a Square, and that likewife is not divifible by a fquare Number, and which alfo divided by the Number 4, fhall leave Unity; provided any one of the Terms p, r, t be odd. For k take fome Integer Divifor of the Quantity $\frac{\lambda}{2nn}$ if p be even, or the half of an odd Divifor if p be odd, or 0 if λ be 0. For Q take the Quantity $\frac{1}{2}\alpha + \frac{1}{2}nkk$. For l fome Divifor of the Quantity $\frac{Qr - QQp - t}{n}$ if Q be an Integer; or the half of an odd Divifor if Q be a Fraction that has for its Denominator the Number 2; or 0, if that Dividual $\frac{Qr - QQp - t}{n}$ be nothing. And for R the Quantity $\frac{1}{2}r - \frac{1}{2}Qp + nkl$. Then try if $RR - v$ can be divided by n, and the Root of the Quotient extracted; and befides, if that Root be equal as well to the Quantity $\frac{QR - \frac{1}{2}t}{nl}$ as to the Quantity $\frac{QQ + pR - nll - s}{2nk}$. If all thefe happen, call that Root m; and in room of the Equation propofed, write this, $x^3 + \frac{1}{2}pxx + Qx + r = \pm\sqrt{n} \times \overline{kxx + lx + m}$. For this Equation, by fquaring its Parts, and taking from both Sides the Terms on the Right-Hand, will produce the Equation propofed. Now if all thefe Things do not happen in the Cafe propofed, the Reduction will be impoffible, provided it appears beforehand that the Equation cannot be reduced by a rational Divifor.

For Example, let there be propofed the Equation

$$x^6 - 2ax^5 + 2bbx^4 + 2abbx^3 \begin{matrix} -2aabb \\ +2a^3b \\ -4ab^3 \end{matrix}\, xx \begin{matrix} +3aab^4 \\ -a^4bb \end{matrix} = 0,$$

and by writing $-2a$, $+2bb$, $+2abb$, $-2aabb + 2a^3b - 4ab^3$, 0, and $3aab^4 - a^4bb$ for p, q, r, s, t, and v refpectively, there will come out $2bb - aa = \alpha$. $4abb - a^3 = \beta$. $2a^3b + 2aabb - 4ab^3 - a^4 = \gamma$. $-b^4 + 2a^3b + 3aabb - 4ab^3 - \frac{5}{4}a^4 = \zeta$. $-\frac{1}{2}a^5 - 3a^3bb - 4ab^4 = \eta$, and $-aab^4 + a^4bb - \frac{1}{4}a^6 = \theta$. And the common Divifor of the Terms 2ζ, η, and 2θ, is $aa - 2bb$, or $2bb - aa$, according as aa or $2bb$ is the greater. But let aa be greater than $2bb$, and $aa - 2bb$ will be n. For n muft always be Affirmative. Moreover, $\frac{\zeta}{n}$ is $-\frac{5}{4}aa + 2ab + \frac{1}{2}bb$, $\frac{\eta}{n}$ is $-\frac{1}{2}a^3 + 2abb$ and $\frac{\theta}{n}$ is $-\frac{1}{4}a^4 + \frac{1}{2}aabb$, and confequently $\frac{\zeta}{2n} \times \frac{\theta}{n} - \frac{\eta\eta}{8nn}$ or $\frac{\lambda}{2nn}$, is $\frac{1}{8}a^6 - \frac{1}{4}a^5b - \frac{1}{8}a^4bb + \frac{1}{2}a^3b^3 - \frac{3}{8}aab^4$, the Divifors whereof are 1, a, aa; but becaufe $\sqrt{n} \times k$ cannot be of more than one Dimenfion, and the $\sqrt{n}$ is of one, therefore k will be of none; and confequently can only be a Number. Wherefore, rejecting a and aa, there remains only 1 for k. Befides, $\frac{1}{2}\alpha + \frac{1}{2}nkk$ gives 0 for Q, and $\frac{Qr - QQp - t}{n}$ is alfo nothing; and confequently l, which ought to be its Divifor, will be nothing. Laftly, $\frac{1}{2}r - \frac{1}{2}pQ + nkl$ gives abb for R. And $RR - v$ is $-2aab^4 + a^4bb$, which may be divided by n or $aa - 2bb$, and the Root of the Quotient $aabb$

$aabb$ be extracted, and that Root taken Negatively, *viz.* $-ab$, is not unequal to the indefinite Quantity $\frac{QR - \frac{1}{2}pt}{nl}$, or $\frac{0}{0}$, but equal to the definite Quantity $\frac{QQ + pR - nll - s}{2nk}$. Wherefore that Root $-ab$ will be m, and in the room of the Equation proposed, there may be writ $x^3 - \frac{1}{2}pxx + Qx + R = \sqrt{n} \times \overline{kxx + lx + m}$, that is, $x^3 - axx + abb = \sqrt{aa - 2bb} \times \overline{xx - ab}$. The Truth of which Conclusion you may prove by squaring the Parts of the Equation found, and taking away the Terms on the Right Hand from both Sides. For from that Operation will be produced the Equation $x^6 - 2ax^5 + 2bbx^4 + 2abbx^3 - 2aabbxx + 2a^3bxx - 4ab^3xx + 3aab^4 - a^4bb = 0$, which was proposed to be reduced.

If the Equation is of eight *Dimensions, let it be* $x^8 + px^7 + qx^6 + rx^5 + sx^4 + tx^3 + vxx + wx + z = 0$, and make $q - \frac{1}{4}pp = \alpha$. $r - \frac{1}{2}p\alpha = \beta$. $s - \frac{1}{2}p\beta - \frac{1}{4}\alpha\alpha = \gamma$. $t - \frac{1}{2}p\gamma - \frac{1}{2}\alpha\beta = \delta$. $v - \frac{1}{2}\alpha\gamma - \frac{1}{4}\beta\beta = \varepsilon$. $w - \frac{1}{2}\beta\gamma = \zeta$, and $z - \frac{1}{4}\gamma\gamma = \eta$. And seek of the Terms 2δ, 2ε, 2ζ, 8η, a common Divisor that shall be an Integer, and neither a Square Number, nor divisible by a Square Number, and which also divided by 4 shall leave Unity, provided any of the alternate Terms, p, r, t, w be odd. If there be no such common Divisor, it is certain, that the Equation cannot be reduced by the Extraction of a Quadratick Surd Root, and if it cannot be so reduced, there will scarce be found a common Divisor of all those four Quantities. The Operation therefore hitherto is a Sort of an Examination, whether the Equation be reducible or not; and consequently, since that Sort of Reductions are seldom possible, it will most commonly end the Work.

And, by a like Reason, if the Equation be of ten, twelve, or more Dimensions, the Impossibility of its Reduction may be known.

As if it be $x^{10} + px^9 + qx^8 + rx^7 + sx^5 + tx^5 + vx^4 + ax^3 + bx^2 + cx + d = 0$, you must make $q - \frac{1}{4}pp = \alpha$, $r - \frac{1}{2}p\alpha = \beta$, $s - \frac{1}{2}p\beta - \frac{1}{4}\alpha\alpha = \gamma$, $t - \frac{1}{2}p\gamma - \frac{1}{2}\alpha\beta = \delta$, $v - \frac{1}{2}p\delta - \frac{1}{2}\alpha\gamma - \frac{1}{4}\beta\beta = \varepsilon$, $a - \frac{1}{2}\alpha\delta - \frac{1}{2}\beta\gamma = \zeta$, $b - \frac{1}{2}\beta\delta - \frac{1}{4}\gamma\gamma = \eta$, $c - \frac{1}{2}\gamma\delta = \theta$, $d - \frac{1}{4}\delta\delta = \kappa$, and seek such a common Divisor to the five Terms, 2ε, 2ζ, 8η, 4θ, 8κ, as is an Integer, and not a Square, and which shall also leave 1 when divided by 4, if any one of the Terms p, r, t, a, c be odd.

So if there be an Equation of *twelve* Dimensions, as $x^{12} + px^{11} + qx^{10} + rx^9 + sx^8 + tx^7 + vx^6 + ax^5 + bx^4 + cx^3 + dx^2 + ex + f = 0$, make $q - \frac{1}{4}pp = \alpha$, $r - \frac{1}{2}p\alpha = \beta$, $s - \frac{1}{2}p\beta - \frac{1}{4}\alpha\alpha = \gamma$, $t - \frac{1}{2}p\gamma - \frac{1}{2}\alpha\beta = \delta$, $v - \frac{1}{2}p\delta - \frac{1}{2}\alpha\gamma - \frac{1}{4}\beta\beta = \varepsilon$, $a - \frac{1}{2}p\varepsilon - \frac{1}{2}\alpha\delta - \frac{1}{2}\beta\gamma = \zeta$, $b - \frac{1}{2}\alpha\varepsilon - \frac{1}{2}\beta\delta - \frac{1}{4}\gamma\gamma = \eta$, $c - \frac{1}{2}\beta\varepsilon - \frac{1}{2}\gamma\delta = \theta$, $d - \frac{1}{2}\gamma\varepsilon - \frac{1}{4}\delta\delta = \kappa$, $e - \frac{1}{2}\delta\varepsilon = \lambda$, $f - \frac{1}{4}\varepsilon\varepsilon = \mu$, and you must seek a common Integer Divisor of the six Terms 2ζ, 8η, 4θ, 8κ, 4λ, 8μ, that is not a Square, but being divided by 4 shall leave Unity, provided any one of the Terms p, r, t, a, c, e be odd.

And thus you may go on *ad infinitum*, and the proposed Equation when it has no common Divisor, will be alway irreduceable by the Extraction of the surd quadratick Root. But if at any Time such a Divisor n being found, there are Hopes of a future Reduction, it may be tried by following the Steps of the Operation we shewed in an Equation of *eight* Dimensions.

Seek a Square Number, to which after it is multiplied by n, the last Term z of the Equation being added under its proper Sign, shall make a Square Number. But that may be expeditiously performed if you add to z, when n is an even Number, or to $4z$ when it is odd, these Quantities successively n, $3n$, $5n$, $7n$, $9n$, $11n$, and so on till the Sum becomes equal to some Number in the Table of Square Numbers, which I suppose to be ready at Hand. And if no such Square Number occurs before the Square Root of that Sum, augmented by the Square Root of the Excess of that Sum above the last Term of the Equation, is four times greater than the greatest of the Terms of the proposed Equation p, q, r, s, t, v, &c. there will be no Occasion to try any farther. For then the Equation cannot be reduced. But if such a Square Number does accordingly occur, let its Root be S, if n is even, or 2 S if n be odd; and call $\sqrt{\frac{SS - z}{n}} = h$. But s and h ought to be Integers if n is even, but if n is odd, they may be Fractions that have 2 for their Denominator. And if one is a Fraction, the other ought to be so too. Which also is to be observed of the Numbers R and m, Q and l, p and k hereafter to be found. And all the Numbers

Ff S and

S and h, that can be found within the prefcribed Limit, muft be collected in a Catalogue.

Afterwards, for k all the Numbers are to be fucceffively tried, which do not make $nk \pm \frac{1}{2}p$ four times greater than the greateft Term of the Equation, and you muft in all Cafes put $\frac{nkk + \alpha}{2} = Q$. Then you are to try fucceffively for l all the Numbers that do not make $nl \pm Q$ four times greater than the greateft Term of the Equation, and in every Trial put $\frac{-npkk + 2\beta}{4} + nkl = R$. Laftly, for m you muft try fucceffively all the Numbers which do not make $nm + R$ four times greater than the greateft of the Terms of the Equation, and you muft fee whether in any Cafe if you make $s - QQ - pR + nll = 2H$, and $H + nkm = S$, let S be fome of the Numbers which were before brought into the Catalogue for S; and befides, if the other Number anfwering to that S, which being fet down for h in the fame Catalogue, will be equal to thefe three, $\frac{2RS - w}{2nm}$, $\frac{2QS + RR - v - nmm}{2nl}$, and $\frac{pS + 2QR - t - 2nlm}{2nk}$. If all thefe Things fhall happen in any Cafe, inftead of the Equation propofed, you muft write this $x^4 + \frac{1}{2}px^3 + Qxx + Rx + S = \sqrt{n} \times \overline{kx^3 + lxx + mx + h}$.

For Example, Let there be propofed the Equation $x^8 + 4x^7 - x^6 - 10x^5 + 5x^4 - 5x^3 - 10xx - 10x - 5 = 0$, and you will have $q - \frac{1}{4}pp = -1 - 4 = -5 = \alpha$. $r - \frac{1}{2}p\alpha = -10 + 10 = 0 = \beta$. $s - \frac{1}{2}p\beta - \frac{1}{4}\alpha\alpha = 5 - \frac{25}{4} = -\frac{5}{4} = \gamma$. $t - \frac{1}{2}p\gamma - \frac{1}{2}\alpha\beta = -5 + \frac{5}{2} = -\frac{5}{2} = \delta$. $v - \frac{1}{2}\alpha\gamma - \frac{1}{4}\beta\beta = -10 - \frac{25}{8} = -\frac{105}{8}$. $w - \frac{1}{4}\beta\gamma = -10 = \zeta$. $z - \frac{1}{4}\gamma\gamma = -5 - \frac{25}{64} = -\frac{345}{64} = \eta$. Therefore 2δ, 2ϵ, 2ζ, 8η refpectively are -5, $-\frac{105}{4}$, -20, and $-\frac{345}{8}$, and their common Divifor 5, which divided by 4, leaves 1, as it ought, becaufe the Term s is odd. Since therefore the common Divifor n, or 5, is found, which gives hope to a future Reduction, and becaufe it is odd, to $4z$, or -20, I fucceffively add n, $3n$, $5n$, $7n$, $9n$, &c. or 5, 15, 25, 35, 45, &c. and there arifes -15, 0, 25, 60, 105, 160, 225, 300, 385, 480, 585, 700, 825, 960, 1105, 1260, 1425, 1600. Of which only 0, 25, 225, and 1600 are Squares. Wherefore the Halves of thefe Roots 0, $\frac{5}{2}$, $\frac{15}{2}$, 20, are to be collected in a Table for the Values of S, and the Values of $\sqrt{\frac{SS - z}{n}}$, that is, 1, $\frac{3}{2}$, $\frac{7}{2}$, 9, refpectively fo: h. But becaufe $S + nh$, if 20 be taken for S and 9 for h, becomes 65, a Number greater than four times the greateft Term of the Equation; therefore I reject 20 and 9, and write only the reft in the Table as follows:

h	1	$\frac{3}{2}$	$\frac{7}{2}$
S	0	$\frac{5}{2}$	$\frac{15}{2}$

Then I try for k all the Numbers which do not make $\frac{1}{2}p \pm nk$, or $2 \pm 5k$, greater than 40, (four times the greateft Term of the Equation) that is, the Numbers -8, -7, -6, -5, -4, -3, -2, -1, 0, 1, 2, 3, 4, 5, 6, 7, putting $\frac{nkk + \alpha}{2}$, or $\frac{5kk - 5}{2}$, that is, the Numbers $\frac{315}{2}$, 120, $\frac{175}{2}$, 60, $\frac{75}{2}$, 20, $\frac{15}{2}$, 0, $-\frac{5}{2}$, 0, $\frac{15}{2}$, 20, $\frac{75}{2}$, 60, $\frac{175}{2}$, 120, refpectively for Q. But even fince $Q \pm nl$, and much more Q, ought not to be greater than 40, I perceive I am to reject $\frac{315}{2}$, 120, $\frac{175}{2}$, and 60, and their Correfpondents -8, -7, -6, -5, 5, 6, 7, and confequently that only -4, -3, -2, -1, 0, 1, 2, 3, 4, muft refpectively be tried for k, and $\frac{75}{2}$, 20, $\frac{15}{2}$, 0, $-\frac{5}{2}$, 0, $\frac{15}{2}$, 20, $\frac{75}{2}$, refpectively for Q. Let us therefore try -1 for k, and 0 for Q, and in this Cafe for l there will be fucceffively to be tried all the Numbers which do not make $Q \pm nl$ greater than 40, that is, all the Numbers between 10 and -10; and for R you are refpectively to try the Numbers $\frac{2\beta - npkk}{4} + nkl$, or $-5 - 5l$, that is, -55, -50, -45, -40, -35, -30, -25, -20, -15, -10, -5, 0, 5, 10, 15, 20, 25, 35, 40, 45, the three former of which and the laft, becaufe they are greater than 40, may be neglected. Let us try therefore -2 for l, and 5 for R, and in this Cafe for m there will be befides to be tried all the Numbers which do not make $R \pm nm$, or $5 \pm 5m$, greater than 40, that is, all the Numbers between 7 and -9, and fee whether or not by putting $s - QQ - pR + nll$, that is $5 - 20 + 20$ or $5 = 2H$, it may be $H + nkm$ or $\frac{5}{2} - 5m = S$; that is, if any of thefe

Ff 2

these Numbers $\frac{-65}{2}$, $\frac{-55}{2}$, $\frac{-45}{2}$, $\frac{-35}{2}$, $\frac{-25}{2}$, $\frac{-15}{2}$, $\frac{-5}{2}$, $\frac{5}{2}$, $\frac{15}{2}$, $\frac{25}{2}$, $\frac{35}{2}$, $\frac{45}{2}$, $\frac{55}{2}$, $\frac{65}{2}$, $\frac{75}{2}$, $\frac{85}{2}$, is equal to any of the Numbers 0, $\pm\frac{5}{2}$, $\pm\frac{15}{2}$, which were first brought into the Catalogue for S. And we meet with four of these $-\frac{15}{2}$, $-\frac{5}{2}$, $\frac{5}{2}$, $\frac{15}{2}$, to which answer $\pm\frac{7}{2}$, $\pm\frac{3}{2}$, $\pm\frac{3}{2}$, $\pm\frac{7}{2}$, written for b in the same Table, as also 2, 1, 0, -1 substituted for m. But let us try $-\frac{5}{2}$ for S, 1 for m, and $\pm\frac{3}{2}$ for b, and you will have $\frac{2RS-w}{2nm} = \frac{-25+10}{10} = -\frac{3}{2}$, and $\frac{2QS+RR-v-nmm}{2nl} = \frac{25+10-5}{-20} = -\frac{3}{2}$, and $\frac{pS+2QR-t-2nlm}{2nk} = \frac{-10+5+20}{-10} = -\frac{3}{2}$. Wherefore, since there comes out in all Cases $-\frac{3}{2}$, or b, I conclude all the Numbers to be rightly found, and consequently that in room of the Equation proposed, you must write $x^4 + \frac{1}{2}px^3 + Qxx + Rx + S = \sqrt{n} \times \overline{kx^3 + lxx + mx + b}$, that is, $x^4 + 2x^3 + 5x - 2\frac{1}{2} = \sqrt{5} \times \overline{-x^3 - 2xx + x - 1\frac{1}{2}}$. For by squaring the Parts of this, there will be produced that Equation of eight Dimensions, which was at first proposed.

But if by trying all the Cases of the Numbers, all the aforesaid Values of b had not in any Case consented, it would be an Argument that the Equation could not be reduced by the Extraction of the Surd Quadratick Root.

But something might be here remarked for the abbreviating of the Work, which however I pass over for the sake of Brevity, seeing the Use of so great Reductions is very little, and I was willing to shew rather the Possibility of the Thing, than a Practice that was commodious. These therefore are the Reductions of Equations by the Extraction of the *Surd Quadratick Root.*

I might now joyn the Reductions of Equations by the *Extraction of the Surd Cubick Root*, but these, as being seldom of Use, for Brevity I pass by.

Yet there are some Reductions of *Cubick Equations* commonly known, which, if I should wholly pass over, the Reader might perhaps think us deficient. Let there be proposed the

the Cubick Equation $x^3 * + qx + r = 0$, the second Term whereof is wanting. For that every Cubick Equation may be reduced to this Form, is evident from what we have said above. Let x be supposed $= a + b$. Then will be $a^3 + 3aab + 3abb + b^3$ (that is x^3) $+ qx + r = 0$. Let $3aab + 3abb$ (that is, $3abx$) $+ qx$ be $= 0$, and then will $a^3 + b^3 + r$ be $= 0$. By the former Equation b is $= -\frac{q}{3a}$, and cubically $b^3 = -\frac{q^3}{27a^3}$. Therefore, by the latter, $a^3 - \frac{q^3}{27a^3} + r$ is $= 0$, or $a^6 + ra^3 = \frac{q^3}{27}$, and by the Extraction of the adfected Quadratick Root, $a^3 = -\frac{1}{2}r \pm \sqrt{\frac{1}{4}rr + \frac{q^3}{27}}$. Extract the Cubick Root and you will have a. And above, you had $-\frac{q}{3a} = b$, and $a + b = x$. Therefore $a - \frac{q}{3a}$ is the Root of the Equation proposed.

For Example, let there be proposed the Equation $y^3 - 6yy + 6y + 12 = 0$. To take away the second Term of this Equation, make $x + 2 = y$, and there will arise $x^3 * - 6x + 8 = 0$. Where q is $= -6$, $r = 8$, $\frac{1}{4}rr = 16$, $\frac{q^3}{27} = -8$, $a^3 = -4 \pm \sqrt{8}$, $a - \frac{q}{3a} = x$, and $x + 2 = y$, that is, $2 + \sqrt[3]{-4 \pm \sqrt{8}} + \frac{2}{\sqrt[3]{-4 \pm \sqrt{8}}} = y$.

And after this Way the Roots of all Cubical Equations may be extracted wherein q is Affirmative; or also wherein q is Negative, and $\frac{q^3}{27}$ not greater than $\frac{1}{4}rr$, that is, *when two of the Roots of the Equation are impossible.* But where q is Negative, and $\frac{q^3}{27}$ at the same time greater than $\frac{1}{4}rr$, $\sqrt{\frac{1}{4}rr - \frac{q^3}{27}}$ becomes an impossible Quantity; and so

ſo the Root of the Equation x or y will, in this Caſe, be impoſſible, *viz.* in this Caſe *there are three poſſible Roots*, which all of them are alike with reſpect to the Terms of the Equations q and r, and are indifferently denoted by the Letters x and y, and conſequently all of them may be extracted by the ſame Method, and expreſſed the ſame Way as any one is extracted or expreſſed; *but it is impoſſible to expreſs all three by the Law aforeſaid.* The Quantity $a - \frac{q}{3a}$, whereby x is denoted, cannot be manifold, and for that Reaſon the Suppoſition that x, in this Caſe wherein it is threefold, may be equal to the Binomial $a - \frac{q}{3a}$, or $a + b$, the Cubes of whoſe Terms $a^3 + b^3$ may together be $= r$, and the triple Rectangle $3ab$ be $= q$, is plainly impoſſible; and it is no Wonder that from an impoſſible Hypotheſis, an impoſſible Concluſion ſhould follow.

There is, moreover, another Way of expreſſing theſe Roots, viz. from $a^3 + b^3 + r$, that is, from nothing take $a^3 + r$, or $\frac{1}{2} r \pm \sqrt{\frac{1}{4} rr + \frac{q^3}{27}}$, and there will remain $b^3 = -\frac{1}{2} r \mp \sqrt{\frac{1}{4} rr + \frac{q^3}{27}}$. Therefore a is $=$

$\sqrt[3]{-\frac{1}{2} r + \sqrt{\frac{1}{4} rr + \frac{q^3}{27}}}$, and $b =$

$\sqrt[3]{-\frac{1}{2} r - \sqrt{\frac{1}{4} rr + \frac{q^3}{27}}}$; or $a =$

$\sqrt[3]{-\frac{1}{2} r - \sqrt{\frac{1}{4} rr + \frac{q^3}{27}}}$, and $b =$

$\sqrt[3]{-\frac{1}{2} r + \sqrt{\frac{1}{4} rr + \frac{q^3}{27}}}$, and conſequently the Sum of theſe $\sqrt[3]{-\frac{1}{2} r + \sqrt{\frac{1}{4} rr + \frac{q^3}{27}}} +$

$\sqrt[3]{-\frac{1}{2} r - \sqrt{\frac{1}{4} rr + \frac{q^3}{27}}}$ will be $= x$.

More-

Moreover, the Roots of Biquadratick Equations may be extracted and expreſſed by means of Cubick ones.

But firſt you muſt take away the ſecond Term of the Equation. Let the Equation that then reſults be $x^4 + qxx + rx + s = 0$. Suppoſe this to be generated by the Multiplication of theſe two $xx + ex + f = 0$, and $xx - ex + g = 0$, that is, to be the ſame with this $x^4 * \begin{matrix} +f \\ +g \\ -ee \end{matrix} xx \begin{matrix} +eg \\ -ef \end{matrix} x + fg = 0$, and comparing the Terms you will have $f + g - ee = q$, $eg - ef = r$, and $fg = s$. Wherefore $q + ee = f + g$, $\frac{r}{e} = g - f$, $\frac{q + ee + \frac{r}{e}}{2} = g$, $\frac{q + ee - \frac{r}{e}}{2} = f$, $\frac{qq + 2eeq + e^4 - \frac{rr}{ee}}{4} (= fg) = s$, and by Reduction $e^6 + 2qe^4 \begin{matrix} +qq \\ -4s \end{matrix} ee - rr = 0$. For ee write y, and you will have $y^3 + 2qyy \begin{matrix} +qq \\ -4s \end{matrix} y - rr = 0$, a Cubick Equation, whoſe ſecond Term may be taken away, and then the Root extracted either by the precedent Rule or otherwiſe. Then that Root being had, you muſt go back again, by putting $\sqrt{y} = e$, $\frac{q + ee - \frac{r}{e}}{2} = f$, $\frac{q + ee + \frac{r}{e}}{2} = g$, and the two Equations $xx + ex + f = 0$, and $xx - ex + g = 0$, their Roots being extracted, will give the four Roots of the Biquadratick Equation $x^4 + qxx + rx + s = 0$, *viz.* $x = -\frac{1}{2} e \pm \sqrt{\frac{1}{4} ee - f}$, and $x = \frac{1}{2} e \pm \sqrt{\frac{1}{4} ee - g}$. Where note, that if the four Roots of the Biquadratick Equation are poſſible, the three Roots of the Cubick Equation $y^3 + 2qyy \begin{matrix} +qq \\ -4s \end{matrix} y - rr = 0$ will be poſſible alſo, and conſequently cannot be extracted by the precedent Rule. *And thus, if the affected Roots of an Equation of five or more Dimenſions are converted into Roots that are not affected, the middle Terms of the Equation being ſome way or other taken away, that Expreſſion*

preſſion of the Roots will be always impoſſible, where more than one Root in an Equation of odd Dimenſions are poſſible, or more than two in an Equation of even Dimenſions, which cannot be reduced by the Extraction of the Surd Quadratick Root, by the Method laid down above.

Monſieur *Des Cartes* taught how to reduce a Biquadratick Equation by the Rules laſt delivered. *E. g.* Let there be propoſed the Equation reduced above, $x^4 - x^3 - 5xx + 12x - 6 = 0$. Take away the ſecond Term, by writing $v + \frac{1}{4}$ for x, and there will ariſe $v^4 - \frac{43}{8}vv + \frac{75}{8}v - \frac{851}{256} = 0$. To take away the Fractions, write $\frac{1}{4}z$ for v, and there will ariſe $z^4 - 86zz + 600z - 851 = 0$. Here is $-86 = q$, $600 = r$, and $-851 = s$, and conſequently $y^3 + 2qyy \begin{matrix} +qq \\ -4s \end{matrix} y - rr = 0$, ſubſtituting what is equivalent, will become $y^3 - 172yy + 10800y - 360000 = 0$. Where trying all the Diviſors of the laſt Term 1, −1, 2, −2, 3, −3, 4, −4, 5, −5, and ſo onwards to 100, you will find at length $y = 100$. Which yet may be found far more expeditiouſly by our Method above delivered. Then having got y, its Root 10 will be e, and $\dfrac{q + ee - \frac{r}{e}}{2}$, that is, $\dfrac{-86 + 100 - 60}{2}$ or -23 will be f, and $\dfrac{q + ee + \frac{r}{e}}{2}$ or 37 will be g, and conſequently the Equations $xx + ex + f = 0$, and $xx - ex + g = 0$, writing z for x, and ſubſtituting equivalent Quantities, will become $zz + 10z - 23 = 0$, and $zz - 10z + 37 = 0$. Reſtore v in the room of $\frac{1}{4}z$, and there will ariſe $vv + 2\frac{1}{2}v - \frac{23}{16} = 0$, and $vv - 2\frac{1}{2}v + \frac{37}{16} = 0$. Reſtore, moreover, $x - \frac{1}{4}$ for v, and there will come out $xx + 2x - 2 = 0$, and $xx - 3x + 3 = 0$, two Equations, the four Roots whereof $x = -1 \pm \sqrt{3}$, and $x = 1\frac{1}{2} \pm \sqrt{-\frac{3}{4}}$, are the ſame with the four Roots of the Biquadratick Equation propoſed at the Beginning, $x^4 - x^3 - 5xx + 12x - 6 = 0$. But theſe might have been more eaſily found by the Method of finding Diviſors, explained before.

A P-

A P P E N D I X.

THE
LINEAR CONSTRUCTION
OF
E Q U A T I O N S.

HITHERTO I have ſhewn the Properties, Traſmutations, Limits, and Reductions of all Sorts of Equations. I have not always joyned the Demonſtrations, becauſe they ſeemed too eaſy to need it, and ſometimes cannot be laid down without too much Tediouſneſs. It remains now only to ſhew, how, after Equations are reduced to their moſt commodious Form, their Roots may be extracted in Numbers. And here the chief Difficulty lies in obtaining the two or three firſt Figures; which may be moſt commodiouſly done by either the Geometrical or Mechanical Conſtruction of an Equation. Wherefore I ſhall ſubjoin ſome of theſe Conſtructions.

The Antients, as we learn from *Pappus*, at firſt in vain endeavoured at the Triſection of an Angle, and the finding out of two mean Proportionals by a right Line and a Circle. Afterwards they began to conſider ſeveral other Lines, as the Conchoid, the Ciſſoid, and the Conick Sections, and by ſome of theſe to ſolve thoſe Problems. At length, having

Gg more

more throughly examined the Matter, and the Conick Sections being received into Geometry, they distinguished Problems into three Kinds; *viz.* Into *Plane ones*, which deriving their Original from Lines on a Plane, may be solved by a right Line and a Circle, into *Solid ones*, which were solved by Lines deriving their Original from the Consideration of a Solid, that is, of a Cone: And *Linear ones*, to the Solution of which were required Lines more compounded. And according to this Distinction, we are not to solve solid Problems by other Lines than the Conick Sections; especially if no other Lines but right ones, a Circle, and the Conick Sections, must be received into Geometry. But the Moderns advancing yet much farther, have received into Geometry all Lines that can be expressed by Equations, and have distinguished, according to the Dimensions of the Equations, those Lines into Kinds; and have made it a Law, that you are not to construct a Problem by a Line of a superior Kind, that may be constructed by one of an inferior one. In the Contemplation of Lines, and finding out their Properties, I approve of their Distinction of them into Kinds, according to the Dimensions of the Equations by which they are defined. But it is not the Equation, but the Description that makes the Curve to be a Geometrical one. The Circle is a Geometrical Line, not because it may be expressed by an Equation, but because its Description is a Postulate. It is not the Simplicity of the Equation, but the Easiness of the Description, which is to determine the Choice of our Lines for the Construction of Problems. For the Equation that expresses a Parabola, is more simple than That that expresses a Circle, and yet the Circle, by reason of its more simple Construction, is admitted before it. The Circle and the Conick Sections, if you regard the Dimension of the Equations, are of the same Order, and yet the Circle is not numbered with them in the Construction of Problems, but by reason of its simple Description, is depressed to a lower Order, *viz.* that of a right Line; so that it is not improper to construct that by a Circle that may be constructed by a right Line. But it is a Fault to construct that by the Conick Sections which may be constructed by a Circle. Either therefore you must fix the Law to be observed in a Circle from the Dimensions of Equations, and so take away as vitious the Distinction between Plane and Solid Problems; or else you must grant, That that Law is not so strictly to be observed in Lines of superior Kinds, but that some, by reason of their more simple Description, may be preferred to others of the same Order, and may be numbered with Lines of inferior Orders in the Construction of Problems. In Constructions that are equally Geometrical, the most simple are always to be preferred. This Law is beyond all Exception. But Algebraick Expressions add nothing to the Simplicity of the Construction. The bare Descriptions of the Lines only are here to be considered. These alone were considered by those Geometricians who joyned a Circle with a right Line. And as these are easy or hard, the Construction becomes easy or hard. And therefore it is foreign to the Nature of the Thing, from any thing else to establish Laws about Constructions. Either therefore let us, with the Antients, exclude all Lines besides a right Line, the Circle, and perhaps the Conick Sections, out of Geometry, or admit all, according to the Simplicity of the Description. If the Trochoid were admitted into Geometry, we might, by its Means, divide an Angle in any given Ratio. Would you therefore blame those who should make use of this Line to divide an Angle in the Ratio of one Number to another, and contend that this Line was not defined by an Equation, but that you must make use of such Lines as are defined by Equations? If therefore, when an Angle was to be divided, for Instance, into 10001 Parts, we should be obliged to bring a Curve defined by an Equation of above an hundred Dimensions to do the Business; which no Mortal could describe, much less understand: and should prefer this to the Trochoid, which is a Line well known, and described easily by the Motion of a Wheel or a Circle, who would not see the Absurdity? Either therefore the Trochoid is not to be admitted at all into Geometry, or else, in the Construction of Problems, it is to be preferred to all Lines of a more difficult Description. And there is the same Reason for other Curves. For which Reason we approve of the Trisections of an Angle by a Conchoid, which *Archimedes* in his Lemma's, and *Pappus* in his Collections, have preferred to the Inventions of all others in this Case; because we ought either to exclude all Lines, besides the Circle and right Line, out of Geometry, or admit them according to the Simplicity of their Descriptions, in which Case the Conchoid yields to none, except the Circle. Equations are Expressions of Arithmetical Computation, and properly have no Place in Geometry, except as far as Quantities truly Geometrical (that is, Lines, Surfaces, Solids, and Proportions) may be said to be some equal to others. Multiplications, Divisions, and

Gg 2 such

such sort of Computations, are newly received into Geometry, and that unwarily, and contrary to the first Design of this Science. For whosoever considers the Construction of Problems by a right Line and a Circle, found out by the first Geometricians, will easily perceive that Geometry was invented that we might expeditiously avoid, by drawing Lines, the Tediousness of Computation. Therefore these two Sciences ought not to be confounded. The Antients did so industriously distinguish them from one another, that they never introduced Arithmetical Terms into Geometry. And the Moderns, by confounding both, have lost the Simplicity in which all the Elegancy of Geometry consists. Wherefore that is *Arithmetically* more simple which is determined by the more simple Equations, but that is *Geometrically* more simple which is determined by the more simple drawing of Lines; and in Geometry, that ought to be reckoned best which is Geometrically most simple. Wherefore, I ought not to be blamed, if, with that Prince of Mathematicians, *Archimedes*, and other Antients, I make use of the Conchoid for the Construction of solid Problems. But if any one thinks otherwise, let him know, that I am here sollicitous not for a Geometrical Construction, but any one whatever, by which I may the nearest Way find the Roots of the Equations in Numbers. For the sake whereof I here premise this Lemmatical Problem.

To place the right Line BC *of a given Length, so between two other given Lines* AB, AC, *that being produced, it shall pass through the given Point* P. [See *Figure* 90.]

If the Line BC turn about the Pole P, and at the same time moves on its End C upon the right Line AC, its other End B shall describe the Conchoid of the Antients. Let this cut the Line AB in the Point B. Join PB, and its Part BC will be the right Line which was to be drawn. And, by the same Law, the Line BC may be drawn, where, instead of AC, some Curve Line is made use of.

If any do not like this Construction by a Conchoid, another, done by a Conick Section, may be substituted in its room. From the Point P to the right Line AD, AE, draw PD, PE, making the Parallelogram EADP, and from the Points C and D to the right Lines AB let fall the Perpendiculars CF, DG, as also from the Point E to the right Line AC, produced towards A, let fall the Perpendicular EH, and making $AD=a$, $PD=b$, $BC=c$, $AG=d$, $AB=x$, and $AC=y$, you will have $AD:AG::AC:AF$, and consequently $AF=\frac{dy}{a}$. Moreover, you will have $AB:AC::PD:CD$, or $x:y::b:a-y$. Therefore $by=ax-yx$, which is an Equation expressive of an Hyperbola. And again, by the 13th of the 2d *Elem.* BCq will be $=ACq+ABq-2FAB$, that is, $cc=yy+xx-\frac{2dxy}{a}$. Both Sides of the former Equation being multiplied by $\frac{2d}{a}$, take them from both Sides of this, and there will remain $cc-\frac{2bdy}{a}=yy+xx-2dx$, an Equation expressing a Circle, where x and y are at right Angles. Wherefore, if you make these two Lines an Hyperbola and a Circle, by the Help of these Equations, by their Intersection you will have x and y, or AB and AC, which determine the Position of the right Line BC. But those right Lines will be compounded after this Way. [*See* Figure 91.]

Draw any two right Lines, KL equal to AD, and KM equal to PD, containing the right Angle MKL. Compleat the Parallelogram KLMN, and with the Asymptotes LN, MN, describe through the Point K the Hyperbola IKX.

On KM produced towards K, take KP equal to AG, and KQ equal to BC. And on KL produced towards K, take KR equal to AH, and RS equal to RQ. Compleat the Parallelogram PKRT, and from the Center T, at the Interval TS, describe a Circle. Let that cut the Hyperbola in the Point X. Let fall to KP the Perpendicular XY, and XY will be equal to AC, and KY equal to AB. Which two Lines, AC and AB, or one of them, with the Point P, determine the Position sought of the right Line BC. To demonstrate which Construction, and its Cases, according to the different Cases of the Problem, I shall not here insist.

I say, by this Construction, if you think fit, you may solve the Problem. But this Solution is too compounded to serve for any particular Uses. It is a bare Speculation, and

and Geometrical Speculations have just as much Elegancy as Simplicity, and deserve just so much Praise as they can promise Use. For which Reason, I prefer a Construction by the Conchoid, as much the simpler, and not less Geometrical; and which is of especial Use in the Resolution of Equations as by us proposed. Premising therefore the preceding Lemma, we Geometrically construct Cubick and Biquadratick Problems [*as which may be reduced to Cubick ones*] as follows. [*See* Figures 92 and 93.]

Let there be proposed the Cubick Equation $x^3 * + qx + r = 0$, *whose second Term is wanting*, but the third is *denoted under its Sign* $+q$, *and the fourth by* $+r$.

Draw any right Line, KA, which call n. On KA, produced on both Sides, take $KB = \frac{q}{n}$ to the same Side as KA, if it be $+q$, otherwise to the contrary Part. Bisect BA in C, and on K, as a Center with the Radius KC, describe the Circle CX, and in it accommodate the right Line CX equal to $\frac{r}{nn}$, producing it each Way. Join AX, which produce also both Ways. Lastly, between these Lines CX and AX inscribe EY of the same Length as CA, and which being produced, may pass through the Point K; then shall XY be the Root of the Equation. [*See* Figure 94.] And of these Roots, those will be Affirmative which fall from X towards C, and those Negative which fall on the contrary Side, if it be $+r$, but contrarily if it be $-r$.

Demonstration.

To demonstrate which, I premise these Lemma's.

Lemma I.

YX *is to* AK *as* CX *to* KE. For draw KF parallel to CX; then because of the similar Triangles ACX, AKF, and EYX, EKF, it will be AC to AK as CX to KF, and YX to YE or AC as KF to KE, and therefore by perturbated Equality YX to AK as CX to KE. Q. E. D.

Lemma II.

YX *is to* AK *as* CY *to* AK + KE. For by Composition of Proportion YX is to AK as YX + CX (*i. e.* CY) to AK + KE. Q. E. D.

Lemma III.

KE − BK *is to* YX *as* YX *to* AK.

For (by 12. *Elem.* 2.) $YKq - CKq$ is $= CYq - CY \times CX = CY \times YX$. That is, if the Theorem be resolved into Proportionals, CY to YK − CK as YK + CK to YX. But YK − CK is = YK − YE + CA − CK = KE − BK. And YK + CK = YK − YE + CA + CK = KE + AK. Wherefore CY is to KE − BK as KE + AK to YX. But by *Lemma* 2. it was CY to KE + AK as YX to AK. Wherefore by Equality it is YX to KE − BK as AK to YX. Or KE − BK to YX as YX to AK. Q. E. D.

These Things being premised, the Theorem will be thus demonstrated.

In the *first Lemma* it was YX to AK as CX to KE, or $KE \times YX = AK \times CX$. In the *third Lemma* it was proved, that KE − BK was to YX as YX to AK. Wherefore, if the Terms of the first Ratio be multiplied by YX, it will be $KE \times YX - BK \times YX$ to XYq as YX : AK that is, $AK \times CX - BK \times YX$ to YXq as YX to AK, and by multiplying the Extremes and Means into themselves, it will be $AKq \times XC - AK \times BK \times YX = YX$ *cube.* Lastly, for YX, AK, BK, and CX, re-substituting x, n, $\frac{q}{n}$, and $\frac{r}{nn}$, this Equation will arise, *viz.* $r - qx = x^3$. Q. E. D. I need not stay to shew you the Variations of the Signs, for they will be determined according to the different Cases of the Problem.

Let now an Equation be proposed wanting the third Term, as $x^3 + pxx + r = 0$; and in order to construct it, n being assumed, take in any right Line two Lengths $KA = \frac{r}{nn}$, and $KB = p$, and let them be taken the same Way if r and p have like Signs; but otherwise, take them towards contrary Sides. Bisect BA in C, and on K, as a Center, with the Radius KC, describe a Circle, into which accommodate $CX = n$, producing it both Ways. Join also AX, and produce it both Ways. Lastly, between these Lines CX and AX inscribe EY = CA, so that if produced it may pass through the Point K, and KE will be the Root of the Equation. And the Roots will be Affirmative, when the Point

Point Y falls on that Side of X which lies towards C; and Negative, when it falls on the contrary Side of X, provided it be $+ r$; but if it be $- r$, it will be the Reverse of this.

To demonstrate this Proposition, look back to the Figures and Lemma's of the former; and then you will find it thus.

By *Lemma* 1. it was Y X to A K as C X to K E, or Y X × K E = A K × C X, and by *Lemma* 3, K E − K B to Y X as Y X to A K, or, (taking K B towards contrary Parts) K E + K B to Y X as Y X to A K, and therefore K E + K B multiplied by K E will be to Y X × K E (or A K × C X) as Y X to A K, or as C X to K E. Wherefore multiplying the Extreams and Means into themselves, K E *cube* + K B × K E *q* is = A K × C X *q*; and then for K E, K B, A K, and C K, restoring their Values assigned above, $x^3 + pxx = r$.

Let now an Equation having three Dimensions, and wanting no Term, be proposed in this Form, $x^3 + pxx + qx + r = 0$, *some of whose Roots shall be Affirmative, and some Negative.* [See *Figure* 95.]

And first suppose *q Negative*, then in any right Line, as K B, let two Lengths be taken, as $KA = \frac{r}{q}$, and $KB = p$, and take them the same Way, if p and $\frac{r}{q}$ have contrary Signs; but if their Signs are alike, then take the Lengths contrary Ways from the Point K. Bisect A B in C, and there erect the Perpendicular C X equal to the Square Root of the Term q; then between the Lines A X and C X, produced infinitely both Ways, inscribe the right Line E Y = A C, so that being produced, it may pass through K; so shall K E be the Root of the Equation, which will be Affirmative when the Point X falls between A and E; but Negative when the Point E falls on that Side of the Point X which is towards A.

But if Q had been Affirmative, then in the Line K B you must have taken those two Lengths thus, *viz.* $KA = \sqrt{\frac{-r}{p}}$, and $KB = \frac{q}{KA}$, and the same Way from K, if $\sqrt{\frac{-r}{p}}$ and $\frac{q}{KA}$ have different Signs; but contrary Ways, if the Signs are of the same Nature. B A also must

be bisected in C; and there the Perpendicular C X erected equal to the Term p; and between the Lines A X and C X, infinitely drawn out both Ways, the right Line E Y must also be inscribed equal to A C, and made to pass through the Point K, as before; then will X Y be the Root of the Equation; Negative when the Point X should fall between A and E, and affirmative when the Point Y falls on the Side of the Point X towards C.

The Demonstration of the first Case.

By the first Lemma, K E was to C X as A K to Y X, and (by Composition) so K E + A K, *i. e.* K Y + K C is to C X + Y X, *i. e.* C Y. But in the right-angled Triangle K C Y, Y C *q* = Y K *q* − K C *q* = $\overline{KY + KC} \times \overline{KY - KC}$; and by resolving the equal Terms into Proportionals, K Y + K C is to C Y as C Y is to K Y − K C; or K E + A K is to C Y as C Y is to E K − K B. Wherefore since K E was to X C in this Proportion, by Duplication K E *q* will be to C X *q* as K E + A K to K E − K B, and by multiplying the Extreams and Means by themselves K E *cube* − K B × K E *q* is = C X *q* × K E × C X *q* × A K. And by restoring the former Values $x^3 - pxx = qx + r$.

The Demonstration of the second Case.

By the first Lemma, K E is to C X as A K is to Y X, then by multiplying the Extreams and Means by themselves, K E × Y X is = C X × A K. Therefore in the preceding Case, put K E × Y X for C X × A K, and it will be K E *cube* − K B × K E *q* = C X *q* × K E + C X × K E × Y X; and by dividing all by K E, there will be K E *q* − K B × K E = C X *q* + C X × Y X; then multiplying all by A K, and you will have A K × K E *q* − A K × K B × K E = A K × C X *q* + A K × C X × Y X. And again, put K E × Y X instead of its equal C X × A K, then A K × K E *q* − A K × K B × K E = E K × C X × Y X + K E × Y X *q*; whence all being divided by K E there will arise A K × K E − A K × K B = Y X × C X + Y X *q*; and when all are multiplied by Y X there will be A K × K E × Y X − A K × K B × Y X = Y X *q* × C X + Y X *cube*. And instead of K E × Y X in the first Term, put C X × A K, and then C X × A K *q* − A K × B K × Y X =

Hh CX

CX × YXq + YX *cube*, or, which is the same Thing, YX *cube* + CX × YXq + AK × KB × YX − CX × AKq = o. And by substituting for YX, CX, AK and KB, their Values x, p, $\sqrt{\frac{-r}{p}}$, $q\sqrt{\frac{p}{-r}}$, there will come out, $x^3 + pxx + qx + r = o$, the Equation to be constructed.

These Equations are also solved, by drawing a right Line from a given Point, in such a Manner that the Part of it, which is intercepted between another right Line and a Circle, both given in Position, may be of a given Length. [See Figure 96.]

For, let there be proposed a Cubick Equation $x^3 * + qx + r = o$, *whose second Term is wanting.*

Draw the right Line KA at Pleasure, which call n. In KA produced both Ways, take KB $= \frac{q}{n}$ on the same Side of the Point K as the Point A is if q be Negative, if not, on the contrary. Bisect BA in C, and from the Center A, with the Distance AC, describe a Circle CX. To this inscribe the right Line CX $= \frac{r}{nn}$, and through the Points K, C, and X describe the Circle KCXG. Join AX, and produce it till it again cuts the Circle KCXG last described in the Point G. Lastly, between this Circle KCXG, and the right Line KC produced both Ways, inscribe the right Line EY = AC, so that EY produced pass through the Point G. And EG will be one of the Roots of the Equation. But those Roots are Affirmative which fall in the greater Segment of the Circle KGC, and Negative which fall in the lesser KFC, if r is Negative, and the contrary will be when r is Affirmative.

In order to demonstrate this Construction, let us premise the following *Lemmas*.

Lemma I.

All Things being supposed as in the Construction, CE *is to* KA *as* CE + CX *is to* AY, *and as* CX *to* KA.

For the right Line KG being drawn, AC is to AK as CX is to KG, because the Triangles ACX and AKG are Similar. The Triangles YEC, YKG are also Similar; for the Angle at Y is common to both Triangles, and the Angles G and C are in the same Segment EGCK of the Circle KGC, and therefore equal. Whence CE will be to EY as KG to KY, that is, CE to AC as KG to KY, because EY and AC were supposed equal. And by comparing this with the Proportionality above, it will follow by perturbated Equality that CE is to KA as CX to KY, and alternately CE is to CX as KA to KY. Whence, by Composition, CE + CX will be to CX as KA + KY to KY, that is, AY to KY, and alternately CE + CX is to AY as CX is to KY, that is, as CE to KA. Q. E. D.

Lemma II.

Let fall the Perpendicular CH *upon the right Line* GY, *and the Rectangle* 2HEY *will be equal to the Rectangle* CE × CX.

For the Perpendicular GL being let fall upon the Line AY, the Triangles KGL, ECH have right Angles at L and H, and the Angles at K and E are in the same Segment CKEG of the Circle CGK, and are therefore equal; consequently the Triangles are Similar. And therefore KG is to KL as EC to EH. Moreover, AM being let fall from the Point A perpendicular to the Line KG, because AK is equal to AG, KG will be bisected in M; and the Triangles KAM and KGL are Similar, because the Angle at K is common, and the Angles at M and L are right ones; and therefore AK is to KM as KG is to KL. But as AK is to KM so is 2AK to 2KM, or KG; (and because the Triangles AKG and ACX are Similar) so is 2AC to CX; also (because AC = EY) so is 2EY to CX. Therefore 2EY is to CX as KG to KL. But KG was to KL as EC to EH, therefore 2EY is to CX as EC to EH, and so the Rectangle 2HEY (by multiplying the Extreams and Means by themselves) is equal to EC × CX. Q. E. D.

Here we took the Lines AK and AG to be equal. For the Rectangles CAK and XAG are equal (by *Cor.* to 36 *Prop.* of the 3d Book of *Euc.*) and therefore as CA is to XA so is AG to AK. But XA and CA are equal by Hypothesis; therefore AG = AK.

Lemma III.

All Things being as above, the three Lines BY, CE, KA *are continual Proportionals.*

Hh 2 For

For (by *Prop.* 12. *Book* 2. *Elem.*) CYq is $= EYq + CEq + 2EY \times EH$. And by taking EYq from both Sides, $CYq - EYq$ is $= CEq + 2EY \times EH$. But $2EY \times EH$ is $= CE \times CX$ (by *Lem.* 2.) and by adding GEq to both Sides, $CEq + 2EY \times EH$ becomes $= CEq + CE \times CX$. Therefore $CYq - EYq$ is $= CEq + CE \times CX$, that is, $\overline{CY+EY} \times \overline{CY-EY} = CEq + CE \times CX$. And by resolving the equal Rectangles into proportional Sides, it will be as $CE + CX$ is to $CY + EY$, so is $CY - EY$ to CE. But the three Lines EY, CA, CB, are equal, and thence $CY + EY = CY + CA = AY$, and $CY - EY = CY - CB = BY$. Write AY for $CY + EY$, and BY for $CY - EY$, and it will be as $CE + CX$ is to YA so is BY to CE. But (*by Lem.* 1.) CE is to KA as $CE + CX$ is to AY, therefore CE is to KA as BY is to CE, that is, the three Lines BY, CE, and KA are continual Proportionals. Q. E. D.

Now, by the Help of these three Lemmas, we may *demonstrate* the Construction of the preceding Problem, thus: *By Lem.* 1. CE is to KA as CX is to KY, so $KA \times CX$ is $= CE \times KY$, and by dividing both Sides by CE, $\frac{KA \times CX}{CE}$ becomes $= KY$. To these equal Sides add BK, and $BK + \frac{KA \times CX}{CE}$ will be $= BY$. Whence (by *Lem.* 3.) $BK + \frac{KA \times CX}{CE}$ is to CE as CE is to KA, and thence, by multiplying the Extreams and Means by themselves, CEq is $= BK \times KA + \frac{KAq \times CX}{CE}$, and both Sides being multiplied by CE, CE *cub.* becomes $= KB \times KA \times CE + KAq \times CX$. CE was called x, the Root of the Equation, KA was $= n$, $KB = \frac{q}{n}$, and $CX = \frac{r}{nn}$. These being substituted instead of CE, KA, KB and CX, there will arise $x^3 = qx + r$, or $x^3 - qx - r = 0$, the Equation to be constructed; when q and r are Negatives, KA and KB having been taken on the same Side of the Point K, and the Affirmative Root being in the greater Segment CGK. This is *one Case* of the Construction to be demonstrated. Draw KB on the contrary Side, that is, let its Sign be changed, or the Sign of $\frac{q}{n}$, or, which is the same Thing, the Sign of the Term q, and there will be had the Construction of the Equation $x^3 + qx - r = 0$. *Which is the other Case*. In these Cases CX, and the Affirmative Root CE, fall towards the same Parts of the Line AK. Let CX and the Negative Root fall towards the same Parts when the Sign of CX, or of $\frac{r}{nn}$, or (which is the same Thing) the Sign of r is changed; and this will be the *third Case* $x^3 + qx + r = 0$, where all the Roots are Negative. And again, when the Sign of KB, or of $\frac{q}{n}$, or only of q, is changed, it will be the *fourth Case* $x^3 - qx + r = 0$. The Constructions of all these Cases may be run through, and particularly demonstrated after the same Manner as the first was. We having demonstrated one Case, thought it sufficient to touch slightly the rest. These are demonstrated with the same Words, by changing only the Situation of the Lines.

Now let the Cubick Equation $x^3 + pxx * + r = 0$, *whose third Term is wanting, be to be constructed.*

In the same Figure n being taken of any Length, take in any infinite right Line AY, $KA = \frac{r}{nn}$ and $KB = p$ and take them on the same Side of the Point K, if the Signs of the Terms p and r are the same, otherwise on contrary Sides. Bisect BA in C, and from the Center K with the Distance KC describe the Circle CXG. And to it inscribe the right Line CX equal to n the assumed Length. Join AX and produce it to G, so that AG may be equal to AK, and through the Points K, C, X, G describe a Circle. And, lastly, between this Circle and the right Line KC, produced both Ways, inscribe the right Line $EY = AC$, so that being produced it may pass through the Point G; then the right Line KY being drawn, will be one of the Roots of the Equation. And those Roots are Affirmative which fall on that Side of the Point K on which the Point A is on, if r is Affir-

Affirmative; but if r is Negative, then the Affirmative Roots fall on the contrary Side. And if the Affirmative Roots fall on one Side, the Negative fall on the other.

This Conftruction is demonftrated by the Help of the three laft *Lemmas* after this Manner:

By the third Lemma, BY, CE, KA are continual Proportionals; and by *Lemma* 1. as CE is to KA fo is CX to KY. Therefore BY is to CE as CX to KY. BY is $=$ KY $-$ KB. Therefore KY $-$ KB is to CE as CX is to KY. But as KY $-$ KB is to CE fo is $\overline{KY-KB} \times KY$ to CE $\times$ KY, by *Prop.* 1. *Book* 6. *Euc.* and becaufe of the Proportionals CE to KA as CX to KY it is CE $\times$ KY $=$ KA $\times$ CX. Therefore $\overline{KY-KB} \times KY$ is to KA $\times$ CX (as KY $-$ KB to CE, that is) as CX to KY. And by multiplying the Extreams and Means by themfelves $\overline{KY-KB} \times KYq$ becomes $=$ KA $\times$ CXq; that is, KY *cub.* $-$ KB $\times$ KYq $=$ KA $\times$ CXq. But in the Conftruction KY was x the Root of the Equation, KB was put $= p$, KA $= \frac{r}{nn}$, and CX $= n$. Write therefore x, p, $\frac{r}{nn}$, and n for KY, KB, KA, and CX refpectively, and $x^3 - pxx$ will become $= r$, or $x^3 - pxx - r = 0$.

This Conftruction may be refolved into thefe four Cafes of Equations, $x^3 - pxx - r = 0$, $x^3 - pxx + r = 0$, $x^3 + pxx - r = 0$, and $x^3 + pxx + r = 0$. The firft Cafe I have already demonftrated; the reft are demonftrated with the fame Words, only changing the Situation of the Lines. To wit, as in taking KA and KB on the fame Side of the Point K, and the Affirmative Root KY on the contrary Side, has already produced KY *cub.* $-$ KB $\times$ KYq $=$ KA $\times$ CXq, and thence $x^3 - pxx - r = 0$; fo by taking KB on the other Side the Point K there will be produced, by the like Reafoning, KY *cub.* $+$ KB $\times$ KYq $=$ KA $\times$ CXq, and thence $x^3 + pxx - r = 0$. And in thefe two Cafes, if the Situation of the Affirmative Root KY be changed, by taking it on the other Side of the Point K, by a like Series of Argumentation you will fall upon the other two Cafes, KY *cub.* $+$ KB $\times$ KYq $= -$ KA $\times$ CXq, or $x^3 + pxx + r = 0$, and KY *cub.* $-$ KB $\times$ KYq $= -$ KA $\times$ CXq, or $x^3 - pxx + r = 0$. Which were all the Cafes to be demonftrated.

Now let this Cubick Equation $x^3 + pxx + qx + r = 0$ *be propofed, wanting no Term (unlefs perhaps the third).* Which is conftructed after this Manner: [*See Figures* 97 and 98.]

Take the length n at Pleafure. Draw any right Line GC $= \frac{n}{2}$, and at the Point G erect a Perpendicular GD $= \sqrt{\frac{r}{p}}$, and if the Terms p and r have contrary Signs, from the Center C, with the Interval CD defcribe a Circle PBE. If they have the fame Signs from the Center D, with the Space GC, defcribe an occult Circle, cutting the right Line GA in H; then from the Center C, with the Diftance GH, defcribe the Circle PBE. Then make GA $= -\frac{q}{n} - \frac{r}{np}$ on the fame Side the Point G that C is on, provided the Quantity $-\frac{q}{n} - \frac{r}{np}$ (the Signs of the Terms p, q, r in the Equation to be conftructed being well obferved) fhould come out Affirmative; otherwife, draw GA on the other Side of the Point G, and at the Point A erect the Perpendicular AY, between which and the Circle PBE already defcribed, infcribe the right Line EY equal to the Term p, fo that being produced, it may pafs through the Point G; which being done, the Line EG will be one of the Roots of the Equation to be conftructed. Thofe Roots are Affirmative when the Point E falls between the Points G and Y, and Negative, when the Point E falls without, if p is Affirmative; and the contrary, if Negative.

In order to demonftrate this Conftruction, let us premife the following *Lemmas*.

Lemma I.

Let EF *be let fall perpendicular to* AG, *and the right Line* EC *be drawn*; EGq $+$ GCq is $=$ ECq $+$ 2CGF.

For

For (by *Prop.* 12. *Book* 2. *Elem.*) EGq is $= ECq + GCq + 2GCF$. Let GCq be added on both Sides, and $EGq + GCq$ will become $= ECq + 2GCq + 2GCF$. But $2GCq + 2GCF$ is $= 2GC \times \overline{GC + CF} = 2CGF$. Therefore $EGq + GCq = ECq + 2CGF$. Q. E. D.

Lemma II.

In the first Case of the Construction, where the Circle PBE *passes through the Point* D, $EGq - GDq$ *is* $= 2CGF$.

For by the *first Lemma* $EGq + GCq$ is $= ECq + 2CGF$, and by taking CGq from both Sides, EGq is $= ECq - GCq + 2CGF$. But $ECq - GCq$ is $= CDq - GCq = GDq$. Therefore $EGq = GDq + 2CGF$, and by taking GDq from both Sides, $EGq - GDq$ is $= 2CGF$. Q. E. D.

Lemma III.

In the second Case of the Construction, where the Circle PBE *does not pass through the Point* D, $EGq + GDq$ is $= 2CGF$.

For in the *first Lemma*, $EGq + GCq$ was $= ECq + 2CGF$. Take ECq from both Sides, and it becomes $EGq + GCq - ECq = 2CGF$. But $GC = DH$, and $EC = CP = GH$. Therefore $GCq - ECq = DHq - GHq = GDq$, and so $EGq + GDq = 2CGF$. Q. E. D.

Lemma IV.

$GY \times 2CGF$ *is* $= 2CG \times AGE$.

For by reason of the similar Triangles GEF and GYA, as GF is to GE so is AG to GY, that is, (by *Prop.* 1. *Book* 6. *Elem.*) as $2CG \times AG$ is to $2CG \times GY$. Let the Extreams and Means be multiplied by themselves, and $2CG \times GY \times GF$ becomes $= 2CG \times AG \times GE$. Q. E. D.

Now, by the Help of these Lemmas, the Construction of the Problem may be thus demonstrated.

2 In

In the *first* Case, $EGq - GDq$ is $= 2CGF$ (by Lemma 2.) and by multiplying all by GY, $EGq \times GY - GDq \times GY$ becomes $= 2CGF \times GY =$ (by Lemma 4.) $2CG \times AGE$. Instead of GY write $EG + EY$, and $EG\ cub. + EY \times EGq - GDq \times EG - GDq \times EY$ becomes $= 2CGA \times EG$, or $EG\ cub. + EY \times EGq - \overline{GDq - 2CGA} \times EG - GDq \times EY = 0$.

In the *second* Case, $EGq + GDq$ is $= 2CGF$ (by Lemma 3.) and by multiplying all by GY, $EGq \times GY + GDq \times GY$ becomes $= 2CGF \times GY = 2CG \times AGE$, by Lemma 4. Instead of GY write $EG + EY$, and $EG\ cub. + EY \times EGq + GDq \times EG + GDq \times EY$ will become $= 2CGA \times EG$, or $EG\ cub. + EY \times EGq + \overline{GDq - 2CGA} \times EG + GDq \times EY = 0$.

But the Root of the Equation EG was called x, $GD = \sqrt{\frac{r}{p}}$, $EY = p$, $2CG = n$, and $GA = -\frac{q}{n} - \frac{r}{np}$, that is, in the first Case, where the Signs of the Terms p and r are different; but in the second Case, where the Sign of one of the two, p or r, is changed, there is $-\frac{q}{n} + \frac{r}{np} = GA$. Let therefore EG be put $= x$, $GD = \sqrt{\frac{r}{p}}$, $EY = p$, $2CG = n$, and $GA = -\frac{q}{n} \mp \frac{r}{np}$, and in the *first* Case it will be $x^3 + px^2 + \overline{q + \frac{r}{p} - \frac{r}{p}} \times x - r = 0$; that is, $x^3 + px^2 \underline{+ qx - r = 0}$; but in the *second* Case, $x^3 + pxx + \overline{q + \frac{r}{p} - \frac{r}{p}} \times x + r = 0$, that is, $x^3 + px^2 + qx + r = 0$. Therefore in both Cases EG is the true Value of the Root x. Q.E.D.

But either Case may be distinguished into its several Particulars; as the former into these, $x^3 + px^2 + qx - r = 0$, $x^3 + px^2 - qx - r = 0$, $x^3 - px^2 + qx + r = 0$, $x^3 - px^2 - qx + r = 0$, $x^3 + px^2 - r = 0$, and $x^3 - px^2 + r = 0$; the latter into these, $x^3 + px^2 + qx + r = 0$, $x^3 + px^2 - qx + r = 0$, $x^3 - px^2 + qx - r = 0$, $x^3 - px^2 - qx - r = 0$, $x^3 + px^2 + r = 0$, and

I i $x^3 -$

$x^3 - px^2 - r = 0$. The Demonſtration of all which Caſes may be carried on in the ſame Words with the two already demonſtrated, by only changing the Situation of the Lines.

Theſe are the chief Conſtructions of Problems, by inſcribing a right Line given in Length ſo between a Circle and a right Line given in Poſition, that the inſcribed right Line produced may paſs through a given Point. And ſuch a right Line may be inſcribed by deſcribing the *Conchoid* of the Antients, of which let that Point, through which the right Line given ought to paſs, be the Pole, the other right Line given in Poſition be the Ruler or Aſymptote, and the Interval be the Length of the inſcribed Line. For this Conchoid will cut the Circle in the Point E, through which the right Line to be inſcribed muſt be drawn. But it will be ſufficient in Practice to draw the right Line between a Circle and a right Line given in Poſition by any Mechanick Method.

But in theſe Conſtructions obſerve, that the Quantity n is undetermined and left to be taken at Pleaſure, that the Conſtruction may be more conveniently fitted to particular Problems. We ſhall give Examples of this in finding two mean Proportionals, and in triſecting an Angle.

Let x and y be two mean Proportionals to be found between a and b. Becauſe a, x, y, b are continual Proportionals, a^2 will be to x^2 as x to b, therefore $x^3 = aab$, or $x^3 - aab = 0$. Here the Terms p and q of the Equation are wanting, and $-aab$ is in the room of the Term r; therefore in the firſt Form of the Conſtructions, where the right Line EY tending to the given Point K, is drawn between other two right Lines EX and YC, given in Poſition, and the right Line CX ſuppoſed $= \frac{r}{nn}$ that is $= \frac{-aab}{nn}$, let n be taken equal to a, and then CX will become $= -b$. From whence the following Conſtruction comes out. [*See* Figure 99.]

I draw any Line, KA $= a$, and biſect it in C, and from the Center K, with the Diſtance KC, deſcribe the Circle CX, to which I inſcribe the right Line CX $= b$, and between AX and CX, infinitely produced, I ſo inſcribe EY $=$ CA, that EY being produced, may paſs through the Point K. So KA, XY, KE, CX will be continual Proportionals, that is, XY and KE two mean Proportionals between a and b. This Conſtruction is known. [*See* Figure 100.]

But in the other Form of the Conſtructions, where the right Line EY converging to the given Point G is inſcribed between the Circle GECX and the right Line AK, and CX is $= \frac{r}{nn}$, that is, (in this Problem) $= \frac{-aab}{nn}$, I put, as before, $n = a$, and then CX will be $= b$, and the reſt are done as follows. [*See* Figure 101.]

I draw any right Line KA $= a$, and biſect it in C, and from the Center A, with the Diſtance AK, I deſcribe the Circle KG, to which I inſcribe the right Line KG $= 2b$, conſtituting the *Iſoſceles* Triangle AKG. Then, through the Points C, K, G I deſcribe the Circle, between the Circumference of which and the right Line AK produced, I inſcribe the right Line EY $=$ CK tending to the Point G. Which being done, AK, EC, KY, $\frac{1}{2}$KG are continual Proportionals, that is, EC and KY are two mean Proportionals between the given Quantities a and b.

Let there be an Angle to be divided into three equal Parts; [See *Figure* 102.] *and let that Angle be* ACB, *and the Parts thereof to be found be* ACD, ECD, *and* ECB.

From the Center C, with the Diſtance CA, let the Circle ADEB be deſcribed, cutting the right Lines CA, CD, CE, CB in A, D, E, B. Let AD, DE, EB be joined, and AB cutting the right Lines CD, CE at F and H, and let DG, meeting AB in G, be drawn parallel to CE. Becauſe the Triangles CAD, ADF, and DFG are Similar, CA, AD, DF, and FG are continual Proportionals. Therefore if AC be $= a$, and AD $= x$, DF will be equal to $\frac{xx}{a}$, and FG $= \frac{x^3}{aa}$. But AB is $=$ BH $+$ HG $+$ FA $-$ GF $= 3$AD $-$ GF $= 3x - \frac{x^3}{aa}$. Let AB be $= b$, then b becomes $= 3x - \frac{x^3}{aa}$, or $x^3 - 3aax + aab = 0$. Here p, the ſecond Term of the Equation, is wanting, and inſtead of q and r we have $-3aa$ and aab. Therefore in the firſt Form of the Conſtructions, where p was $= 0$, KA $= n$, KB $= \frac{q}{n}$, and CX $= \frac{r}{nn}$, that is, in this Pro-

Ii 2 blem,

blem, $KB = -\frac{3aa}{n}$, and $CX = \frac{aab}{nn}$, that these Quantities may come out as simple as possible, I put $n = a$, and so KB becomes $= -3a$, and $CX = b$. Whence this *Construction* of the Problem comes out.

Draw any Line, $KA = a$, and on the contrary Side make $KB = 3a$. [*See* Figure 103.] Bisect BA in C, and from the Center K, with the Distance KC, describe a Circle, to which inscribe the right Line $CX = b$, and the right Line AX being drawn between that infinitely produced and the right Line CX, inscribe the right Line $EY = AC$, and so that it being produced, will pass through the Point K. So XY will be $= x$. But (see the last Figure) because the Circle ADEB = Circle CXA, and the Subtense AB = Subtense CX, and the Parts of the Subtenses BH and XY are equal; the Angles ACB, and CKX will be equal, as also the Angles BCH, XKY; and so the Angle XKY will be one third Part of the Angle CKX. Therefore the third Part XKY of any given Angle CKX is found by inscribing the right Line $EY = AC$ the Diameter of the Circle, between the Chords CX and AX infinitely produced, and converging towards K the Center of the Circle.

Hence, if from K, the Center of the Circle, you let fall the Perpendicular KH upon the Chord CX, the Angle HKY will be one third Part of the Angle HKX; so that if any Angle HKX were given, the third Part thereof HKY may be found by letting fall from any Point X of any Side KX, the Line HX perpendicular to the other Side HK, and by drawing XE parallel to HK, and by inscribing the right Line $YE = 2XK$ between XH and XE, so that it being produced may pass through the Point K. *Or thus.* [See *Figure* 104.]

Let any Angle AXK be given. To one of its Sides AX raise a Perpendicular XH, and from any Point K of the other Side XK let there be drawn the Line KE, the Part of which EY (lying between the Side AX produced, and the Perpendicular XH) is double the Side XK, and the Angle KEA will be one third of the given Angle AXK. Again, the Perpendicular EZ being raised, and KF being drawn, whose Part ZF, between EF and EZ, let be double to KE, and the Angle KFA will be one third of the Angle KEA; and so you may go on by a continual Trisection of an Angle *ad infinitum*. This Method is in the 32d *Prop.* of the 4th Book of *Pappus*.

But if you would trisect an Angle by the other Form of Constructions, where the right Line is to be inscribed between another right Line and a Circle: Here also will KB be $= \frac{q}{n}$, and $CX = \frac{r}{nn}$, that is, in the Problem we are now about, $KB = \frac{-3aa}{n}$, and $CX = \frac{aab}{nn}$; and so by putting $n = a$, KB will be $= -3a$, and $CX = b$. Whence this *Construction* comes out.

From any Point K let there be drawn two right Lines towards the same Way, $KA = a$, and $KB = 3a$. [*See* Figure 105.] Bisect AB in C, and from the Center A with the Distance AC describe a Circle. To which inscribe the right Line $CX = b$. Join AX, and produce it till it cuts the Circle again in G. Then between this Circle and the right Line KC, infinitely produced, inscribe the Line $EY = AC$, and passing through the Point G; and the right Line EC being drawn, will be equal to x the Quantity sought, by which the third Part of the given Angle will be subtended.

This Construction arises from the Form above; which, however, comes out better thus: Because the Circles ADEB and KXG are equal, and also the Subtenses CX and AB, the Angles CAX, or KAG, and ACB are equal, therefore CE is the Subtense of one third Part of the Angle KAG. Whence in any given Angle KAG, that its third Part CAE may be found, inscribe the right Line EY equal to the Semi-Diameter AG of the Circle KCG, between the Circle and the Side KA, of the Angle, infinitely produced, and tending to the Point G. Thus *Archimedes*, in *Lemma* 8. taught to trisect an Angle. The same Constructions may be more easily explained than I have done here; but in these I would shew how, from the general Constructions of Problems I have already explained, we may derive the most simple Constructions of particular Problems.

Besides the Constructions here set down, we might add many more. [*See* Figure 106.] *As if there were two mean Proportionals to be found between a and b.* Draw any right Line $AK = b$, and perpendicular to it $AB = a$. Bisect AK in I, and in AK put AH equal to the Subtense BI; and also in the Line AB produced, AC = Subtense BH. Then

Then in the Line A K on the other Side of the Point A take A D of any Length and D E equal to it, and from the Centers D and E, with the Distances D B and E C, describe two Circles, B F and C G, and between them draw the right Line F G equal to the right Line A I, and converging at the Point A, and A F will be the first of the two mean Proportionals that were to be found.

The Antients taught how to find two mean Proportionals by the *Cissoid*; but no Body that I know of hath given a good manual Description of this Curve. [*See* Figure 107.] Let A G be the Diameter, and F the Center of a Circle to which the *Cissoid* belongs. At the Point F let the Perpendicular F D be erected, and produced *in infinitum*. And let F G be produced to P, that F P may be equal to the Diameter of the Circle. Let the rectangular Ruler P E D be moved, so that the Leg E P may always pass through the Point P, and the other Leg E D must be equal to the Diameter A G, or F P, with its End D, always moving in the Line F D; and the middle Point C of this Leg will describe the *Cissoid* G C K which was desired, as has been already shewn. Wherefore, if between any two Quantities, a and b, there be two mean Proportionals to be found: Take $AM = a$, raise the Perpendicular $MN = b$. Join A N; and move the Rule P E D, as was just now shewn, until its Point C fall upon the right Line A N. Then let fall C B perpendicular to A P, take t to B H, and v to B G, as M N is to B C, and because A B, B H, B G, B C are continual Proportionals, a, t, v, b will also be continual Proportionals.

By the Application of such a Ruler other solid Problems may be constructed.

Let there be proposed the Cubick Equation $x^3 \pm pxx + qx - r = 0$; where let q be always Affirmative, r Negative, and p of any Sign. Make $AG = \frac{r}{q}$, and bisect it in F, and take F R and $GL = \frac{p}{2}$, and that towards A if it be $+p$, if not towards P. Moreover, erect the Perpendicular F D, and in it take $FQ = \sqrt{q}$; to this erect also the Perpendicular Q C. And in the Leg E D of the Ruler, take E D and E C respectively equal to A G and A R, and let the Leg of the Ruler be applied to the Scheme, so that the Point D may touch the right Line F D, and the Point C the right Line Q C, then if the Parallelogram B Q be compleated, L B will be the sought Root x of the Equation.

Thus far, I think, I have expounded the Construction of solid Problems by Operations whose manual Practice is most simple and expeditious. So the Antients, after they had obtained a Method of solving these Problems by a Composition of solid Places, thinking the Constructions by the Conick Sections useless, by reason of the Difficulty of describing them, sought easier Constructions by the Conchoid, Cissoid, the Extension of Threads, and by any Mechanick Application of Figures, preferring useful Things though Mechanical, to useless Speculations in Geometry, as we learn from *Pappus*. So the great *Archimedes* himself neglected the Trisection of an Angle by the Conick Sections, which had been handled by other Geometricians before him, and taught how to trisect an Angle in his Lemmas after the Method we have already explained. If the Antients had rather construct Problems by Figures not received in Geometry in that Time, how much more ought these Figures now to be preferred which are received by many into Geometry as well as the Conick Sections.

However, I do not agree to this new Sort of Geometricians, who receive all Figures into Geometry. Their Rule of admitting all Lines to the Construction of Problems in that Order in which the Equations, whereby the Lines are defined, ascend to the Number of Dimensions, is arbitrary and has no Foundation in Geometry. Nay, it is false; for according to this Rule, the Circle should be joined with the Conick Sections, but all Geometers join it with the right Line; and this being an inconstant Rule, takes away the Foundation of admitting into Geometry all Analytick Lines in a certain Order. In my Judgment, no Lines ought to be admitted into plain Geometry besides the right Line and the Circle, unless some Distinction of Lines might be first invented, by which a circular Line might be joined with a right Line, and separated from all the rest. But truly plain Geometry is not then to be augmented by the Number of Lines. For all Figures are plain that are admitted into plain Geometry, that is, those which the Geometers postulate to be described *in plano*. And every plain Problem is that which may be constructed by plain Figures. So therefore admitting the Conick Sections and other Figures more compounded into plain Geometry, all the solid and more than solid Problems that can be constructed by these Figures

Figures will become plane. But all plane Problems are of the same Order. A right Line is Analytically more simple than a Circle; neverthelefs, Problems which are constructed by right Lines alone, and those that are constructed by Circles, are of the same Order. These Things being postulated, a Circle is reduced to the same Order with a right Line. And much more the Ellipse, which differs much lefs from a Circle than a Circle from a right Line, by postulating in like manner the Description thereof *in plano*, will be reduced to the same Order with the Circle. If any, in considering the Ellipse, should fall upon some solid Problem, and should construct it by the Help of the same Ellipse, and a Circle: This would be counted a plane Problem, because the Ellipse was supposed to be described *in plano*, and all the Construction besides will be solved by the Description of the Circle only. Wherefore, for the same Reason, every plane Problem whatever may be constructed by a given Ellipse. For Example, [*See* Figure 108.] If the Center O of the given Ellipse A D F G be required, I would draw the two Parallels A B, C D meeting the Ellipse in A, B, C, D; and also two other Parallels E F, G H meeting the Ellipse in E, F, G, H, and I would bisect them in I, K, L, M, and produce I K, L M, till they meet in O. This is a real Construction of a plane Problem by an Ellipse. It imports nothing that an Ellipse is Analytically defined by an Equation of two Dimensions. Nor that it be generated Geometrically by the Section of a solid Figure. The Hypothesis, only considering it as already described *in plano*, reduces all solid Problems constructed by it to the Order of plane ones, and concludes, that all plane ones may be rightly constructed by it. And this is the State of a *Postulate*. Whatever may be supposed done, it is permitted to assume it, as already done and given. Therefore let this be a Postulate to describe an Ellipse *in plano*, and then all those Problems that can be constructed by an Ellipse, may be reduced to the Order of plane ones, and all plane Problems may be constructed by the Ellipse.

It is necessary therefore that either plane and solid Problems be confounded among one another, or that all Lines be flung out of plane Geometry, besides the right Line and the Circle, unlefs it happens that sometime some other is given in the State of constructing some Problem. But certainly none will permit the Orders of Problems to be confused. Therefore the Conick Sections and all other Figures must be cast out of plane Geometry, except the right Line and the Circle, and those which happen to be given in the State of the Problems. Therefore all these Descriptions of the Conicks *in plano*, which the Moderns are so fond of, are foreign to Geometry. Neverthelefs, the Conick Sections ought not to be flung out of Geometry. They indeed are not described Geometrically *in plano*, but are generated in the plane Superficies of a Geometrical Solid. A Cone is constituted geometrically, and cut by a Geometrical Plane. Such a Segment of a Cone is a Geometrical Figure, and has the same Place in solid Geometry, as the Segment of a Circle has in Plane, and for this Reason its Base, which they call a Conick Section, is a Geometrical Figure. Therefore a Conick Section hath a Place in Geometry so far as it is the Superficies of a Geometrical Solid; but is Geometrical for no other Reason than that it is generated by the Section of a Solid, and therefore was not in former Times admitted but only into solid Geometry. But such a Generation of the Conick Sections is difficult, and generally uselefs in Practice, to which Geometry ought to be most serviceable. Therefore the Antients betook themselves to various Mechanical Descriptions of Figures *in plano*. And we, after their Example, have framed the preceding Constructions. Let these Constructions be Mechanical; and so the Constructions by Conick Sections described *in plano* (as is wont now to be done) are Mechanical. Let the Constructions by Conick Sections given be Geometrical; and so the Constructions by any other given Figures are Geometrical, and of the same Order with the Constructions of plane Problems. There is no Reason that the Conick Sections should be preferred in Geometry before any other Figures, unlefs so far as they are derived from the Section of a Cone; they being altogether unserviceable in Practice in the Solution of Problems. But least I should wholly neglect Constructions by the Conick Sections, it will be proper to say something concerning them, in which also we will consider some commodious manual Description.

The Ellipse is the most simple of the Conick Sections, most known, and nearest of Kin to a Circle, and easiest described by the Hand *in plano*. Many prefer the Parabola before it, for the Simplicity of the Equation by which it is expressed. But by this Reason the Parabola ought to be

K k preferred

preferred before the Circle it ſelf, which it never is. Therefore the reaſoning from the Simplicity of the Equation will not hold. The modern Geometers are too fond of the Speculation of Equations. The Simplicity of theſe is of an Analytick Conſideration. We treat of Compoſition, and Laws are not given to Compoſition from Analyſis. Analyſis does lead to Compoſition: But it is not true Compoſition before its freed from Analyſis. If there be never ſo little Analyſis in Compoſition, that Compoſition is not yet real. Compoſition in it ſelf is perfect, and far from a Mixture of Analytick Speculations. The Simplicity of Figures depend upon the Simplicity of their Geneſis and Ideas, and it is not an Equation but a Deſcription (either Geometrical or Mechanical) by which a Figure is generated and rendered more eaſy to the Conception. Therefore we give the Ellipſe the firſt Place, and ſhall now ſhew how to conſtruct Equations by it.

Let there be any Cubick Equation propoſed, $x^3 = px^2 + qx + r$, *where* p, q, *and* r *ſignify given Co-efficients of the Terms of the Equation, with their Signs* $+$ *and* $-$, *and either of the Terms* p *and* q, *or both of them, may be wanting.* For ſo we ſhall exhibit the Conſtructions of all Cubick Equations in one Operation, which follows:

From the Point B in any given right Line, take any two right Lines, BC and BE, on the ſame Side the Point B, and alſo BD, ſo that it may be a mean Proportional between them. [*See* Figure 109.] And call BC, n, in the ſame right Line alſo take $BA = \frac{q}{n}$, and that towards the Point C, if $-q$, if not, the contrary Way. At the Point A erect a Perpendicular AI, and in it take $AF = p$, $FG = AF$, $FI = \frac{r}{nn}$, and FH to FI as BC is to BE. But FH and FI are to be taken on the ſame Side of the Point F towards G, if the Terms p and r have the ſame Signs; and if they have not the ſame Signs, towards the Point A. Let the Parallelograms IACK and HAEL be compleated, and from the Center K, with the Diſtance KG, let a Circle be deſcribed. Then in the Line HL let there be taken HR on either Side the Point H, which let be to HL as BD to BE; let GR be drawn, cutting EL in S, and let the Line GRS be moved with its Point R falling on the Line HL, and the Point S upon the Line EL, until its third Point G in deſcribing the Ellipſe, meet the Circle, as is to be ſeen in the Poſition of $\gamma\varrho\sigma$. For half the Perpendicular γX let fall from γ the Point of meeting to AE will be the Root of the Equation. But G or γ the End of the Rule GRS, or $\gamma\varrho\sigma$, can meet the Circle in as many Points as there are poſſible Roots. And thoſe Roots are Affirmative which fall towards the ſame Parts of the Line EA, as the Line FI drawn from the Point F does, and thoſe are Negative which fall towards the contrary Parts of the Line AE if r is Affirmative; and contrarily if r is Negative.

But this Conſtruction is *demonſtrated* by the Help of the following *Lemmas.*

LEMMA I.

All being ſuppoſed as in the Conſtruction, $2CAX - AXq$ is $= \gamma Xq - 2AI \times \gamma X + 2AG \times FI$.

For from the Nature of the Circle, $K\gamma q - CXq$ is $= \overline{\gamma X - AI}|^2$. But $K\gamma q$ is $= GIq + ACq$, and $CXq = \overline{AX - AC}|^2$, that is, $= AXq - 2CAX + ACq$, and ſo their Difference $GIq + 2CAX - AXq$ is $= \overline{\gamma X - AI}|^2 = \gamma Xq - 2AI \times \gamma X + AIq$. Subtract GIq from both, and there will remain $2CAX - AXq = \gamma Xq - 2AI \times \gamma X + AIq - GIq$. But (by *Prop.* 4. *Book* 2. *Elem.*) AIq is $= AGq + 2AGI + GIq$, and ſo $AIq - GIq$ is $= AGq + 2AGI$, that is, $= 2AG \times \overline{\tfrac{1}{2}AG + GI}$, or $= 2AG \times FI$, and thence $2CAX - AXq$ is $= \gamma Xq - 2AI \times \gamma X + 2AG \times FI$. Q. E. D.

LEMMA II.

All Things being conſtructed as above $2EAX - AXq$ *is* $= \frac{FI}{FH} X\gamma q - \frac{2FI}{FH} AH \times X\gamma + 2AG \times FI$.

For it is known, that the Point γ, by the Motion of the Ruler $\gamma\varrho\sigma$ aſſigned above, deſcribes an Ellipſe, the Center whereof is L, and the two Axis's coincide with the two right Lines LE and LH, of which that which is in LE is $= 2\gamma\varrho$, or $= 2GR$, and the other which is in LH is $= 2\gamma\sigma$, or $= 2GS$. And the Ratio of theſe to one another

Kk 2 is

is the same as that of the Line HR to the Line HL, or of the Line BD to the Line BE. Whence the *Latus Transversum* is to the principal *Latus Rectum*, as BE is to BC, or as FI is to FH. Wherefore since γT is ordinately applied to HL, it will be from the Nature of the Ellipse $GSq - LTq = \frac{FI}{FH} T\gamma$ squared. But LT is $= AE - AX$, and $T\gamma = X\gamma - AH$. Let the Squares of which be put instead of LTq and $T\gamma q$, and then $GSq - AEq + 2EAX - AXq$ will become $= \frac{FI}{FH} \times X\gamma q - 2AH \times X\gamma + AHq$. But $GSq - AEq$ is $= \overline{GH+LS}|^2$, because GS is the Hypothenuse of a Rectangled Triangle, the Sides whereof are equal to AE and $GH + LS$. And (by reason of the similar Triangles RGH and RSL) LS is to GH as LR is to HR, and by Composition $GH + LS$ is to GH as HL is to HR, and by squaring the Proportions $\overline{CH+LS}|^2$ is to GHq as HLq is to HRq, that is, (by Construction) as BEq is to BDq, that is, as BE is to BC, or as FI is to FH, and so $\overline{GH+LS}|^2$ is $= \frac{FI}{FH} GHq$. Therefore $GSq - AEq$ is $= \frac{FI}{FH} GHq$, and so $\frac{FI}{FH} GHq + 2EAX - AXq = \frac{FI}{FH} \times X\gamma q - 2AH \times X\gamma + AHq$. Subtract $\frac{FI}{FH} GHq$ from both Sides, and there will remain $2EAX - AXq = \frac{FI}{FH} \times X\gamma q - 2AH \times X\gamma + AHq - GHq$. But AH is $= AG + GH$, and so $AHq = AGq + 2AGH + GHq$, and by subtracting GHq from both, there will remain $AHq - GHq = AGq + 2AGH$, that is, $= 2AG \times \overline{\tfrac{1}{2}AG + GH} = 2AG \times FH$, and therefore $2EAX - AXq$ is $= \frac{FI}{FH} \times X\gamma q -$

2 AH

$2AH \times X\gamma + 2AG \times FH$, that is, $= \frac{FI}{FH} X\gamma q - \frac{2FI}{FH} AH \times X\gamma + 2AG \times FI$. Q.E.D.

LEMMA III.

All Things standing as before, AX will be to $X\gamma - AG$ as $X\gamma$ is to 2BC.

For if from the Equals in the *second Lemma* there be subtracted the Equals in the *first Lemma*, there will remain $2CE \times AX = \frac{HI}{FH} X\gamma q - \frac{2FI}{FH} AH \times X\gamma + 2AI \times X\gamma$. Let both Sides be multiplied by FH, and $2FH \times CE \times AX$ will become $= HI \times X\gamma q - 2FI \times AH \times X\gamma + 2AI \times FH \times X\gamma$. But AI is $= HI + AH$, and so $2FI \times AH - 2FH \times AI = 2FI \times AH - 2FHA - 2FHI$. But $2FI \times HA - 2FHA = 2AHI$, and $2AHI - 2FHI = 2HI \times AF$. Therefore $2FI \times AH - 2FH \times AI = 2HI \times AF$, and so $2FH \times CE \times AX = HI \times X\gamma q - 2HI \times AF \times X\gamma$. And thence as HI is to FH, so is $2CE \times AX$ to $X\gamma q - 2AF \times X\gamma$. But by Construction HI is to FH as CE is to BC, and consequently as $2CE \times AX$ is to $2BC \times AX$, and therefore $2BC \times AX$ will be $= X\gamma q - 2AF \times X\gamma$, (by *Prop.* 9. *Book* 5. *Elem.*) But because the Rectangles are equal, the Sides are proportional, AX to $X\gamma - 2AF$, (that is, $X\gamma - AG$) as $X\gamma$ is to 2BC. Q.E.D.

LEMMA IV.

The same Things being still supposed, 2FI *is to* $AX - 2AB$ *as* $X\gamma$ *is to* 2BC.

For if from the Equals in the *third Lemma*, to wit, $2BC \times AX = X\gamma q - 2AF \times X\gamma$, the Equals in the *first Lemma* be subtracted, there will remain $-2AB \times AX + AXq = 2FI \times X\gamma - 2AG \times FI$, that is, $AX \times \overline{AX - 2AB} = 2FI \times \overline{X\gamma - AG}$. But because the Rectangles are Equal, the Sides are Proportional, 2FI is to $AX - 2AB$ as AX is to $X\gamma - AG$, that is, (by the *third Lemma*) as $X\gamma$ is to 2BC. Q.E.D.

At

At length, by the Help of theſe Lemmas, the Conſtruction of the Problem is thus demonſtrated.

By the *fourth Lemma*, $X\gamma$ is to $2BC$ as $2FI$ is to $AX - 2AB$, that is, (by *Prop.* 1. *Book* 6. *Elem.*) as $2BC \times 2FI$ is to $2BC \times \overline{AX - 2AB}$, or to $2BC \times AX - 2BC \times 2AB$. But by the *third Lemma*, AX is to $X\gamma - 2AF$ as $X\gamma$ is to $2BC$, or $2BC \times AX = X\gamma q - 2AF \times X\gamma$, and conſequently $X\gamma$ is to $2BC$ as $2BC \times 2FI$ is to $X\gamma q - 2AF \times X\gamma - 2BC \times 2AB$. And by multiplying the Means and Extreams into themſelves, $X\gamma$ *cub.* $- 2AF \times X\gamma q - 4BC \times AB \times X\gamma = 8BCq \times FI$. And by adding $2AF \times X\gamma q + 4BC \times AB \times X\gamma$ to both Sides $X\gamma$ *cub.* is $= 2AF \times X\gamma q + 4BC \times AB \times X\gamma + 8BCq \times FI$. But $\frac{1}{2}X\gamma$ in the Conſtruction to be demonſtrated was equal to the Root of the Equation $= x$, and $AF = p$, $BC = n$, $AB = \frac{q}{n}$, and $FI = \frac{r}{nn}$, and therefore $BC \times AB = q$. And $BCq \times FI = r$. Which being ſubſtituted, will make $x^3 = px^2 + qx + r$. Q. E. D.

Corol. Hence if AF and AB be ſuppoſed equal to nothing, by the third and fourth *Lemma*, $2FI$ will be to AX as AX is to $X\gamma$, and $X\gamma$ to $2BC$. From whence ariſes the Invention of two mean Proportionals between any two given Quantities, FI and BC.

Scholium. Hitherto I have only expounded the Conſtruction of a Cubick Equation by the Ellipſe; but the Rule is of a more univerſal Nature, extending it ſelf indifferently to all the Conick Sections. For, if inſtead of the Ellipſe you would uſe the Hyperbola, take the Lines BC and BE on the contrary Side of the Point B, then let the Points A, F, G, I, H, K, L, and R be determined as before, except only that FH ought to be taken on the Side of F not towards I, and that HR ought to be taken in the Line AI not in HL, on each Side the Point H, and inſtead of the right Line GRS, two other right Lines are to be drawn from the Point L to the two Points R and R for Aſymptotes to the Hyperbola. With theſe Aſymptotes LR, LR deſcribe an Hyperbola through the Point G, and a Circle from the Center K with the Diſtance GK: And the halves of the Perpendiculars let fall from their Interſections to the right Line AE will be the Roots of the Equation propoſed. All which, the Signs $+$ and $-$ being rightly changed, are demonſtrated as above.

But

But if you would uſe the Parabola, the Point E will be removed to an infinite Diſtance, and ſo not to be taken any where, and the Point H will coincide with the Point F, and the Parabola will be to be deſcribed about the Axis HL with the principal *Latus Rectum* BC through the Points G and A, the Vertex being placed on the ſame Side of the Point F, on which the Point B is in reſpect of the Point C.

Thus the Conſtructions by the Parabola, if you regard Analytick Simplicity, are the moſt ſimple of all. Thoſe by the Hyperbola next, and thoſe which are ſolved by the Ellipſe, have the third Place. But if in deſcribing of Figures, the Simplicity of the manual Operation be reſpected, the Order muſt be changed.

But it is to be obſerved in theſe Conſtructions, that by the Proportion of the principal *Latus Rectum* to the *Latus Tranſverſum*, the Species of the Ellipſe and Hyperbola may be determined, and that Proportion is the ſame as that of the Lines BC and BE, and therefore may be aſſumed: But there is but one Species of the Parabola, which is obtained by putting BE infinitely long. So therefore we may conſtruct any Cubick Equation by a Conick Section of any given Species. To change Figures given in Specie into Figures given in Magnitude, is done by encreaſing or diminiſhing in a given Ratio, all the Lines by which the Figures were given in Specie, and ſo we may conſtruct all Cubick Equations by any given Conick Section whatever. Which is more fully explained thus.

Let there be propoſed any Cubick Equation $x^3 = pxx \,.\, qx \,.\, r$, *to conſtruct it by the Help of any given Conick Section.* [See *Figures* 110 and 111.]

From any Point B in any infinite right Line BCE, take any two Lengths BC, and BE towards the ſame Way, if the Conick Section is an Ellipſe, but towards contrary Ways if it be an Hyperbola. But let BC be to BE as the principal *Latus Rectum* of the given Section, is to the *Latus Tranſverſum*, and call BC, n, take $BA = \frac{q}{n}$, and that towards C, if q be Negative, and contrarily if Affirmative. At the Point A erect a Perpendicular AI, and in it take $AF = p$, and $FG = AF$; and $FI = \frac{r}{nn}$. But let FI be taken towards G if the Terms p and r have the ſame Signs, if not, towards A. Then make as FH is to FI ſo is BC to BE,

and

and take this F H from the Point F towards I, if the Section is an Ellipse, but towards the contrary Way if it is an Hyperbola. But let the Parallelograms I A C K and H A E L be compleated, and all these Lines already described transferred to the given Conick Section; or, which is the same Thing, let the Curve be described about them, so that its Axis or principal transverse Diameter might agree with the right Line L H, and the Center with the Point L. These Things being done, let the Line K L be drawn as also G L cutting the Conick Section in g. In L K take L k, which let be to L K as L g to L G, and from the Center k, with the Distance $k\,g$, describe a Circle. From the Points where it cuts the given Curve, let fall Perpendiculars to the Line L H, whereof let T γ be one. Lastly, towards γ take T Y, which let be to T γ as L G to L g, and this T Y produced will cut A B in X, and $\frac{1}{2}$ X Y will be one of the Roots of the Equation. But those Roots are Affirmative which lie towards such Parts of A B as F I lies from F, and those are Negative which lie on the contrary Side, if r is $+$, and the contrary if r is $-$

After this Manner are Cubick Equations constructed by given Ellipses and Hyperbolas: But if a Parabola should be given, the Line B C is to be taken equal to the *Latus Rectum* it self. Then the Points A, F, G, I, and K, being found as above, a Circle must be described from the Center K with the Distance K G, and the Parabola must be so applied to the Scheme already described, (or the Scheme to the Parabola) that it may pass through the Points A and G, and its Axis through the Point F parallel to A C, the Vertex falling on the same Side of the Point F as the Point B falls of the Point C; these being done, if Perpendiculars were let fall from the Points where the Parabola intersects the Circle to the Line B C, their Halves will be equal to the Roots of the Equation to be constructed.

And take Notice, that where the second Term of the Equation is wanting, and so the *Latus Rectum* of the Parabola is the Number 2, the Construction comes out the same as that which *Des Cartes* produced in his Geometry, with this Difference only, that these Lines are the double of them.

This is a general Rule of Constructions. But where particular Problems are proposed, we ought to consult the most simple Forms of Constructions. For the Quantity n remains free, by the taking of which the Equation may, for the most part, be rendered more simple. One Example of which I will give.

Let there be given an Ellipse, and let there be two mean Proportionals to be found between the given Lines a and b. Let the first of them be x, and $a \,.\, x \,.\, \frac{xx}{a} \,.\, b$ will be continual Proportionals, and so $ab = \frac{x^3}{a}$, or $x^3 = aab$, is the Equation which you must construct. Here the Terms p and q are wanting, and the Term $r = aab$, and therefore B A and A F are $= 0$, and F I is $= \frac{aab}{nn}$. That the last Term may be more simple, let n be assumed $= a$, and let F I be $= b$. And then the Construction will be thus:

From any Point A in any infinite right Line A E [*See Figure* 112.] take A C $= a$, and on the same Side of the Point A take A C to A E as the principal *Latus Rectum* of the Ellipse is to the *Latus Transversum*. Then in the Perpendicular A I take A I $= b$, and A H to A I as A C to A E. Let the Parallelograms I A C K, H A E L be compleated. Join L A and L K. Upon this Scheme lay the given Ellipse, and it will cut the right Line A L in the Point g. Make L k to L K as L g to L A. From the Center k, with the Distance $k\,g$, describe a Circle cutting the Ellipse in γ. Upon A E let fall the Perpendicular γ X, cutting H L in T, and let that be produced to Y, that T Y may be to T as L A to L g. And so $\frac{1}{2}$ X Y will be equal to x the first of the two mean Proportionals. Q. E. I.

L l A

"Lexicon Technicum. Or, an Universal Dictionary of Arts and Sciences." By John Harris. Volume 2 (London 1710). Article: "Curves, by Sir Isaac Newton."

CURVES. *The incomparable Sir* Isaac Newton *gives this following Ennumeration of Geometrical Lines of the Third or Cubick Order; in which you have an admirable account of many Species of* Curves *which exceed the* Conick-Sections, *for they go no higher than the Quadratick or Se-Second Order.*

The Orders of Geometrick Lines.

1: GEOMETRICK-LINES, are best distinguish'd into *Classes*, *Genders*, or *Orders*, according to the Number of the Dimensions of an Equation, expressing the relation between the *Ordinates* and the *Abscissæ*; or which is much at one, according to the Number of Points in which they may be cut by a Right Line. Wherefore, a Line of the *First Order* will be only a *Right Line*: These of the *Second* or *Quadratick Order*, will be the *Circle* and the *Conick-Sections*; and these of the *Third* or *Cubick Order*, will be the *Cubical* and *Nelian Parabola's*, the *Cissoid* of the Antients, and the rest as belew ennumerated. But a *Curve* of the *First Gender* (becausе a Right Line can't be reckoned among the *Curves*) is the same with a Line of the *Second Order*, and a *Curve* of the *Second Gender*; the same with a Line of the *Third Order*, and a Line of an *Infinitesimal Order*, is that which a Right Line may cut in infinite Points, as the *Spiral*, *Cycloid*, the *Quadratrix*, and every Line generated by the Infinite Revolutions of a *Radius* or *Rota*.

2. The chief Properties of the *Conick-Sections* are every where treated of by Geometers; and of the same Nature are the Properties of the *Curves* of the *Second Gender*, and of the rest, as from the following Ennumeration of their Principle Properties will appear.

3. For if any right and parallel Lines be drawn and terminated on both Sides by one and the same *Conick-Section*; and a Right Line bisecting any two of them, shall bisect all the rest; and therefore such a Line is called the Diameter of the Figure; and all the Right Lines so bisected, are called *Ordinate Applicates* to that Diameter, and the Point of Concourse to all the Diameters is called the *Center* of the *Figure*; as the Intersection of the *Curve* and of the Diameter, is called the *Vertex*, and that Diameter the *Axis* to which the Ordinates are *Normally* applied. And so in *Curves* of the *Second Gender*, if any two right and parallel Lines are drawn occurring to the Curve in Three Points; a right Line which shall so cut those Parallels, that the Sum of Two Parts terminated at the Curve on one Side of the Intersecting Line shall be equal to the third Part terminated at the Curve on the other side, this Line shall cut, after the same manner, all others parallel to these, and occurring to the Curve in Three-Points; that is, shall so cut them that the Sum of the Two Parts on one Side of it, shall be equal to the Third Part on the other.

And therefore these Three Parts one of which is thus every where equal to the Sum of the other two, may be called *Ordinate Applicates* also: And the Intersecting Line to which the Ordinates are applied, may be called the *Diameter*; the Intersection of the Diameter and the Curve, may be called the *Vertex*, and the Point of Concourse of any two Diameters, the *Center*.

And if the Diameter be Normal to the Ordinates, it may be called the *Axis*; and that Point where *all* the Diameters terminate, the *General Centre*.

Assymptotes and their Properties.

4. The Hyperbola of the First Gender has Two *Assymptotes*, that of the Second, Three; that of the Third, Four, and it can have no more, and so of the rest. And as the Parts of any Right Line lying between the *Conical Hyperbola* and its Two Assymptotes are every where equal; so in the Hyperbola's of the Second Gender, if any Right Line be drawn, cutting both the Curve and its Three Assymptotes, in Three Points; the Sum of the Two Parts of that Right Line, being drawn the same way from any Two Assymptotes to Two Points of the Curve, will be equal to the Third Part drawn a contrary way from the Third Assymptote to a Third Point of the Curve.

Latera Transversa and Recta.

5. And as in *Non Parabolick Conick Sections*, the Square of the Ordinate Applicate, that is, the Rectangle under the Ordinates, drawn at contrary Sides of the Diameter, is to the Rectangle of the Parts of the Diameter, which are terminated at the Vertex's of the *Ellipsis* or *Hyperbola*; as a certain Given Line which is called the *Latus Rectum*, is to that Part of the Diameter which lies between the Vertex's, and is called the *Latus Transversum*: so in *Non-Parabolick Curves* of the Second Gender, a Parallelopiped under the Three Ordinate Applicates, is to a Parallelopiped, under the Parts of the Diameter terminated at the Ordinates, and the Three Vertex's of the Figure in a certain Given Ratio; in which Ratio, if you take Three Right Lines to the Three Parts of a Diameter scituated between the Vertex's of the Figure, one answering to another, then these Three Right Lines may be called the *Latera Recta* of the Figure, and the Parts of the Diameter between the *Vertices*, the *Latera Transversa*. And as in the Conick Parabola having to one and the same Diameter but one only Vertex, the Rectangle under the Ordinates is equal to that under the Part of the Diameter cut off between the Ordinates and the Vertex, and a certain Line called the *Latus Rectum*: So in the Curves of the Second Gender, which have but two Vertex's to the same Diameter; the Parallelopiped under Three Ordinates, is equal to the Parallelopiped under the Two Parts of the Diameter cut off between the Ordinates and those Two Vertexes, and a given Right Line, which therefore may be called the *Latus Rectum*.

The Ratio of the Rectangles under the Segments of Parallels.

Lastly, As in the Conick-Sections when two parallels terminated on each side at the Curve, are cut by two other Parallels terminated on each side by the Curve, the First being cut by the Third, and the Second by the Fourth; as here the Rectangle under the Parts of the First, is to the Rectangle under the Parts of the Third; as the Rectangle under the Parts of the Second is to that under the Parts of the Fourth: So when Four such Right Lines occur to a Curve of the Second Gender, each one in Three Points, then shall the Parallelopiped under the Parts of the First right Line be to that under the Parts of the Third, and as the Parallelopiped under the Parts of the Second Line into that under the Pares of the Fourth.

Hyperbolick and Parabolick Legs.

All the Legs of Curves of the second and higher Genders, as well as of the first, infinitely drawn out, will be of the *Hyperbolick* or *Parabolick* Gender; and I call that an *Hyperbolick* Leg, which infinitely approaches to some *Asymptote*; and that a *Parabolick* one, which hath no *Asymptote*. And these Legs are best known from the Tangents: For if the Point of Contact be at an infinite Distance, the Tangent of an *Hyperbolick Leg* will coincide with the *Asymptote*, and the Tangent of a Parabolick Leg will recede *in infinitum*, will vanish and no where be found. Wherefore the Asymptote of any Leg is found, by seeking the Tangent to that Leg at a Point infinitely distant: And the *Course*, *Place* or *Way* of an infinite Leg, is found by seeking the Position of any Right Line, which is parallel to the Tangent where the Point of Contact goes off *in infinitum*: For this Right Line is directed towards the same way with the infinite Leg.

The Reduction of all Curves of the Second Gender, to Four Cases of Equations.

CASE I

All Lines of the First, Third, Fifth and Seventh Order, and so of any one, proceeding in the Order of the odd Numbers, have at least two Legs or Sides proceeding on *ad infinitum*, and towards contrary ways. And all Lines of the Third Order have two such Legs or Sides running out contrary ways, and towards which no other of their infinite Legs (except in the *Cartesian Parabola*) do tend. If the Legs are of the Hyperbolick Gender, let GAS be their Asymptote; and to it let the Parallel CBc be drawn, terminated (if possible) at both Ends at the Curve. Let this Parallel be bisected in X; and then will the Place of that Point X

Fig. 1.

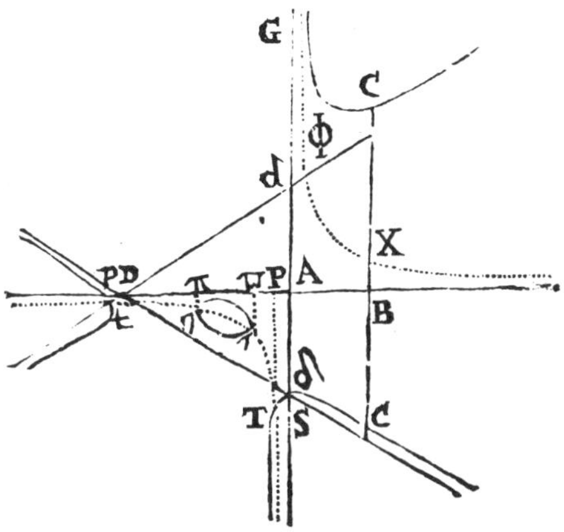

be the *Conical Hyperbola* $X\Phi$, one of whose Asymptotes is AS: Let its other Asymptote be AB; then the *Equation* by which the Relation between the Ordinate BC and the Abscissa AB is determimined, if AB be put $=x$ and $BC=y$, will always be in this Form, $xyy+ey=ax^3+bxx+cx+d$, where the Terms e, a, b, c and d denote given Quantities, affected with their Signs $+$ and $-$; of which any one may be wanting, so the Figure, through their Defect, don't turn into a Conick-Section. And this Conical Hyperbola may coincide with its Asymptotes, that is, the Point X may come to be in the Line AB, and then the Term $+ey$ will be wanting.

CASE II.

9. But if the Right Line CBc cannot be terminated both ways at the Curve, but will occur to the Curve only in one Point; then draw any Line in a given Position, which shall cut the Asymptote AS in A; as also any other Right Line, as BC, parallel to the Asymptote, and meeting the Curve in the Point C: And then the Equation by which the Relation between the Ordinate BC and the Abscissa AB is determined, will always put on this Form, $xy=ax^3+bxx+cx+d$.

CASE III.

10. But if the opposite Legs are of the Parabolick Gender, draw the Right Line CBc, terminated at both Ends, if it's possible, at the Curve; and running according to the Course of the Legs; which bissect in B: Then shall the Place of B be a Right Line. Let that Right Line be AB, terminated at any given Point, as A; and then the Equation by which the Relation between the Ordinate BC and the Abscissa AB is determined, will always be in this Form, $yy=ax^3+bxx+cx+d$.

CASE IV.

11. But if the Right Line CBc meet the Curve but in one Point, and therefore can't be terminated at the Curve at both Ends; let the Point where it occurs to the Curve be C; and let that Right Line at the Point B, fall on any other Right Line given in Position, as AB, and terminated at any given Point, as A: Then will the Equation, by which the Relation between the Ordinate BC and the Abscissa $A\beta$ is determined, always be in this Form, $yy=ax^3+bxx+cx+d$.

The Names of the Forms.

12. In the Enumeration of Curves of these Cases, we call that an *Inscribed Hyperbola*, which lies entirely within the Angle of the Asymptotes, like the *Conical Hyperbola*; and that a *Circumscribed* one, which cuts the Asymptotes, and contains the Parts cut off within its own proper Space; and that an *Ambigenal* one, which hath one of its innite Legs inscribing it, and the other circumscribing it. I call that a *Converging* one, whose Concave Legs bend inwards towards one another, and run both the same way; but that I call a *Diverging* one, whose Legs turn their Convexities towards each other, and tend towards quite contrary ways. I call that *Hyperbola contrary leg'd*, whose Legs are Convex towards contrary Parts, and run infinitely on towards contrary ways; and that a *Conchoidal one*, which is applied to its Asymptote with its Concave Vertex and diverging Legs; and that an *Anguineal or Eel-like* one, which cuts its Asymptote with contrary Flexions, and is produced both ways into contrary Legs. I call that a *Cruciform or Cross-like one*, which cuts its Conjugate cross-wise; and that *Nodate*, which, by returning round into, decussates it self. I call that *Cuspidate*, whose two Parts meet and terminate in the Angle of Contact; and that *Punctate*, whose Oval *Conjugate* is infinitely small, or a Point: And that Hyperbola I

call *Pure*, which, by the Impoſſibility of its two Roots, is without any Oval Node, Spike, or Conjugate Point. And in the ſame Senſe I denominate a Parabola alſo, to be *Converging*, *Diverging*, *contrary leg'd*, *Cruciform*, *Nodate*, *Cuſpidate*, *Punctate*, and *Pure*.

Of the Redundant Hyperbola and its Aſymptotes.

13. In the Firſt Caſe, if the Term ax^3 be Affirmative, then the Figure will be a triple Hyperbola with ſix Hyperbolical Legs, which will run on infinitely by the three Aſymptotes, of which none are parallel, two Legs towards each Aſymptote, and towards contrary Parts; and theſe Aſymptotes, if the Term bxx be not wanting in the Equation, will mutually interſect each other in three Points, forming thereby the Triangle $Dd\delta$. But if the Term bxx (ſee *Fig.* 1.) be wanting, they will all converge to the ſame Point. In the former Caſe take $AD = \frac{-b}{2a}$, and $Ad = A\delta = \frac{b}{2\sqrt{d}}$, and join Dd,

Fig. 30.

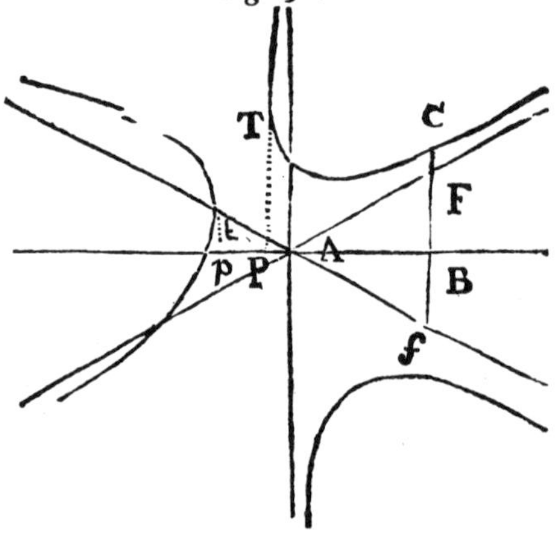

$D\delta$; ſo ſhall AD, Dd, and $D\delta$, be the three Aſymptotes. In the latter Caſe, draw any Ordinate, as BC, in which, both ways produced, take, on each Side, BF and Bf equal to one another, and in the ſame Ratio with AB that $\sqrt{a}$ hath to I; and then joining AF, Af; AB, AF, and Af, ſhall be the three Aſymptotes. And this kind of *Hyperbola* I call *Redundant*, becauſe it exceeds the Conick-Sections in the Number of its Hyperbolick Legs.

Of the Diameters of this Hyperbola, and the Poſition of its infinite Legs.

14. In every Redundant Hyperbola, if neither the Term ey be wanting, nor $bb - 4ac$ equal to $+ae\sqrt{:a}$, the Curve will have no Diameter; but if either of thoſe happen, it will have *one only Diameter*, and *three* if they both happen. And the Diameter will always paſs through the Interſection of two of the Aſymptotes, and biſſect all Right Lines which are terminated each way by thoſe Aſymptotes, and which are parallel to the third Aſymptote: And the *Abſciſſa* AB will be the Diameter of the Figure, as often as the Term ey is wanting. I take the Word *Diameter* here, and in the following Pages, *Abſolutely*; and in the common Acceptation of it, *viz.* for an Abſciſſa which hath every-where two equal Ordinates, one on eaeh Side, inſiſting at the ſame Point.

Nine Redundant Hyperbola's, having no Diameter, but three Aſymptotes, which form a Triangle.

m 15. If the Redundant Hyperbola have no Diameter, let the four Roots or Values of x in this quation $ax^4 + bx^3 + cxx + dx + \frac{1}{4}ee = 0$, be ſought: And ſuppoſe them to be AP, $A\varpi$, $A\pi$, and Ap. Let the Ordinates PT, $\varpi\tau$, $\pi\tau$, and pt, be erected, and thoſe ſhall touch the Curve in the Points T, τ, τ, t, and by that Contact ſhall give the Limits of the Curve, by which its *Species* will be diſcovered.

For if all the Roots AP, $A\varpi$, $A\pi$, Ap, (ſee *Fig.* 1.) are real, having the ſame Sign, and are unequal, the Curve conſiſts of three Hyperbola's,

Fig. 2.

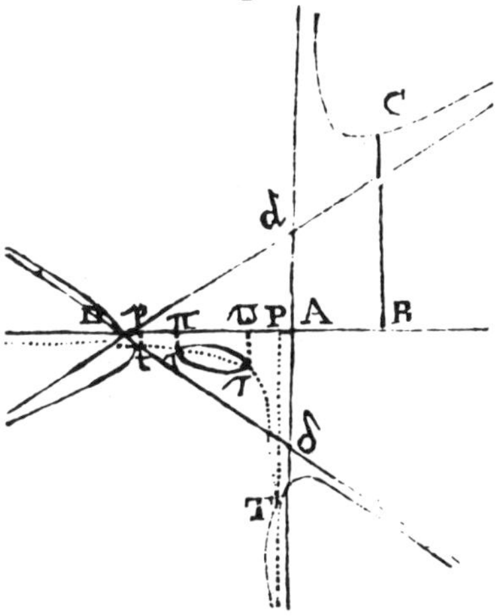

(an *Inſcribed*, a *Circumſcribed*, and an *Ambigeneal* one) *with an Oval*: And one of the Hyperbola's will lie towards *D*, another towards *d*, and the Third toward *δ*; and the Oval will always lie within the Triangle *D d δ*, and alſo within the middle Limits 7 and τ, where it will be touch'd by the Ordinates *π* 7 and *ϖ τ*. And this is the *Firſt Species*.

But if either the two greateſt Roots, *A π*, *A p*; or the two leaſt, *A P*, *A ϖ*, are equal to one another, and have the ſame Sign with the other two; then the *Oval* and *Circumſcribed Hyperbola* will join with one another, the Points of Contact 7 and *t*, or *T* and τ, co-inciding; and the Legs of the Hyderbola decuſſating one another, will be continued in the Oval, and make the *Nodate* Figure. Which is the *Second Species*.

If the three greateſt of the Roots, *A p*, *A π*, *A ϖ*; or the three leaſt, *A π*, *A ϖ*, *A P*, are equal

Fig. 3.

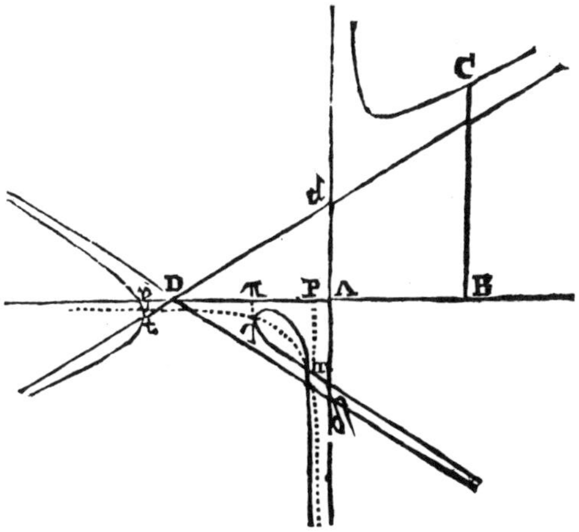

Fig. 4.

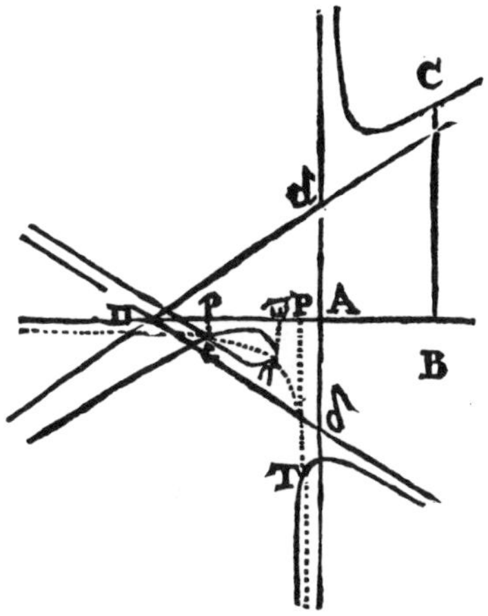

Fig. 5.

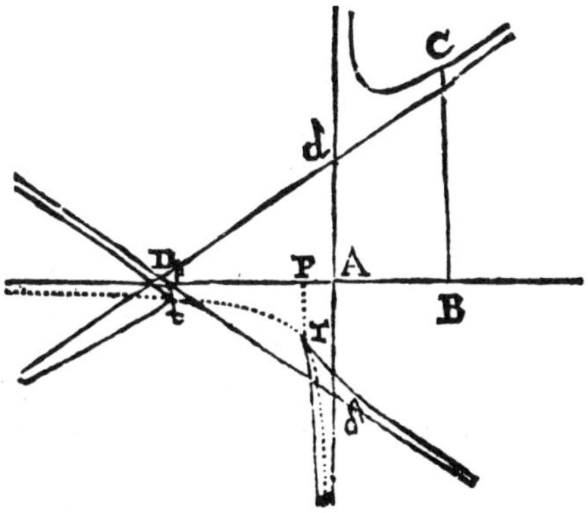

Fig. 6.

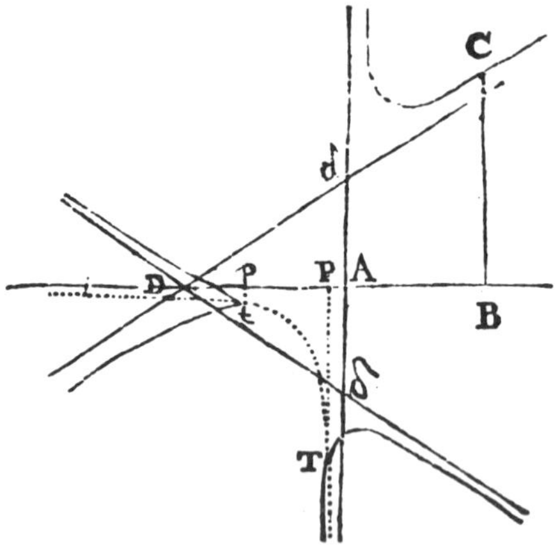

to one another, the *Nodus* will be turned into a very ſharp *Cuſpis*; for the two Legs of the Circumſcribed Hyperbola's will then concur in the Angle of Contact, and not be produced further. And this is the *Third Species*.

If the two middle Roots *A ϖ* and *A π* are equal, the Points of Contact τ and 7 will be coincident; wherefore the *Oval* will vaniſh into a Point, and the Figure will conſiſt of three Hyperbola's, an *Inſcribed*, a *Circumſcribed*, and an *Ambigenal* one with a Conjugate *Point*: Which makes a *Fourth Species*.

Fig. 7.

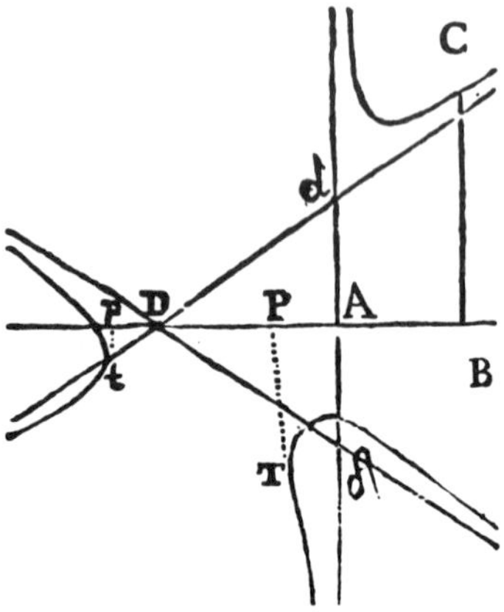

If two of the Roots are impoſſible, and the other two unequal, and of the ſame Sign, (for they

(See *Fig.* 7.)

Fig. 8.

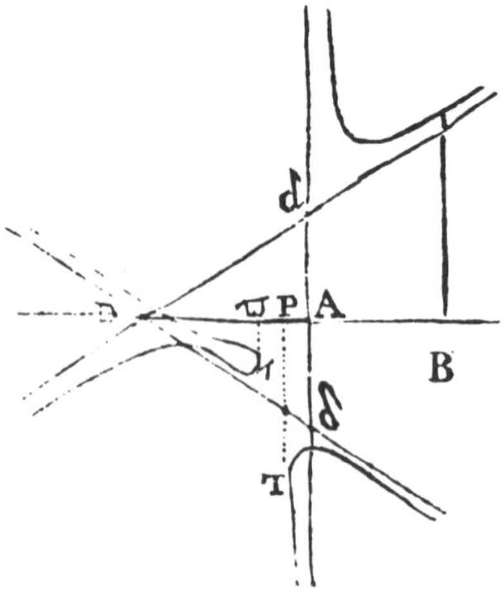

Fig. 13.

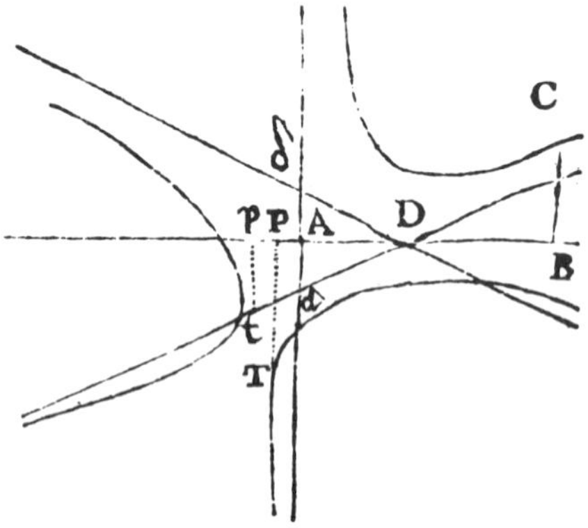

Fig. 14.

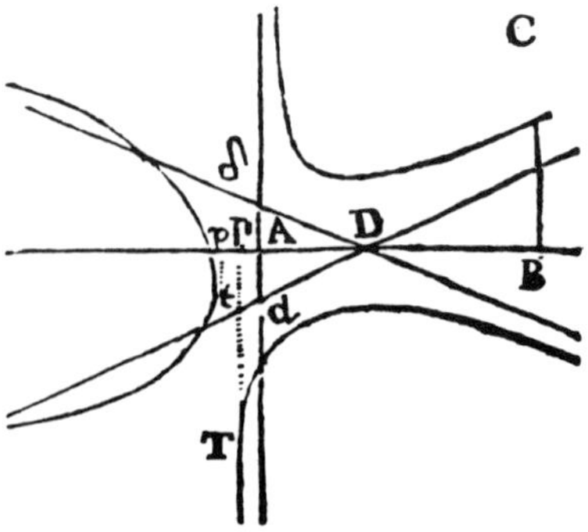

can't have contrary Signs); there will be three *Pure* Hyperbola's, without any *Oval, Node, Cusp,* or *Point Conjugate*; and these Hyperbola's will either lie at the Sides or the Angles of the Triangle made by the Asymptotes: Which makes a *Fifth* or *Sixth Species.*

If two of the Roots are equal, and the other two either Impossible or Real, with Signs contra-

Fig. 9.

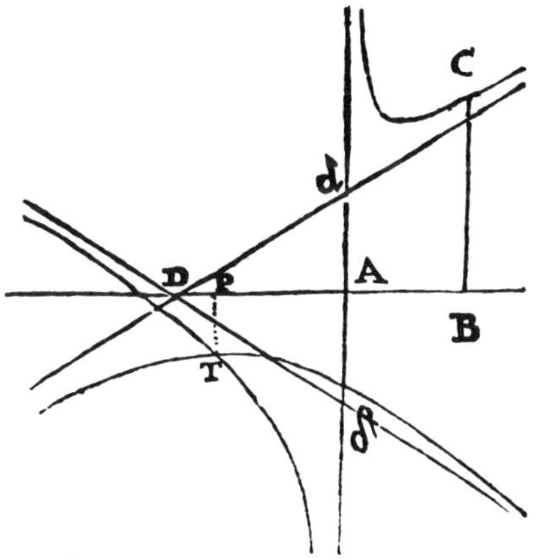

Fig. 10.

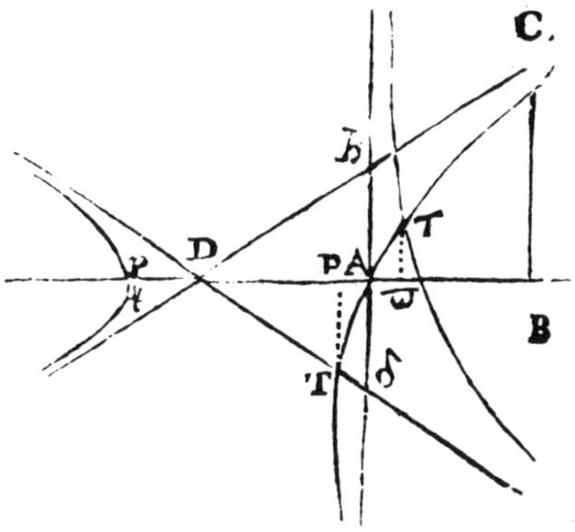

Fig. 15.

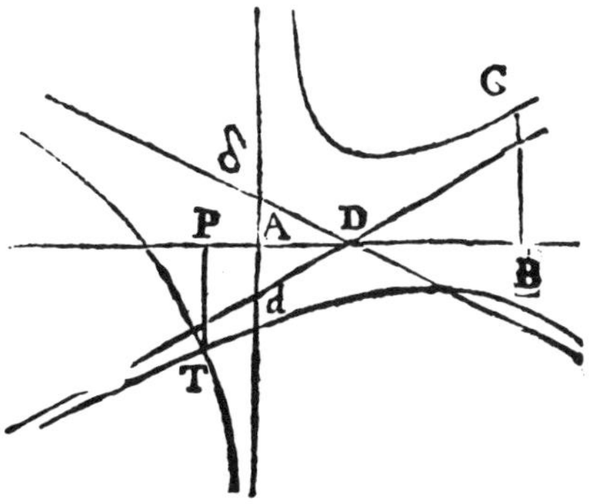

Fig. 16.

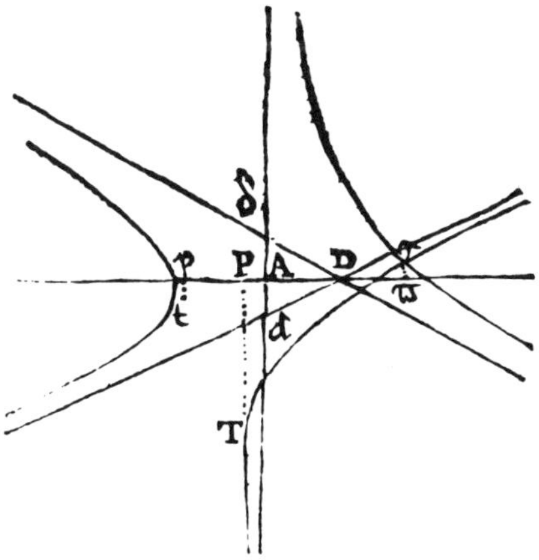

ry to those of the equal Roots; the *Cruciform* Figure will be produced: For two of the *Hyperbola* will decussate one another; and that either at the Vertex of the Triangle made by the Asymptotes, or at its Base; and these two are the *Seventh* and *Eighth Species.*

Lastly, If all the Roots are impossible, or if they are all real and unequal, and two of them are Affirmative and two Negative; then there will be two Hyperbola's at the Opposite Angles of the two Asymptotes, with an *Anguineal* or *Serpentine Hyperbola* about the third Asymptore. Which is the *Ninth Species.*

Fig. 11.

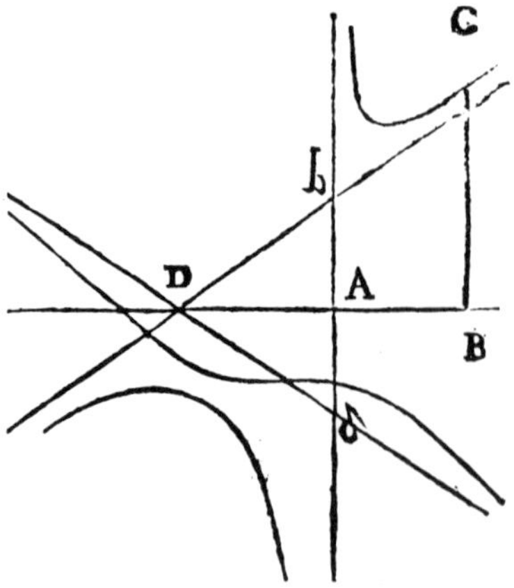

Fig. 12.

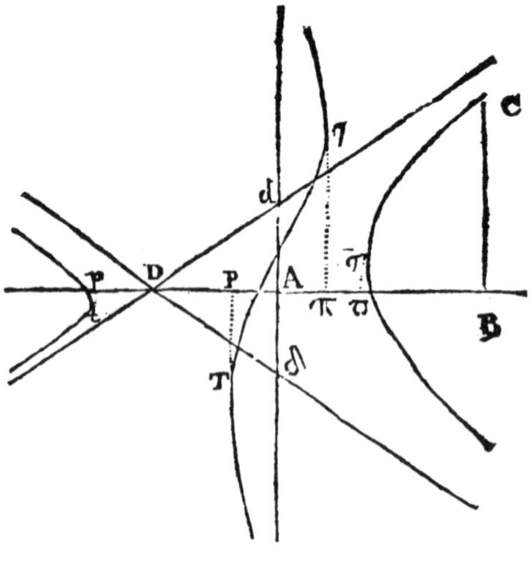

And these are all the possible Cases of the Roots; for if any two Roots are equal to one another, and the other two are equal also, the Figure will become a *Conick-Section* with a Right Line.

Twelve Redundant Hyperbola's with one only Diameter.

16. If the Redundant Hyperbola have one only Diameter, let it be the Abscissa *AB*; and in the Equation $ax^3 + bxx + cx + d = 0$, seek the three Values of x, or the three Roots. Then, If those Roots are all real, and have the same Sign, the Figure shall consist of an *Oval* lying with-

Fig. 17.

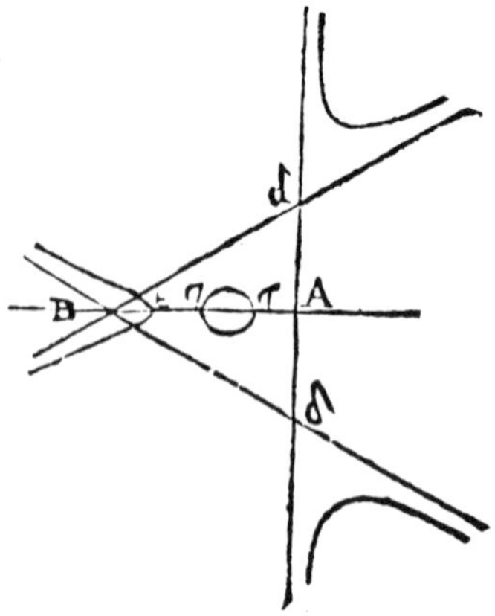

in the Triangle $D\,d\,\delta$, and of three Hyperbola's at its Angles, *viz.* one circumscribed at the Angle *D*, and the other two inscribed at *d* and δ; and this makes a *Tenth Species.*

If the two greater Roots are equal, and the Third of the same Sign with them, the Legs of

Fig. 18.

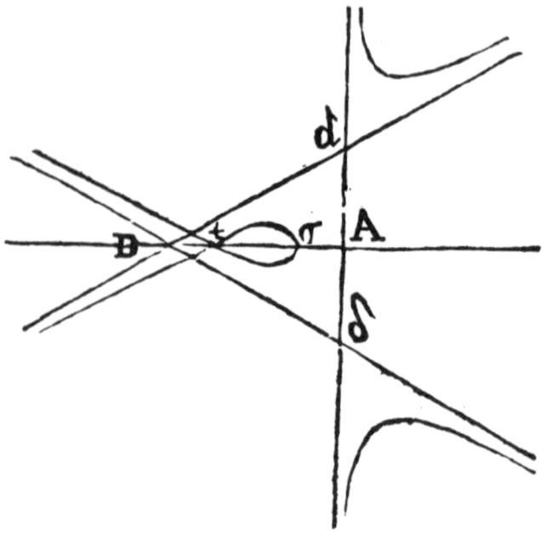

the Hyperbola lying towards *D*, will decussate one another in the Form of a *Node*, by reason of the Contact of the *Oval.* Which is the *Eleventh Species.*

If the three Roots are equal, the Hyperbola be-

Fig. 19.

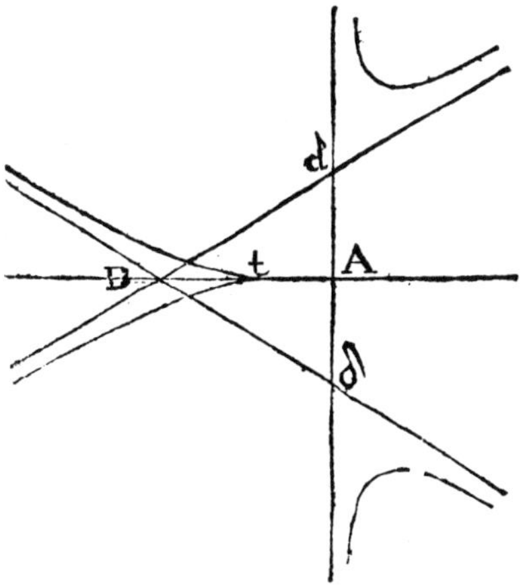

comes *Cuspidate*, without any *Oval*. Which is the *Twelfth Species*

If the two least Roots are equal, and the Third of the same Sign with them, then the *Oval* va-

Fig. 20.

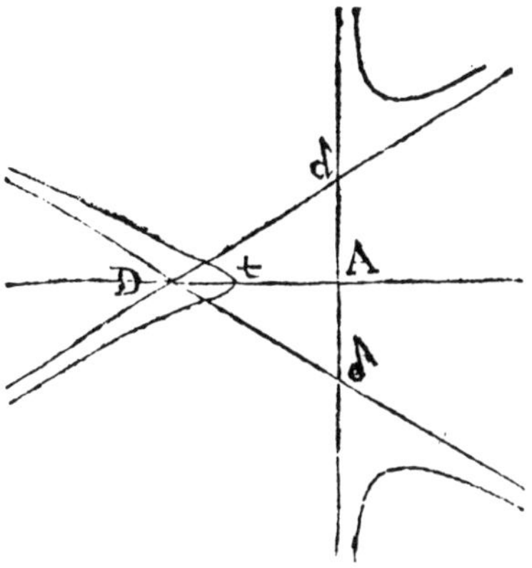

nishes into a Point. Which makes a *Thirteenth Species*.

In the Four last *Species*, the Hyperbola lying towards *D* contains its Asymptote within it; but the other two are themselves contained within the Asmptotes.

If two of the Roots are impossible, then there will be three *Pure Hyperbola's*, without any *Oval*, (See *Fig.* 20.)

Fig. 21.

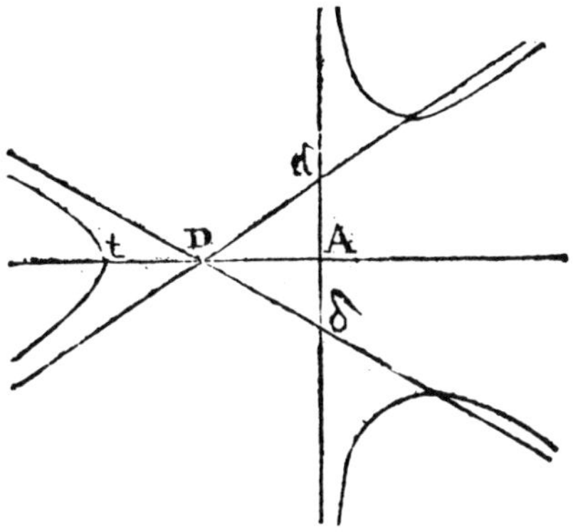

Fig. 22.

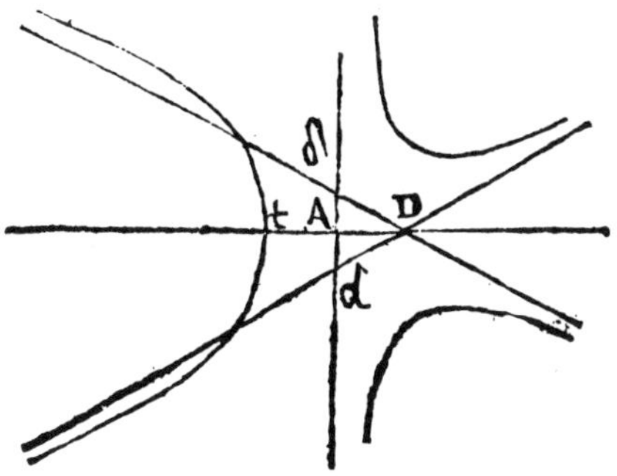

Fig. 23.

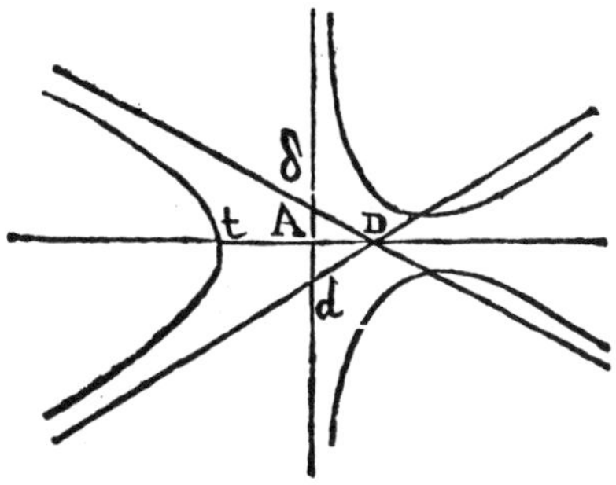

Decussation, or *Cuspis*. And there are Four Cases of this *Species*, *viz*. a *Fourteenth*, if the circumscribed Hyperbola lie towards *D*, and a *Fifteenth*,

if the inſcribed Hyperbola lie towards *D*; a ***Sixteenth***, if the circumſcribed Hyperbola lie under the Baſe *D δ* of the Triangle *D d δ*, and a ***Seventeenth***, when the inſcribed Hyperbola lies under the ſame Baſe.

If two Roots are equal, and the Third of a different Sign from them, the Figure will be ***Cruciform***; for two of the three Hyperbola's will decuſſate one another, either at the ***Vertex***, or at the Baſe of the Triangle made by the Aſymptotes. Which two *Species* are the *Eighteenth* and *Nineteenth*.

Fig. 24.

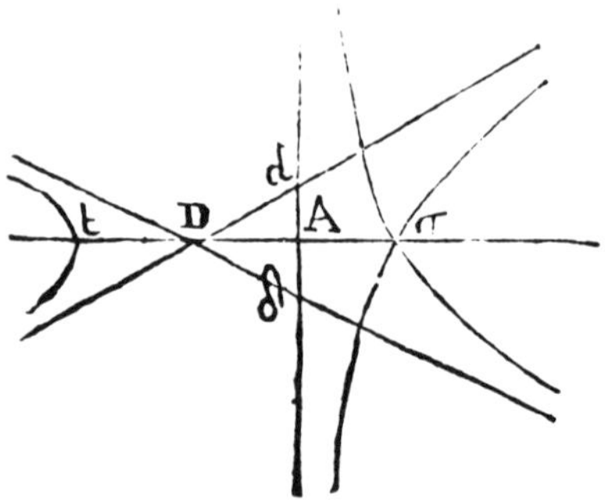

Fig. 25.

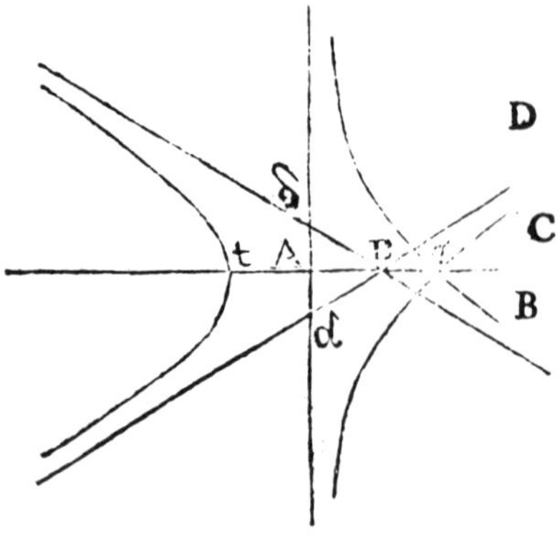

If two Roots are unequal, and of the ſame Sign, and the Third be of a different one, there will be two Hyperbola's in the oppoſite Angles of

Fig. 26.

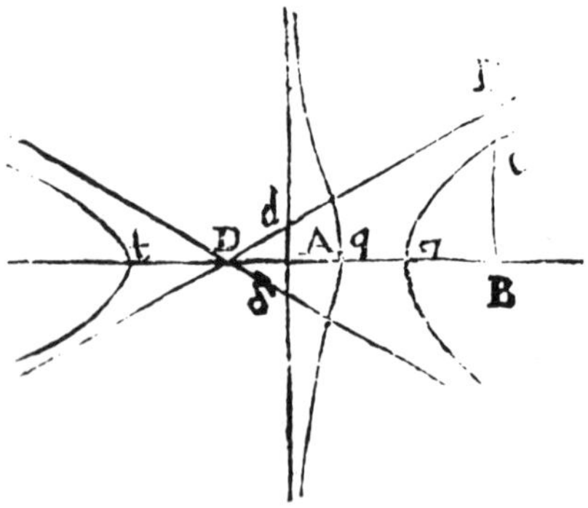

Fig. 27.

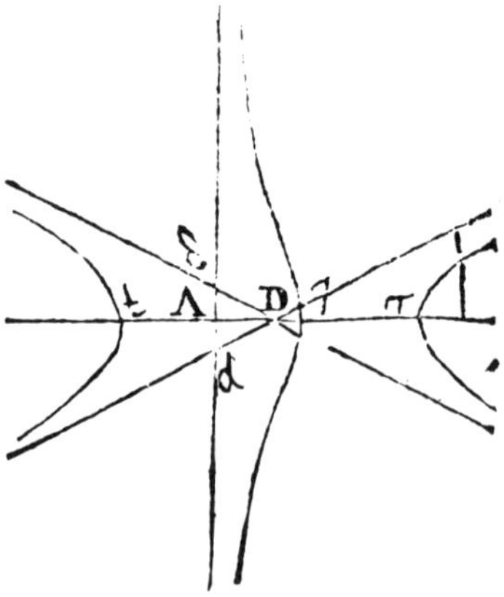

the two Aſypmtotes, with an intermediate ***Conchoidal one***. And this ***Conchoidal*** Hyperbola will either lie on the ſame Side of its Aſymptote that the Aſymptotick Triangle doth, or contrarily: And theſe two Caſes conſtitute two other ***Species***, which are the ***Twentieth*** and ***Twenty Firſt***.

Two Redundant Hyperbola's with three Diameters.

17. The Redundant Hyperbola which hath three Diameters, conſiſts of three Hyperbola's lying within the Aſymptotes, and that either at the Sides,

Fig. 28.

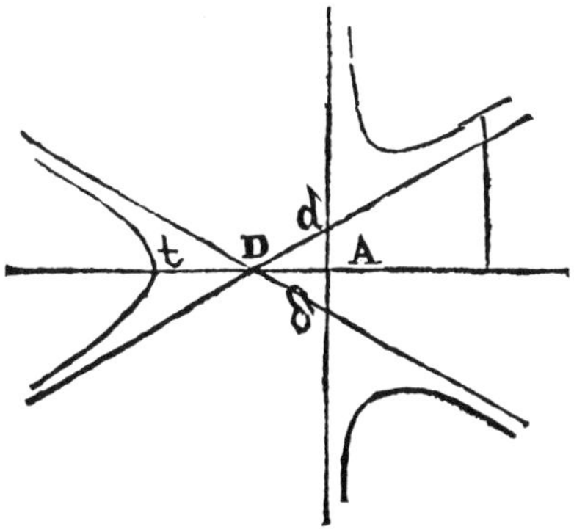

Fig. 29.

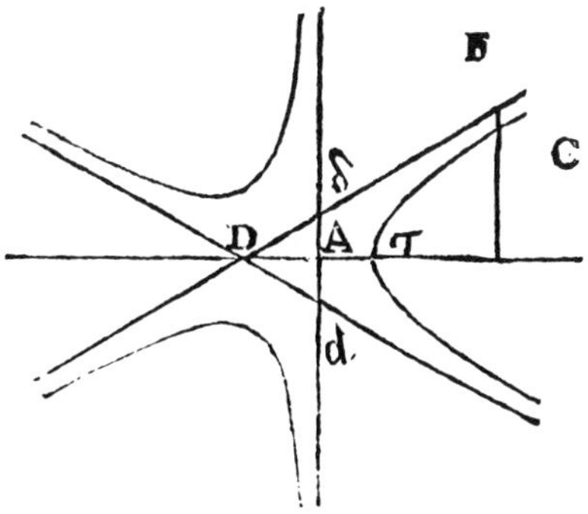

or at the Angles of the Aſymptotick Triangle. The Former Caſe makes the *Twenty Second,* this Latter the *Twenty Third Species.*

Nine Redundant Hyperbola's with three Aſmptotes, converging towards one common Point.

18. If the three Aſymptotes do interſect one another in one common Point, the 5th and 6th Species will be changed into a *Twenty Fourth,* the Seventh

Fig. 30

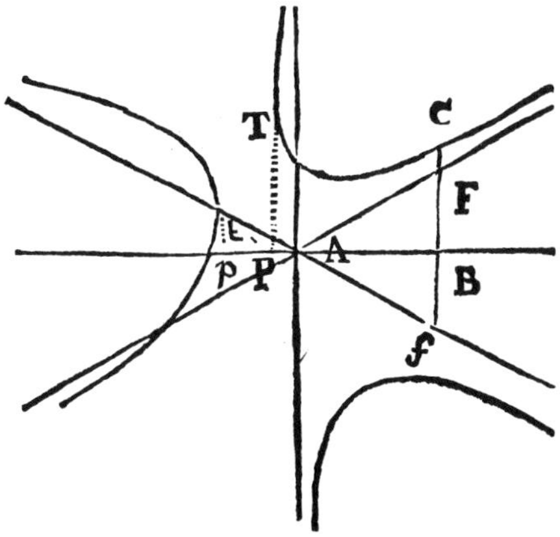

Fig. 31.

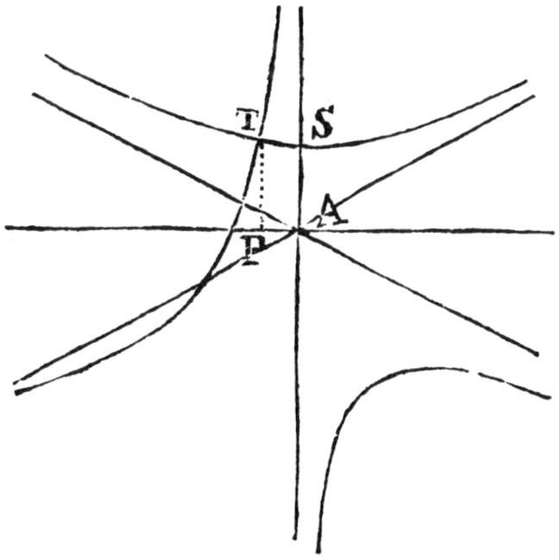

Fig. 32.

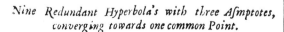

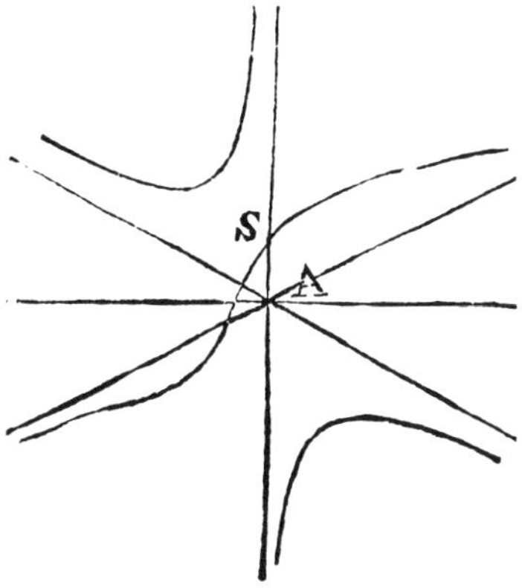

Fig. 33.

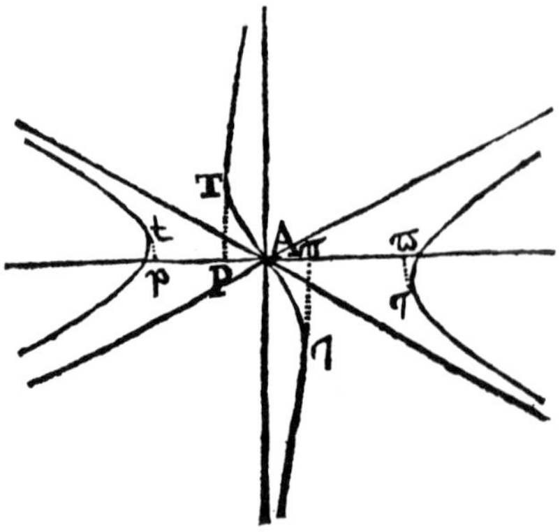

and Eighth into a ***Twenty Fifth,*** and the Ninth into a ***Twenty Sixth*** Species, where the Anguineal doth not paſs through the Concourſe of the Aſymptote, and into a ***Twenty Seventh,*** where it doth ſo; in which Caſe the Terms *b* and *d* are wanting, and the Concourſe of the Aſymptotes is the Center of the Figure, equally diſtant from all its oppoſite Parts. And theſe Four Species have no Diameter.

The Fourteenth and Sixteenth Species may be changed alſo into a ***Twenty Eighth Species,*** and the Fifteenth and Seventeenth into a ***Twenty Ninth:*** The

Fig. 34.

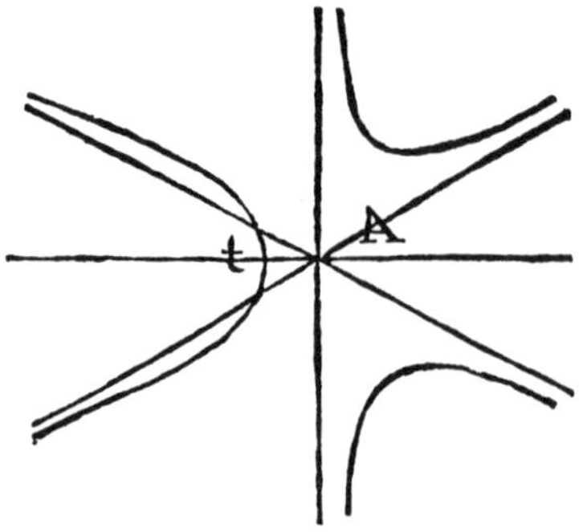

Fig. 35.

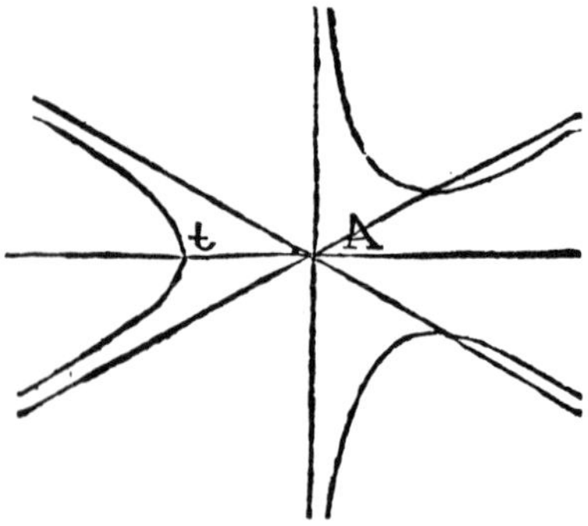

Fig. 36.

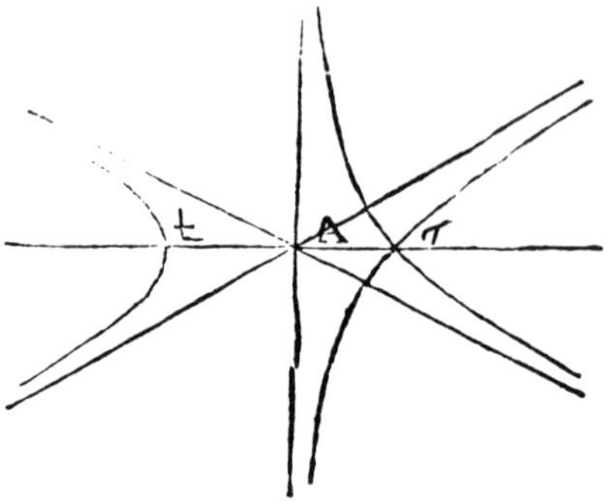

ig. 37.

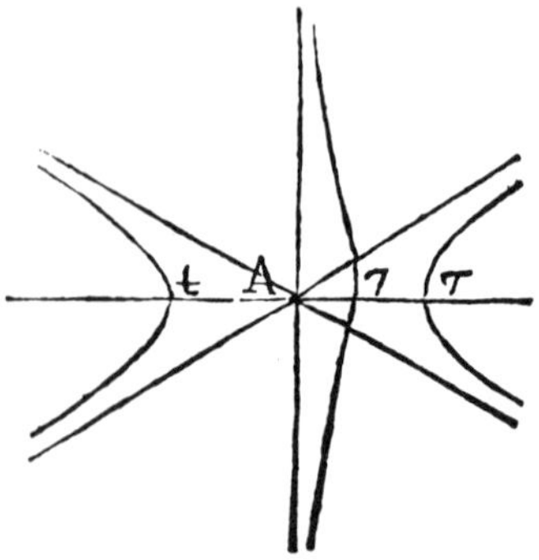

Eighteenth and and Nineteenth into a ***Thirtieth*** and the Twentieth and Twenty Firſt into a ***Thirty Firſt.*** And all theſe Species have but one only Diameter. And finally, the Twenty Second and Twenty Third Species may be changed into a ***Thirty Second,*** which hath three Diameters paſſing through the Point of Concourſe of the Aſymptotes.

Fig. 38.

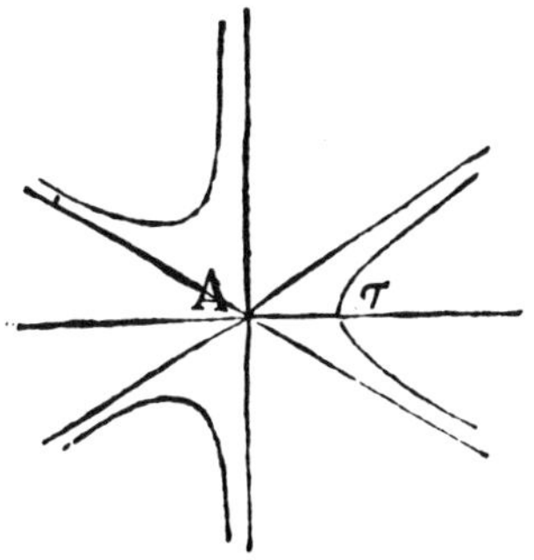

All which Changes will be easily understood, if you suppose the Asymptotick Triangle to be diminished till it vanish into a Point.

Six Deficient Hyperbola's, having no Diameter.

19. If, in the first Case of the Equations, the Term ax^3 be Negative, the Figure will be a *Deficient* Hyperbola, having one only Asymptote, and only two Hyperbolick Legs running out infinitely towards the Side of the Asymptote, but quite contrary ways; and this Asymptote is the first and principal Ordinate *AG*. If the Term *ey* be not wanting, the Figure will have no Diameter; but if it be wanting, it will have but one: In the former Case the Species are thus enumerated:

If all the Roots *Aτ*, *AP*, *Ap*, *Aϖ*, of this Equation $ax^4 = bx^3 + cxx + dx + \frac{1}{4}ee$; be real and unequal, the Figure will be an Anguineal Hyperbola approaching towards the common Asymptote by a contrary Flexion, and with a Conjugate *Oval*. Which makes the *Thirty Third Species*.

Fig. 39.

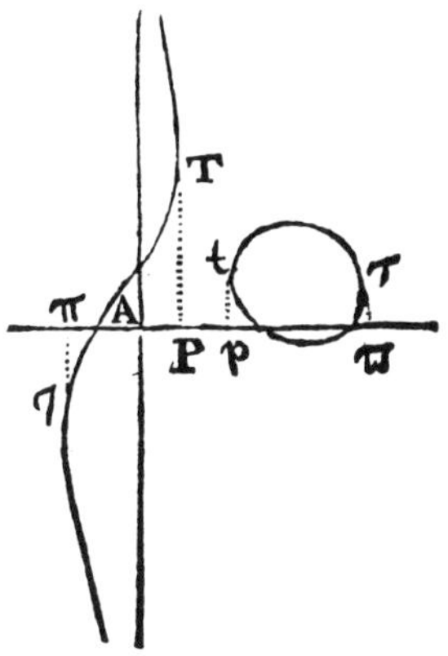

If the two middle Roots *AP* and *Ap* be equal one to another, then the Oval and the Anguineal will be joined, decussating one another in th Form of a *Node*. And this is the *Thirty Fourth Species*.

Fig. 40.

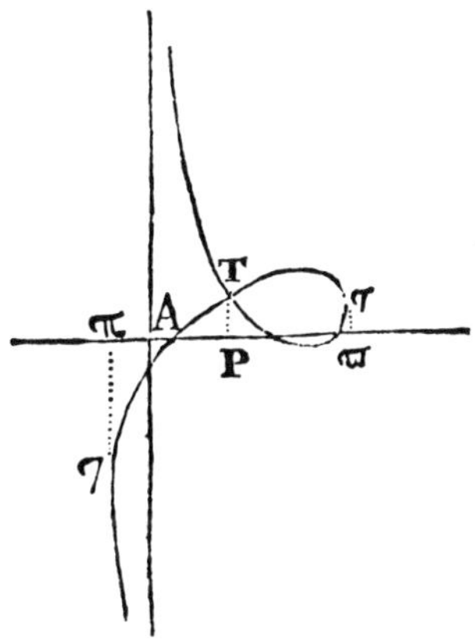

If three of the Roots are equal, the Node will be changed into a most Acute *Cuspis* in the Vertex of the Anguineal. And this constitutes a *Thirty Fifth Species*.

Fig. 41.

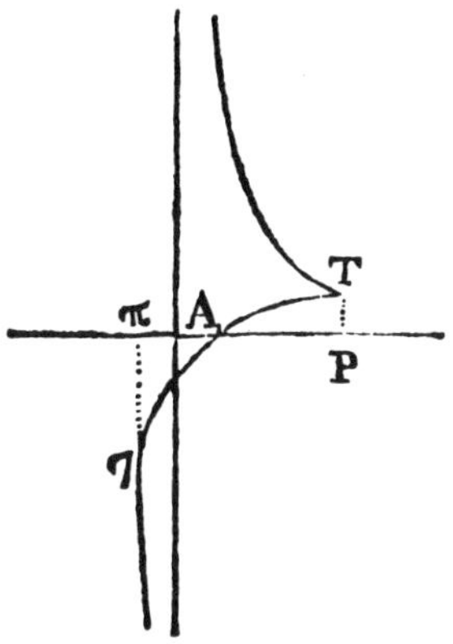

If of the three Roots, having the ſame Sign, the two greateſt, *A p* and *A π*, are equal to one another; then the *Oval* vaniſhes into a *Point*. Which makes a *Thirty ſixth Species*. (See *Fig.* 43.)

If any two Roots are imaginary, there will remain the *Anguineal* alone, and this *Pure*, without any *Oval*, *Decuſſation*, *Cuſpis*, or *Conjugate Point*.

Fig. 42.

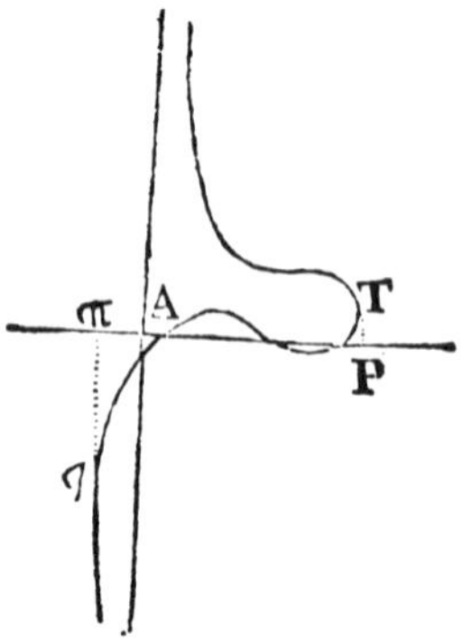

Fig. 43.

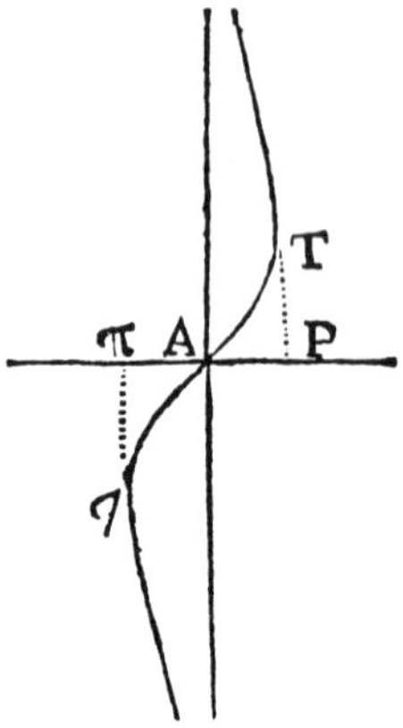

If the *Anguineal* don't paſs through the Point *A*, it makes the *Thirty ſeventh Species*; but if it doth paſs through *A*, (as it will do when the Terms *b* and *d* are wanting) then that Point will be the Center of the Figure, biſſecting all Right Lines drawn through it, and terminated both ways by the Curve. And this is a *Thirty eighth Species*.

Seven defective Hyperbola's, having a Diameter.

20. In the other Caſe, where the Term *ey* is wanting, and conſequently the Figure hath a Diameter, if all the Roots *A T*, *A t*, *A τ*, of the Equation

Fig. 45.

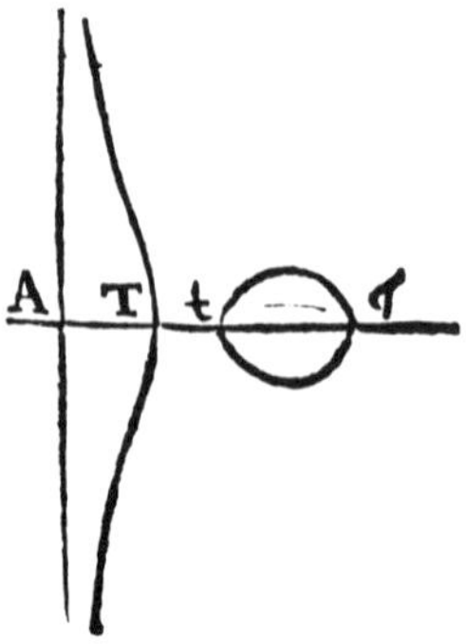

$ax^3 + bxx + cx + d$, are real, unequal, and of the ſame Sign; then the Figure will be a *Conchoidal Hyperbola*, with an *Oval* on its Convex Side And this is a *Thirty Ninth Species*.

If two of the Roots are equal, and of the ſame Sign, but the Third with a contrary Sign, the *Oval*

Fig. 44.

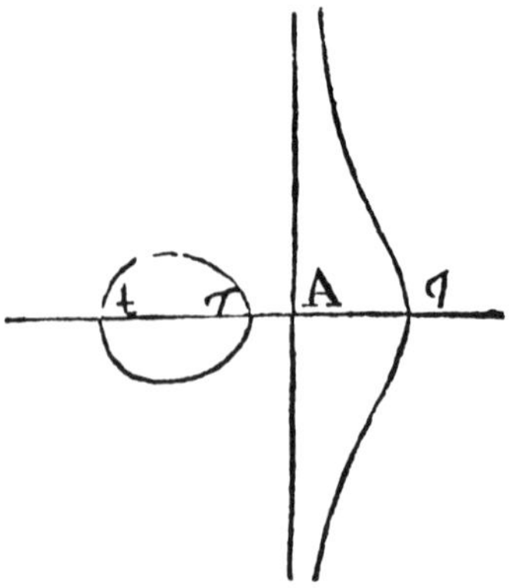

will lie on the Concave Side of the Conchoidal Hyperbola. And this makes a *Fortieth Species*.

If the two leſſer Roots *A T*, *A t*, are equal, and the Third, *A τ*, be of the ſame Sign with

Fig. 46.

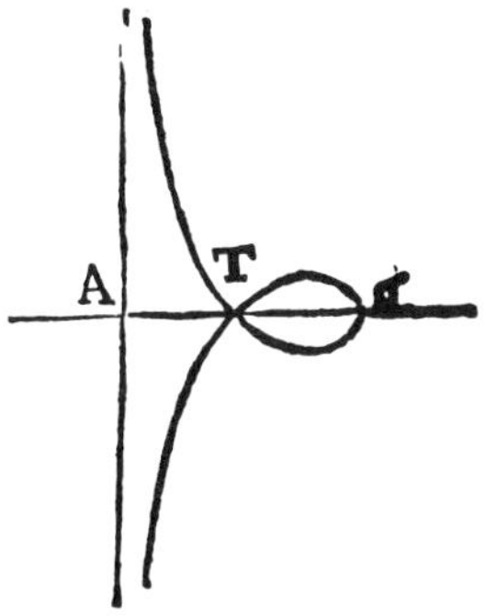

them, then the *Oval* and the *Conchoidal* will be join-ed, decuſſating one another like a *Node*. Which is a *Forty firſt Species*.

If the three Roots are equal, the *Nodus* will be changed into a *Cuſpis*, and the Figure will be the

Fig. 47.

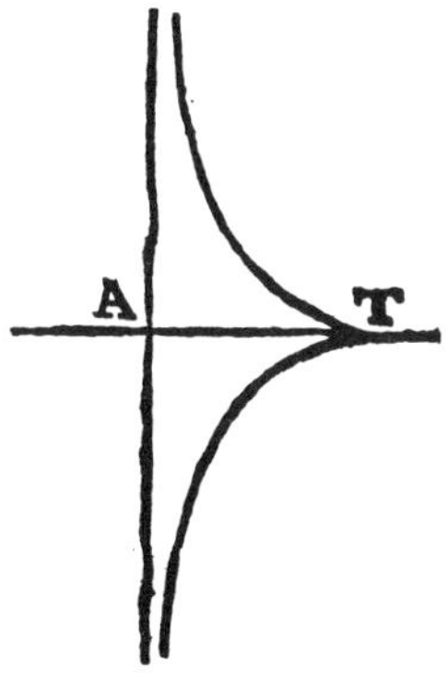

Ciſſoid of the Ancients. And this makes a *Forty ſecond Species*.

If the two greater Roots are equal, and the Third of the ſame Sign with them, then the Con-

Fig. 49.

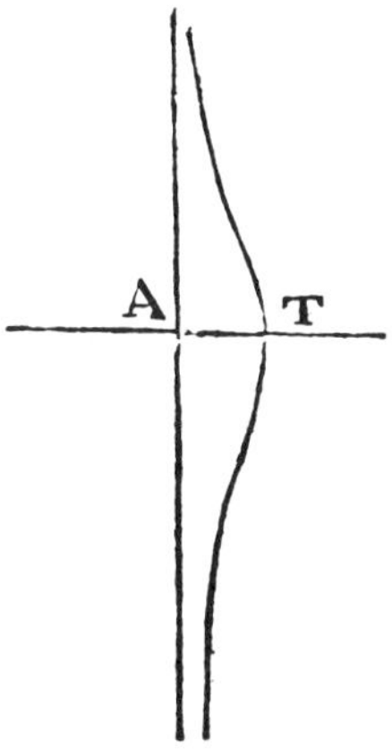

choidal Hyperbola will have a Conjugate *Point* at its Convexity. Which is a *Forty third Species*.

If two of the Roots are equal, and the Third have a contrary Sign; the Conchoidal Hyperbola will then have a *Conjugate Point* at its Concavity. Which makes a *Forty fourth Species*.

If two of the Roots are impoſſible, there will be a *Pure* Conchoidal without either Oval, Node,

Fig. 48.

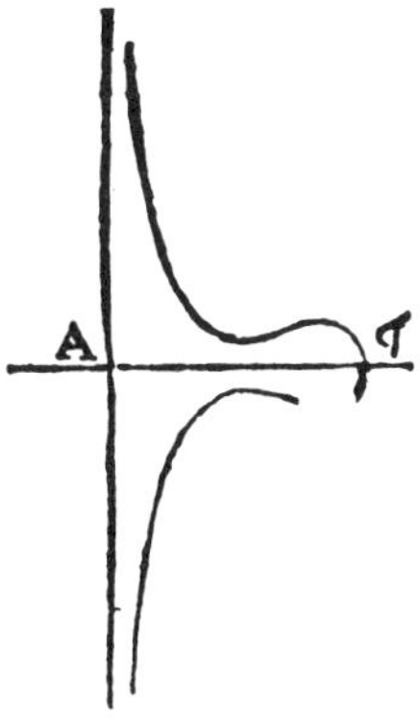

Cuſp, or Conjugate Point. And this is a *Forty fifth Species*. (See *Fig.* 49.)

Seven Parabolick Hyperbola's, having no Diameter.

21. If, in the first Case of the Equations, the Term ax^3 be wanting, but the bbx be not wanting; then the Figure will be a Parabolick Hyperbola, having two Hyperbolick Legs to one Asymptote SAG, converging towards one and the same Side. If the Term ey be not wanting, the Figure will have no Diameter; but if it be wanting, it will have one onely: In the former Case the *Species* will be these.

If the three Roots AP, $A\varpi$, $A\pi$, of this Equation $bx^3 + cx^2 + dx + \frac{ee}{4} = 0$, be unequal, and have the same Sign, the Figure will consist of an *Oval*, and of two other Curves, which are partly Hyperbolical and partly Parabolical; that is, the Parabolick Legs, by being continually

Fig. 50.

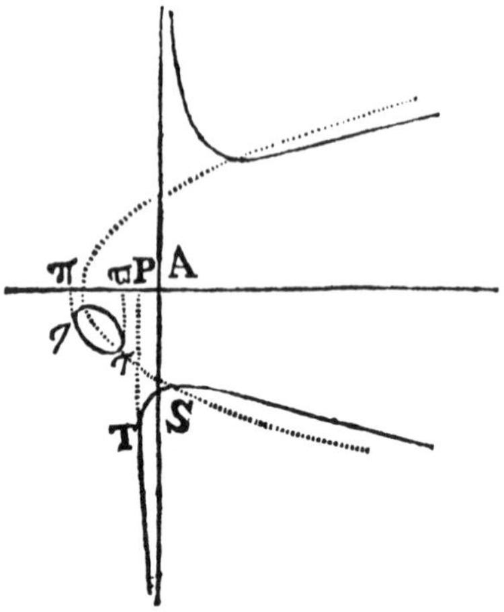

drawn out, are joined with the Hyperbolical Legs which are next to them. And this is the *Forty sixth Species.*

If the two lesser Roots are equal, and the Third of the same Sign with them; then will the Oval,

Fig. 51.

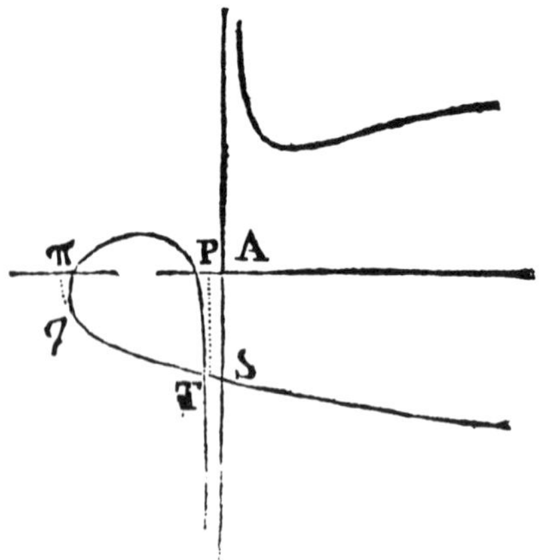

and one of those Hyperbolo-Parabolick Curves be joined, and intersect one another in the Form of a Node. Which is the *Forty seventh Species.*

If the three Roots are equal, the *Node* will turn

Fig. 52.

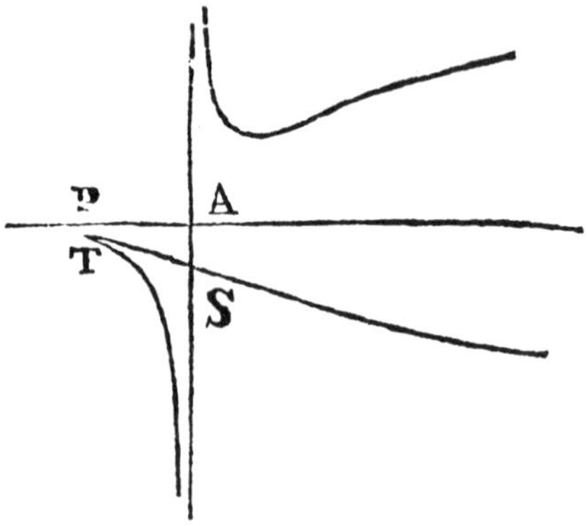

into a *Cusp*. Which makes a *Forty eighth Species.*

If the two greatest Roots are equal, and the Third hath the same Sign with them, the *Oval*

Fig. 53.

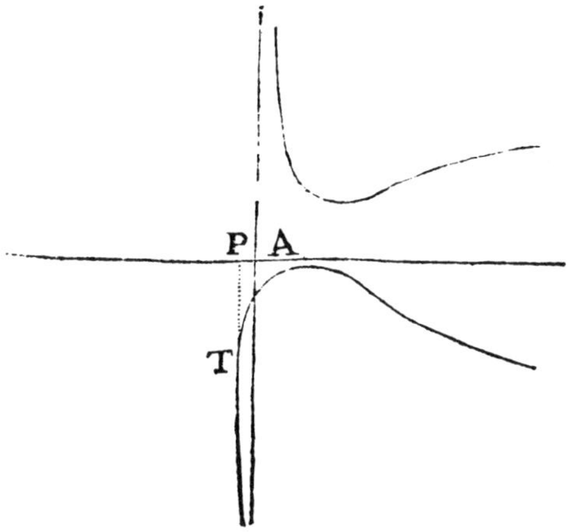

will vanifh into a ***Conjugate Point.*** Which is the *Forty ninth Species.*

If two of the Roots are impoffible, the two Hyperbolo-Parabolick Curves will remain *Pure,* (See *Fig.* 53.)

Fig. 54.

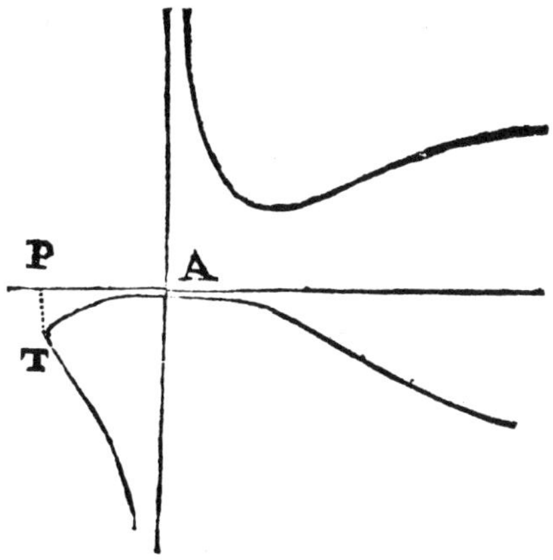

without any ***Oval. Decuffation, Cufp,*** or ***Conjugate Point.*** And this will make a ***Fiftieth Species.***

If two of the Roots be equal, and the Third have a contrary Sign to them, then the Hyperbolo-Parabolick Curves will be joined, decuffating one another in the Form of a Crofs. And this is the *Fifty firft Species.*

Fig. 55.

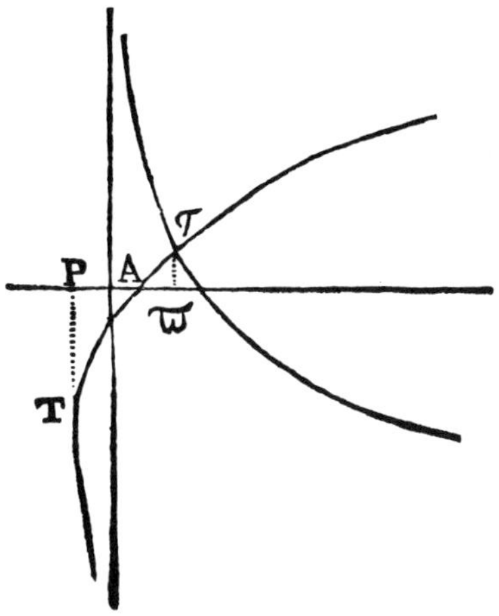

If the two Roots are unequal, and of the fame Sign, and the Third have a contrary Sign, the Figure will become an Anguineal Hyperbola about

Fig. 56.

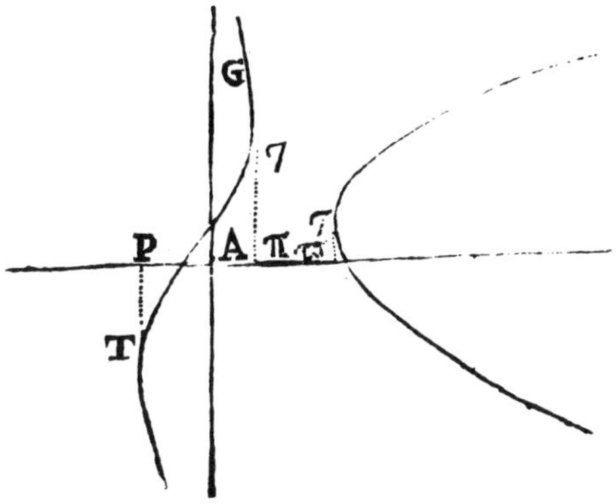

the Afymptote *A G*, together with a *Conjugate Parabola.* And this will be a *Fifty fecond Species.*

Four Parabolick Hyperbola's which have a Diameter.

22. In the other Cafe, where the Term ey is wanting, and the Figure hath a Diameter, if the two Roots of this Equation $bxx + cx + d = 0$

Fig. 57.

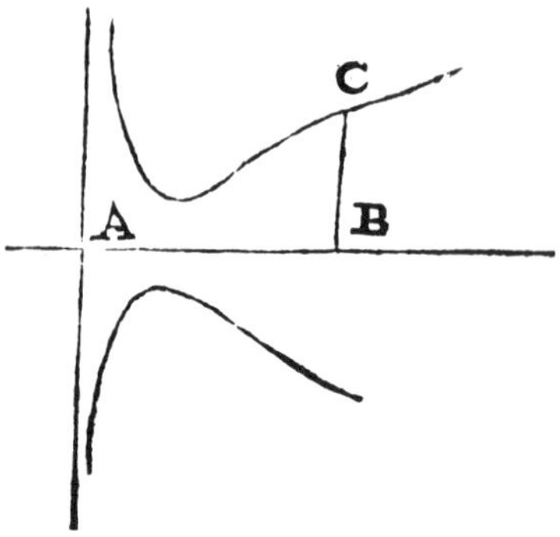

are impoſſible; there will be two Hyperbolo-Parabolick Figures equally diſtant from the Diameter *AB*, and one on one Side, and the other on the other, which will conſtitute a *Fifty third Species.*

If the two Roots of this Equation be impoſſible, the Hyperbolo-Parabolick Figures will join, and

Fig. 58.

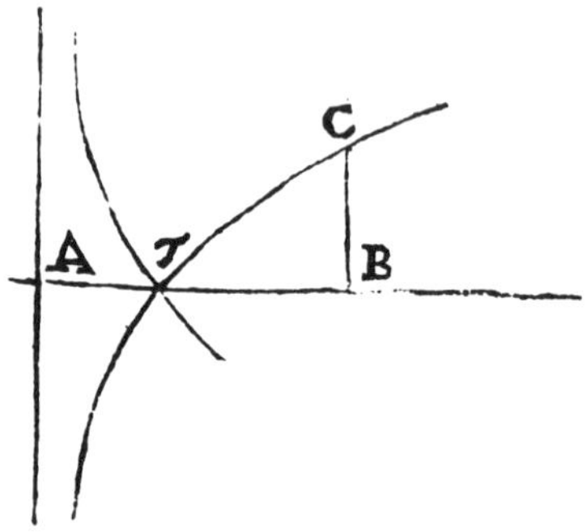

interſect one another in the Form of a Croſs. And this will be a *Fifty fourth Species.*

If the Roots are equal, and have the ſame Sign, there will be a Conchoidal Hyperbola with

Fig. 59.

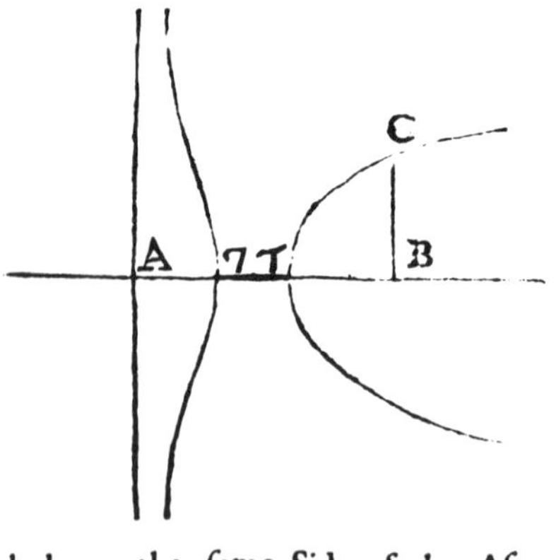

a Parabola on the ſame Side of the Aſymptote. And this makes a *Fifty fifth Species.*

If the Roots have contrary Signs, there will be a Conchoidal Hyperbola on one Side of the Aſymptote, and a Parabola on the other. And this makes a *Fifty ſixth Species.*

Fig. 60.

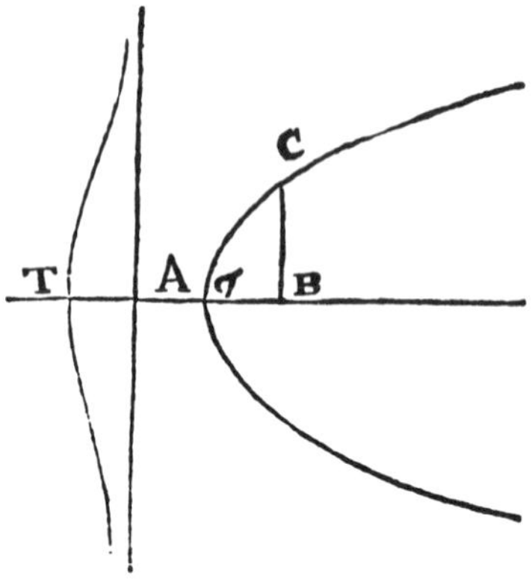

Four Hyperboliſms of the Hyperbola.

23. When-ever, in the firſt Caſe of the Equations, the Terms ax^3 and bxx are both wanting, the Figure will be a *Hyperboliſm* of ſome Conick-Section.

I call that the *Hyperboliſm* of a Figure, when the Ordinate comes out by dividing the Rectangle under the Ordinate of that Figure and a given Right Line, by the common *Abſciſſa.* By this

means a Right Line is changed into a Conick-Section, and every Conick-Section into some one of those Figures which I here call the Hyperbolisms of the Conick-Sections. For the Equation for the Figure, of which we now speak, *viz.* $xyy + ey = cx + d$, gives the Ordinate $y = \frac{e \pm \sqrt{ee + 4dx + 4cxx}}{2x}$; which is generated by dividing the Rectangle under the Ord. of the Conick-Section, $\frac{e \pm \sqrt{ee + dx + 4cxx}}{2m}$, and a given Right Line m, by the common Abscissa x. Whence it is plain, that the Figure produced will be the Hyperbolism of an Hyperbola, Ellipsis or Parabola, according as the Term cx is Affirmative or Negative, or quite wanting.

The Hyperbolism of an Hyperbola hath three Asymptotes, of which one is the first and principal Ordinate Ad, the other two are Parallels to the Abscissa AB, and equi-distant from it on each Side of it.

In the principal Ordinate Ad, take Ad, $A\delta$ equal both ways to the Quantity $\sqrt{:c}$; and thro' the Point d and δ, draw dg, $\delta\gamma$ as Asymptotes, parallel to the Abscissa AB.

When the Term ey is not wanting, the Figure hath no Diameter. In this Case, if AP and Ap, the two Roots of the Equation $cxx + dx + \frac{ee}{4} = 0$, are *real* and *unequal*, (for *equal* they cannot be, unless the Figure be a Conick-Section;) then will the Figure consist of three Hyperbola's opposite to one another; of which, one lies between the parallel Asymptotes, and the other two without them. And this is a *Fifty seventh Species.*

Fig. 61.

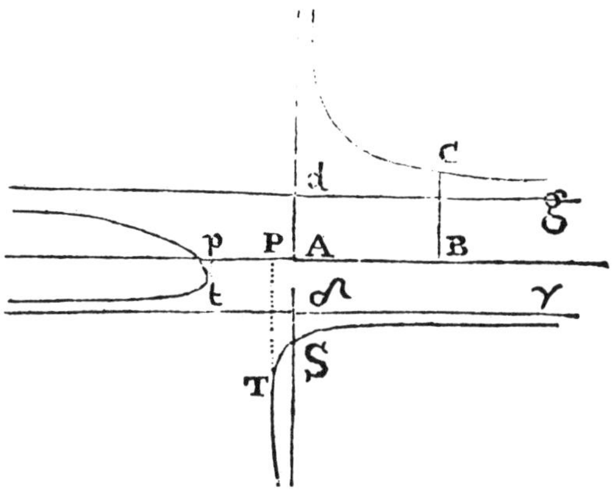

If the two Roots are impossible, there will be two opposite Hyperbola's without the parallel Asymptotes, and an Hyperbolical Anguineal within them. This Figure is of two Species; for it hath no Center when the Term d is not wanting, but if d be wanting, the Point A is its Center. The Former of these makes a *Fifty eighth*, the Latter a *Fifty ninth Species.*

Fig. 62.

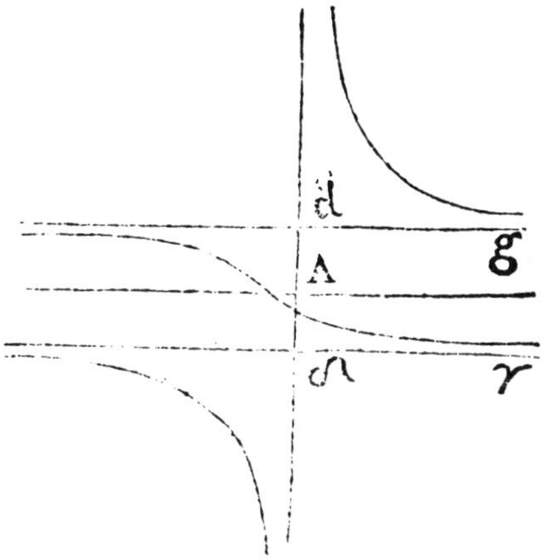

Fig. 63.

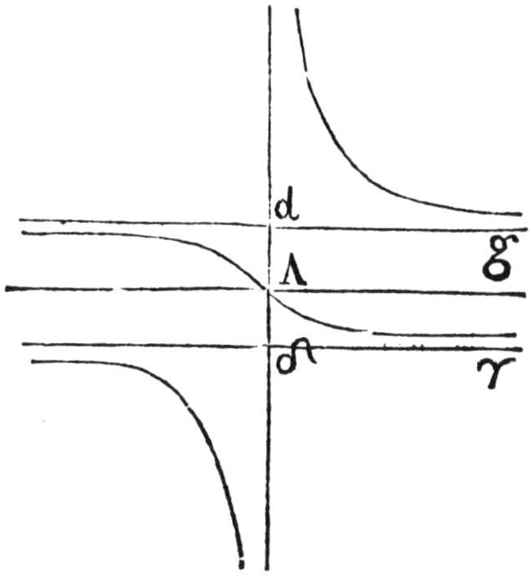

But if the Term *e y* is wanting, the Figure will confiſt of three oppoſite Hyperbola's; of which one will lie between the parallel Aſymptotes, and

Fig. 64.

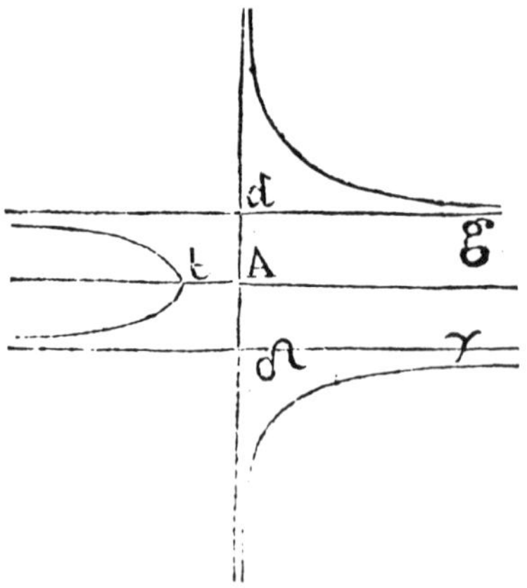

the other two without, as in the 54th Species: And beſides this, it will have a Diameter, which is the Abſciſſa *A* B. And this conſtitutes a *Sixtieth Species*.

Three Hyperboliſms of the Ellipſe.

24. The Hyperboliſm of an Ellipſis is determined by this Equation *x y y* + *e y* = *c x* + *d*; and hath only one Aſymptote, which is the principal Ordinate *A d*. If the Term *e y* be not wanting, the Figure will be an Anguineal Hyperbola without any Diameter, and even without any Center, if the Term *d* be not wanting. Which makes the *Sixty firſt Species*.

Fig. 65.

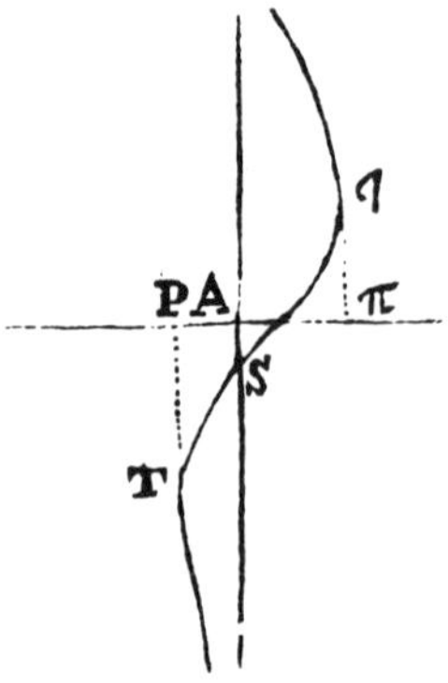

But if the Term *d* be wanting, the Figure will have a Center without any Diameter, which will

Fig. 66.

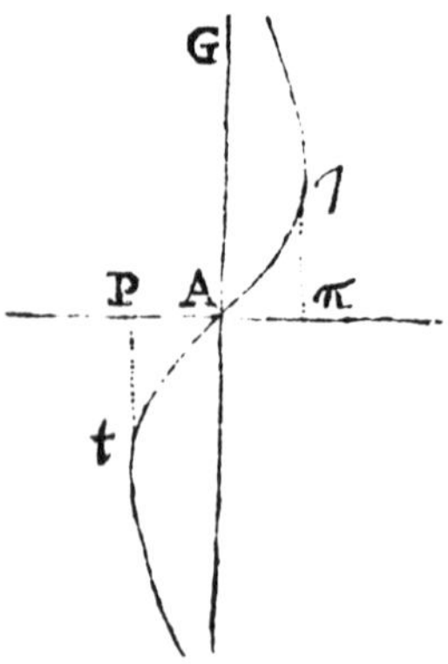

be the Point *A*. And this makes a *Sixty ſecond Species*.

And if the Term *e y* be wanting, and not *d*, the Figure will be a Conchoidal Hyperbola to the

Fig. 67.

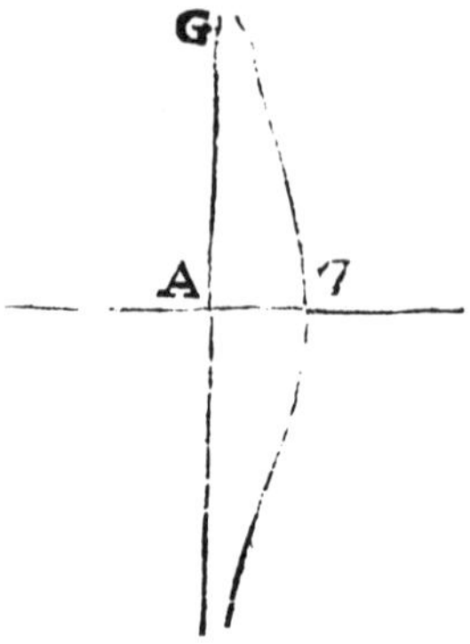

Aſymptote *A G*, and will have a Diameter without any Center, that is, the Abſciſſa *A B*. Which makes a *Sixty third Species*.

Two Hyperboliſms of the Parabola.

25. The Hyperboliſm of a Parabola is determined by this Equation *x y y* + *e y* = *d*; and hath two Aſymptotes, the Abſciſſa *A B*, and the firſt and principal Ordinate *A G*. But the Hyperbola's in this Figure are two, not lying in the oppoſite Ans

gles of the Aſymptotes, but in the contiguous or adjoining ones, and that on each Side the Abſciſſa

Fig. 68.

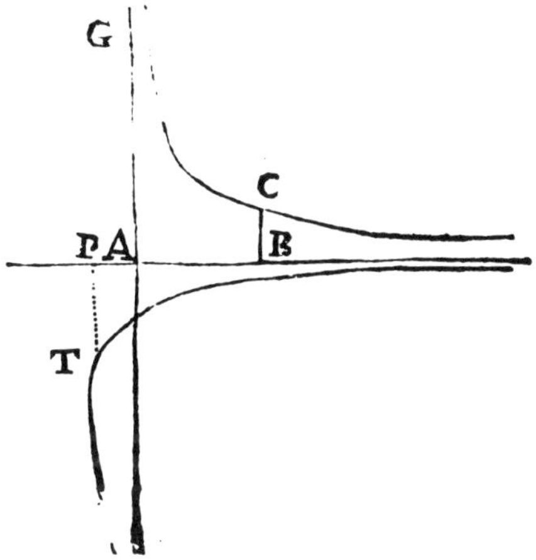

Fig. 69.

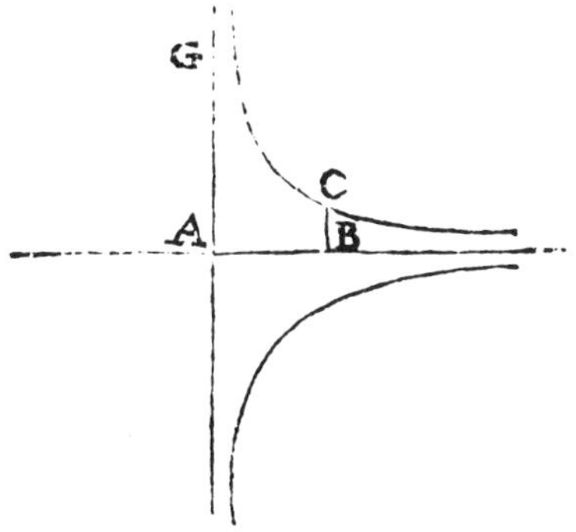

AB; and even without any Diameter, if the Term *ey* be there, but with one if that be wanting. Which two *Species* are the *Sixty fourth* and *Sixty fifth.*

A Trident.

26. In the ſecond Caſe of the Equations there is $xy = ax^3 + bxx + cx + d$: And the Figure in this Caſe will have four infinite Legs, of which

Fig. 76.

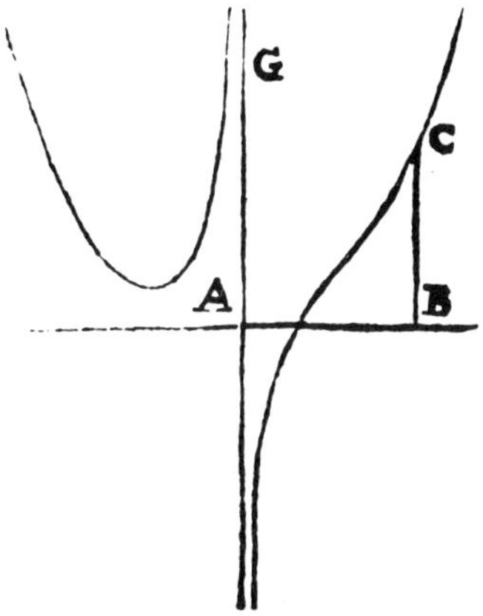

two are Hyperbola's about the Aſymptote *AG* tending towards contrary Parts; and two converging Parabola's, and, with the Former, making as it were the Figure of a *Trident.* And this Figure is that Parabola by which *D. Cartes* conſtructed Equations of ſix Dimenſions. This therefore is the *Sixty ſixth Species.*

Five Diverging Parabola's.

27. In the third Caſe the Equation was $yy = ax^3 + bxx + cx + d$; and deſigns a Parabola, whoſe Legs diverge from one another, and run out infinitely contrary ways. The Abſciſſa *AB* is its Diameter, and its five Species are theſe:

If, of the Equation $ax^3 + bxx + cx + d = 0$, all the Roots $A\tau$, AT, At, are real and unequal; then the Figure is a diverging Parabola

Fig. 70.

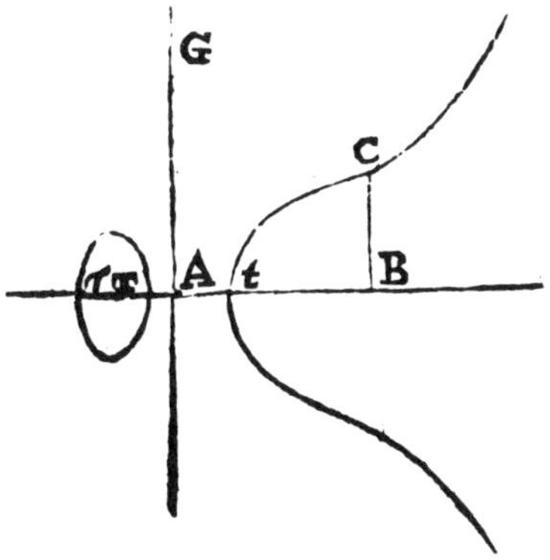

Fig. 71.

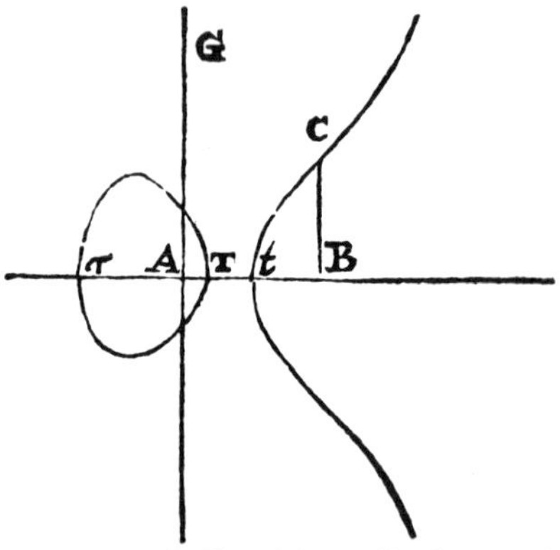

of the Form of a Bell, with an Oval at its Vertex. And this makes a *Sixty seventh Species.*

If two of the Roots are equal, a Parabola will be formed, either *Nodated* by touching an Oval,

Fig. 72.

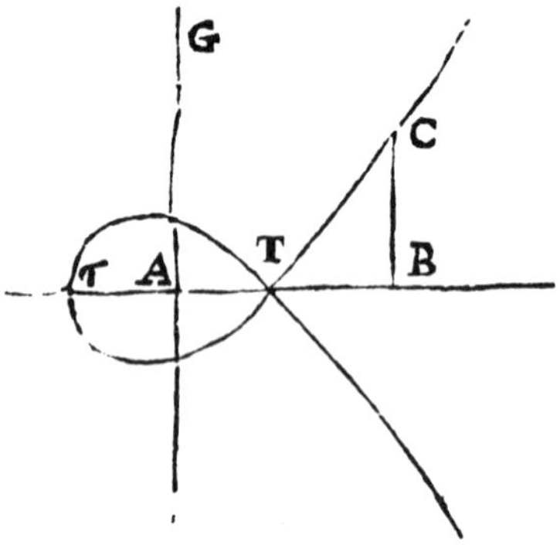

Fig. 73.

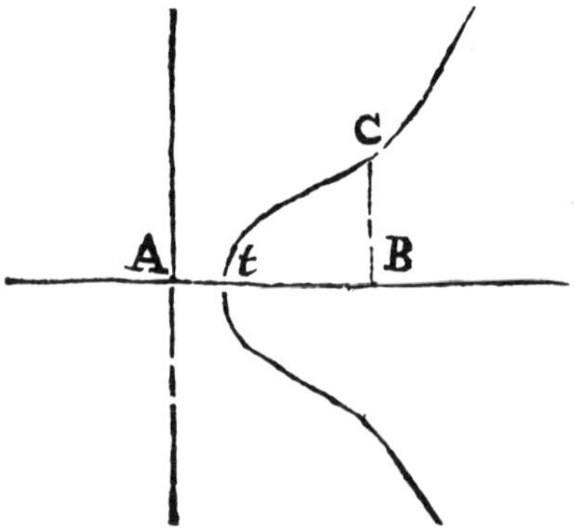

or *Punctate*, by having the Oval infinitely small. Which two *Species* are the *Sixty eighth* and *Sixty ninth.*

If three of the Roots are equal, the Parabola will be *Cuspidate* at the Vertex. And this is the

Fig. 75.

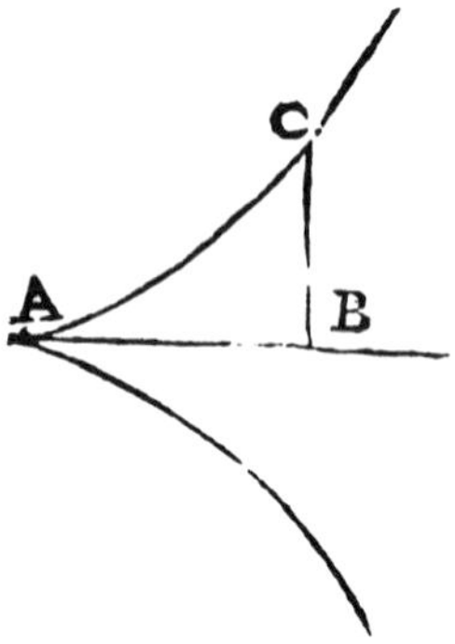

Neilian Parabola, commonly called Semi-cubical. Which makes the *Seventieth Species.*

If two of the Roots are impossible, there will (See *Fig.* 73.)

Fig. 73.

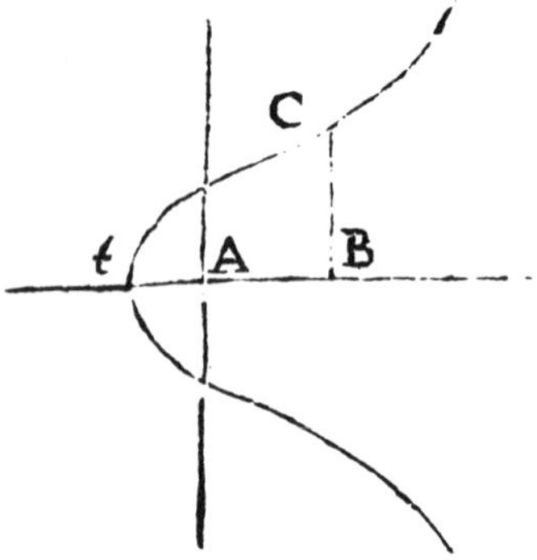

be a *Pure* Parabola of a Bell-like Form. And this makes the *Seventy first Species.*

The Cubical Parabola.

28. in the Fourth Cafe, let the Equation be $y = a x + b x x + c x + d$; then will it denote

Fig. 77.

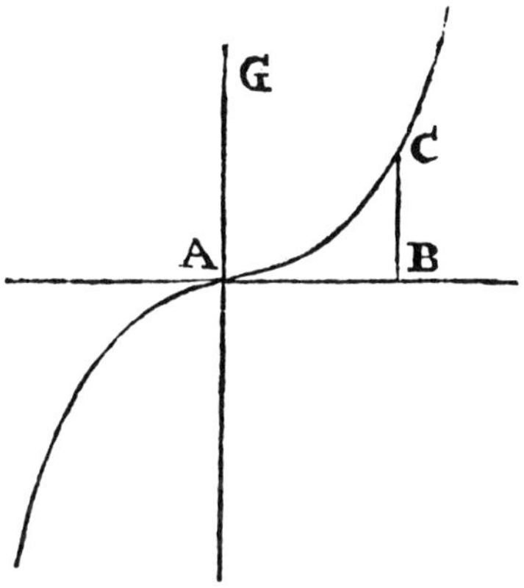

the *Cubical Parabola* with contrary turn'd Legs. And this makes up, or compleats, the Number of the Species of thefe Curves to be in all *Seventy two.*

Of the Genefis of Curves by Shadows.

29. If the Shadows of Figures are projected on an infinite Plane illuminated from a lucid Point, the Shadows of the Conick-Sections will always be Conick-Sections; thofe of the Curves of the Second Gender, will always be Curves of the Second Gender; and the Shadows of Curves of the Third Gender, will themfelves be of the fame Gender, and foon *in infinitum.* And as a Circle, by the Projection of its Shade, generates all the Conick-Sections; fo will the five diverging Parabola's fpoken of in *ch.* 28. by their Shadows generate and exhibit all Curves of the Second Gender; and fo fome more fimple Curves of other Genders may be found, which, by the Projection of their Shadows from a lucid Point upon a Plane, fhall from all other Curves of the fame kinds.

Of the double Points of Curves.

30. I faid above, that Curves of the Second Gender might be cut by a Right Line in three Points; but two of thofe Points are fometimes coincident. As when the Right Line paffes by an Oval infinitely fmall, or by the Concourfe of two Parts of a Curve mutually interfecting each other, or running together into a *Cufpis.* And if at any time all the Right Lines tending the fame way with the infinite Leg of any Curve, do cut it in one only Point, (as happens in the Ordinates of the *Cartefian,* and in the *Cubical Parabola*, and in the Right Lines which are parallel to the Abfciffa of the Hyperbolifms of Hyperbola's and Parabola's;) then you are to conceive that thofe Right Lines pafs through two other Points of the Curve (as I may fay) placed at at an infinite Diftance; and thefe two co-incident Interfections, whether they be at a finite or an infinite Diftance, I call the ***Double Point.*** And fuch Curves as have this ***Double Point,*** may be defcribed by the following Theorems.

Theorems for the Organical Defcription of Curves.

31. *Theor.* I. If two Angles, as PAD and PBD, whofe Magnitude is given, be turned round the Poles A and B, given alfo in Pofition; and their Legs AP, BP, by their Point of Concourfe

Fig. 78.

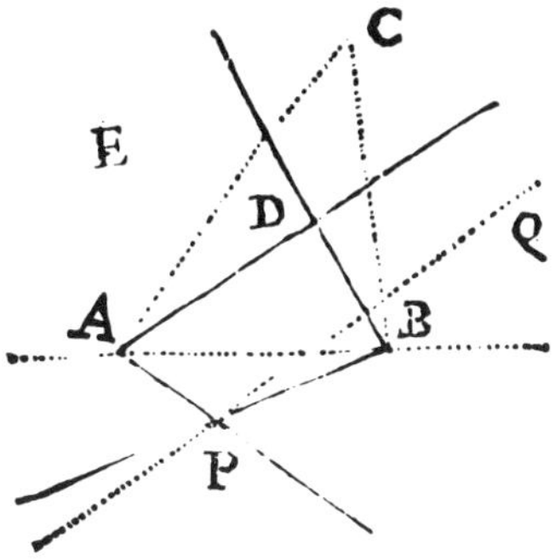

P, defcribe a Conick-Section paffing thro' their Poles A and B; except when that Right Line happens to pafs through either of the Poles A or B; or when the Angles BAD and ABD vanifh together into nothing; for in fuch Cafes the Point will defcribe a Right Line.

II. If the firft Legs AP, BP, by their Point of Concourfe P, do defcribe a Conick-Section paf-

ſing thro' the Pole *A*; then will the two other Legs *A D*, *B D*, by their Point of Concourſe *D*, deſcribe a Curve of the Second Gender, paſſing through the other Pole *B*, and having a *Double Point* in the firſt Pole *A*, through which the Conick-Section; except when the Angles *B A D*, *A B D*, vaniſh both away together; for then the Point *D* will deſcribe another Conick-Section paſſing through the Pole *A*.

III. But if the Conick-Section which the Point *P* deſcribes, paſs through neither the Pole *A* nor *B*; then the Point *D* will deſcribe a Curve of the Second or Third Gender, having a *Double Point*; and that *Double Point* will be in the Concourſe of the deſcribent Legs *A D* and *B D*, when the Angles *B A P*, *A B P* vaniſh together: And the Curve deſcribed will be one of the Second Gender, if the Angles *B A D*, *A B D* vaniſh together; otherwiſe 'twill be one of the Third kind, and then it will have two other *Double Points* in the Poles *A* and *B*.

The Deſcription of the Conick-Section by Five given Points.

32. A Conick-Section is determined by having five of its Points given; and may be thus deſcribed by them: Let the five Points be *A*, *B*, *C*, *D*, and *E*; join any three of them together, as ſuppoſe *A*, *B* and *C*, and form the Triangle *A B C*, and ſuppoſe any two of its Angles, as *C A B* and *C B A*, to revolve round their Vertices *A* and *B*; and when *C*, the Interſection of the Legs *A C*, *B C*, is ſucceſſively applied to the other two Points *D*, *E*, let the Interſection of the other Legs *A B* and *B A*, fall in the Points *P* and *Q*. Let alſo the Line *P Q* be drawn, and infinitely produced; and let the moveable Angles be ſo turned round, that the Interſection of the Legs *A P* and *B P* may deſcribe the Right Line *P Q*: And then will the Interſection of the two other Legs, *C*, deſcribe the propoſed Conick-Section, by *Theor.* I.

The Deſcription of Curves of the Second Gender, having a Double Point, by ſeven given Points.

33. All Curves of the Second Gender which have a *Double Point*, are determined from their ſeven given Points, of which one is that *Double Point*. And by means of thoſe Points they may be thus deſcribed: Let there be given any ſeven Points of the Curve to be deſcribed, as *A*, *B*, *C*, *D*, *E*, *F*, and *G*; of which *A* is the *Double Point*. Join *A* with any two other Points, as ſuppoſe *B* and *C*; and then let both the Angle *C A B*, and alſo either of the other two Angles of the Triangle *A B C* (as the Angle *A B C*) revolve round the two Vertexes *A* and *B*. And when the Point of Concourſe *C*, of the Legs *A C*, *B C*, is ſucceſſively applied to the four remaining Points *D*, *E*, *F*, and *G*, let the Concourſe of the two other Legs *A B* and *B A*, fall in the four Points *P*, *Q*, *R*, *S*. Through thoſe four Points, and the fifth Point *A*, deſcribe a Conick-Section; and let the aforeſaid Angles *C A B* and *C B A*, ſo revolve, that the Points of Concourſe of the Legs *A P*, *P B*, may deſcribe that Conick-Section: Then ſhall the Point of Concourſe of the other Legs *A C*, *B C*, deſcribe the Curve propoſed, by *Theor.* the *Second*.

If inſtead of the Point *C*, the Right Line *B C* be given in Poſition, and which ſhall touch the Curve to be deſcribed in *B*; then the Lines *A D*, *A P*, will be co-incident; and inſtead of the Angle *D A P*, there will be a Right Line revolving round the Pole *A*.

If the *Double Point* *A* be infinitely diſtant, the Right Line will perpetually tend with a Direction towards that Point, and will be carried with a parallel Motion, while the Angle *A B C* revolves about the Pole *B*.

Theſe Curves may alſo be deſcribed after another manner by the Third Theorem; but 'tis enough to ſhew you the moſt ſimple way of their Deſcription.

After the ſame Method may Curves of the Third, Fourth, and yet higher Genders, be deſcribed; not all indeed, but ſuch as by ſome commodious Ratio may be deſcribed by local Motion: For how commodiouſly, to deſcribe ſome Curves of the Second or higher Genders, when they have no *Common Point*, is a Problem that muſt be reckoned amongſt the more difficult ones.

The Conſtruction of Equations by the Deſcription of Curves.

The Uſe of Curves in Geometry is, that by their Interſections Problems may be ſolved. Let an Equation be propoſed to be conſtructed having Nine Di-

menſions, as $x^9 * + bx^7 + cx^6 + dx^5 + ex^4 + fx^3 + gxx + hx + k = 0$; where b, c,
$+m$
d, &c. ſignify any given or known Co-efficients, adfected with the Signs + and —. Let an Equation to a Cubical Parabola $x^3 = y$ be aſſumed: Then will the former Equation, putting y for x^3, ſtand thus, $y^3 + bxyy + cyy + dxxy + exy + my + fx^3 + gxx + hx + k = 0$, be an Equation to another Curve of the Second Gender, where m or f may either be wanting or aſſumed at pleaſure. And by the Deſcriptions of theſe Curves and their Interſections, there will be found the Roots of the Equation at firſt given to be conſtructed.

Note, 'Tis enough to deſcribe the Cubical Parabola once.

If the Equation to be conſtructed, by reaſon of the two laſt Terms hx and k being wanting, is depreſſed to ſeven Dimenſions; the other Curve, by expunging m, will have a *Double Point* in the Beginning of the Abſciſſa, and therefore may eaſily be deſcribed as above.

If the Equation to be conſtructed hath the three laſt Terms $gxx + hx + k$ wanting, and therefore is but of ſix Dimenſions, the other Curve, expunging f, will become a Conick-Section.

And if the ſix laſt Terms being wanting, the Curve be reduced to three Dimenſions, its Conſtruction will fall in with Dr. *Wallis*'s, by the Cubical Parabola and a Right Line.

Equations may alſo be conſtructed by the Hyperboliſm of a Parabola with a Diameter. Suppoſe this Equation of nine Dimenſions, and wanting its laſt Term ſave one, were to be conſtructed,

$$a + cxx + dx^3 + ex^4 + fx^5 + gx^6 + hx^7 + kx^8 + lx^9 = 0.$$
$$+m$$

Let there be an Equation aſſumed to that Hyperboliſm; thus, $xxy = 1$; and ſubſtituting y for $\frac{1}{xx}$, the Equation to be conſtructed will be changed into this Form, $ay^3 + cyy + dxyy + ey + fxy + mxxy + g + hx + kxx + lx^3 = 0$, which denotes a Curve of the Second Gender, by whoſe Deſcription the Problem may be ſolved, and of the Quantities m and g, either may be wanting or aſſumed at pleaſure.

By the Cubical Parabola and Curves of the Third Genders, all Equations may be conſtructed not exceeding twelve Dimenſions; and by the ſame Parabola, and a Curve of the Fourth Gender, all Equations not exceeding fifteen Dimenſions; and ſo on infinitely. And theſe Curves of the third, fourth, and ſuperior Genders, may always be deſcribed by finding their Points by plain Geometry.

As if this Equation were to be conſtructed, $x^{12} * + ax^{10} + bx^9 + cx^8 + dx^7 + ex^6 + fx^5 + gx^4 + hx^3 + ixx + kx + l = 0$, and the Cubical Parabola be ſuppoſed to be deſcribed; let the Equation for that Cubical Parabola be $x = y^3$: Wherefore ſubſtituting y for x^3, the Equation will put on this Form,

$$\begin{array}{llllll} y^4 & + ayy^3 & + cxxyy & + fxxy & + ixx & = 0 \\ & + b & + dx & + gx & + kx & \\ & & + e & + h & + l & \end{array}$$

Which is an Equation to a Curve of the Third Gender, by whoſe Deſcription the Problem may be ſolved. And this Curve may be deſcribed by finding its Points by plain Geometry, becauſe the indeterminate Quantities relate not to above Two Dimenſions.

Journal of the Institute of Actuaries, Volume 51
(London 1918). Article: "Newton's Interpolation
Formulas" by D. C. Fraser. Pages 94–101.

METHODUS DIFFERENTIALIS.

Prop. I.

If the abscissa of a curve consist of a given quantity A *and an indeterminate quantity* x, *and if the ordinate consist of any number of quantities* b, c, d, e, *&c., multiplied respectively into a corresponding number of terms of the* G. P. x, x^2, x^3, x^4, *&c., and if ordinates be erected at as many points of the abscissa; then the first differences of the ordinates are divisible by their intervals; and the differences of the differences so divided are divisible by the intervals between alternate ordinates; and the differences of these differences so divided are divisible by the intervals between every third ordinate, and so on indefinitely.*

Thus if given quantities p, q, r, s, t, &c., be substituted in succession for the indeterminate portion of the abscissa, and ordinates α, β, γ, δ, ϵ, &c., be erected at the extremities of the abscissæ so determined; the abscissæ and the ordinates, and the differences of ordinates divided by the differences of abscissæ (which are in fact the intervals of the ordinates), and the differences of the quotients divided by the differences of alternate ordinates, and so on, are shewn in the following table.

Abscissæ	Ordinates
$A+p$	$A+bp+cp^2+dp^3+ep^4=\alpha$
$A+q$	$A+bq+cq^2+dq^3+eq^4=\beta$
$A+r$	$A+br+cr^2+dr^3+er^4=\gamma$
$A+s$	$A+bs+cs^2+ds^3+es^4=\delta$
$A+t$	$A+bt+ct^2+dt^3+et^4=\epsilon$
Divisor Ord. Diffs.	Quotients produced by division.
$p-q)\ \alpha-\beta$	$b+c(p+q)+d(p^2+pq+q^2)+e(p^3+p^2q+pq^2+q^2)=\zeta$
$q-r)\ \beta-\gamma$	$b+c(q+r)+d(q^2+qr+r^2)+e(q^3+q^2r+qr^2+r^3)=\eta$
$r-s)\ \gamma-\delta$	$b+c(r+s)+d(r^2+rs+s^2)+e(r^3+r^2s+rs^2+s^3)=\theta$
$s-t)\ \delta-\epsilon$	$b+c(s+t)+d(s^2+st+t^2)+e(s^3+s^2t+st^2+t^3)=\kappa$
$p-r)\ \xi-\eta$	$c+d(p+q+r)+e(p^2+pq+q^2+pr+qr+r^2)=\lambda$
$q-s)\ \eta-\theta$	$c+d(q+r+s)+e(q^2+qr+r^2+qs+rs+s^2)=\mu$
$r-t)\ \theta-\kappa$	$c+d(r+s+t)+e(r^2+rs+s^2+rt+st+t^2)=\nu$
$p-s)\ \lambda-\mu$	$d+e(p+q+r+s)=\xi$
$q-t)\ \mu-\nu$	$d+e(q+r+s+t)=\pi$
$p-t)\ \xi-\pi$	$e=\sigma$

PROP. II.

Making the same suppositions and assuming the number of terms b, c, d, e, &c., to be finite, the last quotient will be equal to the last of the terms b, c, d, e, &c., and the remaining terms will be found by means of the remaining quotients; and, when these terms are known, a parabolic curve is determined which passes through the extremities of all the ordinates.

Thus, in the preceding table, the last quotient σ is equal to the last term e; and the product of this term by the known sum $p+q+r+s$ when subtracted from the quotient ξ leaves as remainder d, the last term but one. The quantities $d(p+q+r) + e(p^2+pq+q^2+pr+qr+r^2)$ which are then known, being deducted from the quotient λ, give the term c. The quantities $c(p+q) + d(p^2+pq+q^2) + e(p^3+p^2q+pq^2+q^3)$, which are then known, being deducted from the quotient ζ, leave the term b. By a similar calculation, other terms, if any, would be obtainable by means of a corresponding series of quotients. Finally, the ascertained quantities $bp+cp^2+dp^3+ep^4$, when deducted from the first ordinate α, leave the first term a of the expression for the ordinate. And the quantity $a+bx+cx^2+dx^3+ex^4$, &c., is the ordinate of a parabolic curve which passes through the extremities of all the given ordinates, the abscissa being $A+x$.

From these propositions those which follow are easily inferred.

PROP. III.

If a straight line A_1A_9 be divided into any number of equal parts A_1A_2, A_2A_3, A_3A_4, A_4A_5, &c., and if parallel straight lines A_1B_1, A_2B_2, A_3B_3, &c., be erected at the points of division, it is required to find a parabolic curve which shall pass through the extremities of all these lines.

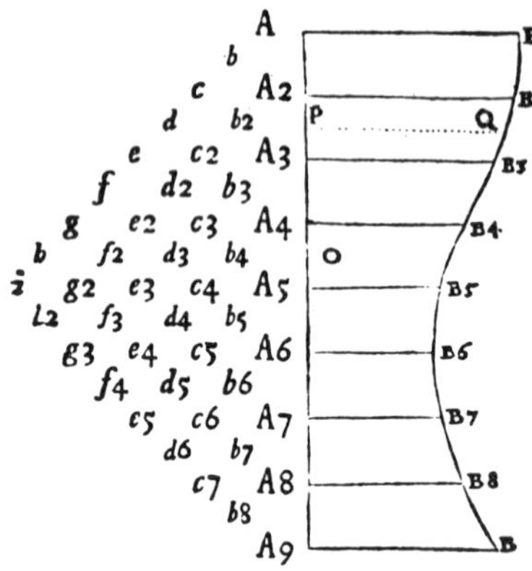

Find the first differences b_1, b_2, b_3, &c., of the ordinates A_1B_1, A_2B_2, A_3B_3, &c. ; the second differences c_1, c_2, c_3, &c. ; the third differences d_1, d_2, d_3, &c. ; and so on, up to the last difference and let that difference be called i.

Then beginning at the last difference, take the central differences in the alternate columns or orders of differences, and the arithmetic means between the two central differences in the remaining columns, proceeding in order up to the series of primary terms A_1B_1, A_2B_2, A_3B_3, A_4B_4, &c. Call the terms extracted k, l, m, n, o, p, q, r, s, &c. ; the last of these symbols representing the last difference ; the last but one, the mean between the two differences in the last column but one, the last but two, the central difference of the three differences in the last column but two, and so on to the first of the symbols, which will represent either the central ordinate of the series A_1B_1, A_2B_2, A_3B_3, &c., or the mean between the two central ordinates, the former happening when the number of the ordinates is odd, and the latter when the number is even.

CASE I.

In the former case let A_5B_5 be the central ordinate, that is put

$$A_5B_5 = k, \quad \frac{b_4 + b_5}{2} = l, \quad c_4 = m, \quad \frac{d_3 + d_4}{2} = n,$$

$$e_3 = o, \quad \frac{f_2 + f_3}{2} = p, \quad g_2 = q, \quad \frac{h_1 + h_2}{2} = r, \quad i = s.$$

Erect the ordinate PQ and let $AP = x$. Now multiply continuously into one another the terms of the progression,

$$1,\ x,\ \frac{x}{2},\ \frac{x^2-1}{3x},\ \frac{x}{4},\ \frac{x^2-4}{5x},\ \frac{x}{6},\ \frac{x^2-9}{7x},\ \frac{x}{8},\ \frac{x^2-16}{9x},\ \frac{x}{10},\ \frac{x^2-25}{11x},\ \frac{x}{12},\ \frac{x^2-36}{13x},$$

&c., the resulting terms being

$$1,\ x,\ \frac{x^2}{2},\ \frac{x^3-x}{6},\ \frac{x^4-x^2}{24},\ \frac{x^5-5x^3+4x}{120},\ \frac{x^6-5x^4+4x^2}{720},$$

$$\frac{x^7-14x^5+49x^3-36x}{5040},\ \text{\&c.}$$

Then if these terms be respectively multiplied into the terms of the series k, l, m, n, o, p, &c., the sum of the products, namely

$$k+x.l+\frac{x^2}{2}\cdot m+\frac{x^3-x}{6}\cdot n+\frac{x^4-x^2}{24}\cdot o+\frac{x^5-5x^3+4x}{120}\cdot p+\&c.$$

will be the length of the ordinate PQ.

CASE II.

In the latter case let A_4B_4 and A_5B_5 be the two central ordinates, that is, put

$$\frac{A_4B_4+A_5B_5}{2}=k,\ b_4=l,\ \frac{c_3+c_4}{2}=m,\ d_3=n,$$

$$\frac{e_2+e_3}{2}=o,\ f_2=p,\ \frac{g_1+g_2}{2}=q,\ \&\ h=r.$$

Erecting the ordinate PQ take the middle point O of A_4A_5, and call $OP=x$.

Now multiply continuously into one another the terms of the progression

$$1,\ x,\ \frac{x^2-\frac{1}{4}}{2x},\ \frac{x}{3},\ \frac{x^2-\frac{9}{4}}{4x},\ \frac{x}{5},\ \frac{x^2-\frac{25}{4}}{6x},\ \frac{x}{7},\ \frac{x^2-\frac{49}{4}}{8x},\ \&c.$$

the resulting terms being

$$1,\ x,\ \frac{4x^2-1}{8},\ \frac{4x^3-x}{24},\ \frac{16x^4-40x^2+9}{384},\ \&c.$$

Then if these terms be respectively multiplied into the terms of the series k, l, m, n, o, p, q, &c., the sum of the products, namely,

$$k+x.l+\frac{4x^2-1}{8}\cdot m+\frac{4x^3-x}{24}\cdot n+\frac{16x^4-40x^2+9}{384}\cdot o+\&c.$$

will be the length of the ordinate PQ.

It is to be noted that each of the intervals A_1A_2, A_2A_3, A_3A_4, &c., is here assumed to be unity; also that the differences are to be obtained by deducting the lower quantities from the upper, A_2B_2 from A_1B_1, A_3B_3 from A_2B_2, b_2 from b_1, &c., so that $A_1B_1-A_2B_2=b_1$, $A_2B_2-A_3B_3=b_2$, $b_1-b_2=c_1$, &c., and further that when any of the differences taken in this way turn out to be negative, effect must be given to the negative signs.

PROP. IV.

If a straight line be divided into any number of unequal parts A_1A_2, A_2A_3, A_3A_4, A_4A_5, *&c., and if parallel straight lines* A_1B_1, A_2B_2, A_3B_3, *&c., be erected at the points of division; it is required to find a parabolic curve which shall pass through the extremities of all the lines so erected.*

Let the given points be B_1, B_2, B_3, B_4, B_5, B_6, B_7, &c., and let fall ordinates B_1A_1, B_2A_2, &c., perpendicularly on the abscissa A_1A_7. Put

$$\frac{A_1B_1 - A_2B_2}{A_1A_2} = b_1, \quad \frac{A_2B_2 - A_3B_3}{A_2A_3} = b_2, \quad \frac{A_3B_3 - A_4B_4}{A_3A_4} = b_3,$$

$$\frac{A_4B_4 - A_5B_5}{A_4A_5} = b_4, \quad \frac{A_5B_5 - A_6B_6}{A_5A_6} = b_5, \quad \frac{A_6B_6 + A_7B_7}{A_6A_7} = b_6, \quad \frac{-A_7B_7 - A_8B_8}{A_7A_8} = b_7.$$

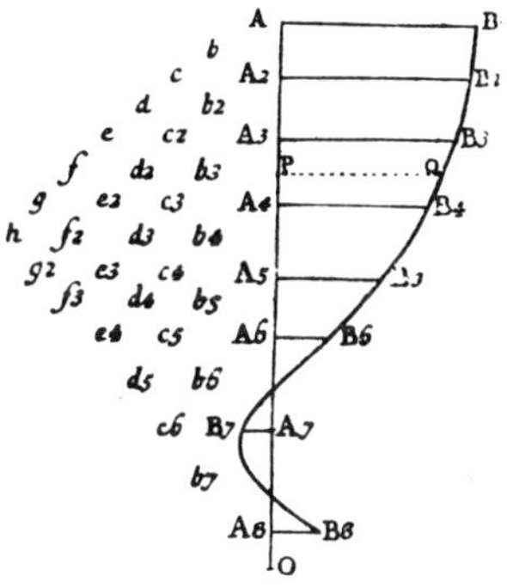

Thence derive

$$\frac{b_1 - b_2}{A_1A_3} = c_1, \quad \frac{b_2 - b_3}{A_2A_4} = c_2, \quad \frac{b_3 - b_4}{A_3A_5} = c_3, \text{ \&c.};$$

and then

$$\frac{c_1 - c_2}{A_1A_4} = d_1, \quad \frac{c_2 - c_3}{A_2A_5} = d_2, \quad \frac{c_3 - c_4}{A_3A_6} = d_3, \text{ \&c.};$$

and

$$\frac{d_1 - d_2}{A_1A_5} = e_1, \quad \frac{d_2 - d_3}{A_2A_6} = e_2, \quad \frac{d_3 - d_4}{A_3A_7} = e_3, \text{ \&c.};$$

the process being continued in the same way until the last difference is reached.

After the differences have been collected and divided by the intervals between the ordinates, the next step is to pick out the central terms in the alternate columns (or series, or lines), reckoning from the last difference, and the arithmetic means between the two central terms in the remaining columns, right up to the series of primary terms A_1B_1, A_2B_2, &c. Let the terms extracted be k, l, m, n, o, p, q, r, &c., of which the last symbol denotes the last difference; the last but one, the mean between the two differences in the last column but one; the last but two, the central difference of the three differences in the last column but two, &c. Then the first symbol k will represent the central ordinate if the number of ordinates is odd, or the arithmetic mean between the two central ordinates if their number is even.

CASE I.

In the former case let A_4B_4 be the central ordinate, that is, put $A_4B_4 = k$, $\frac{b_3+b_4}{2} = l$, $c_3 = m$, $\frac{d_2+d_3}{2} = n$, $e_2 = o$, $\frac{f_1+f_2}{2} = p$, $g = q$. Having erected the ordinate PQ, take a fixed point O in the base A_1A_5 and call $OP = x$. Then multiply into one another in succession the terms of the progression,

$$1,\ x - OA_4,\ x - \frac{OA_3 + OA_5}{2},\ \frac{(x - OA_3)(x - OA_5)}{x - \frac{1}{2}(OA_3 + OA_5)},$$

$$x - \frac{OA_2 + OA_6}{2},\ \&c.,$$

and take the resulting progression.

Or, what comes to the same thing, multiply into one another in succession the terms of the progression,

$$1,\ x - OA_4,\ (x - OA_3)(x - OA_5),\ (x - OA_2)(x - OA_6),$$

$$(x - OA_1)(x - OA_7),\ \&c.$$

Then multiply the resulting terms respectively into the terms of the progression,

$$1,\ x - \frac{OA_3 + OA_5}{2},\ x - \frac{OA_2 + OA_6}{2},\ x - \frac{OA_1 + OA_7}{2},\ \&c.,$$

and intermediate terms will be obtained, the complete progression being

$$1,\ x - OA_4,\ x^2 - \frac{OA_3 + 2OA_4 + OA_5}{2} \cdot x + \frac{OA_3 + OA_5}{2} \times OA_4,\ \&c.$$

Otherwise, let $OA_1 = \alpha$, $OA_2 = \beta$, $OA_3 = \gamma$, $OA_4 = \delta$, $OA_5 = \epsilon$,

$$OA_6 = \zeta,\ OA_7 = \eta,\ \frac{OA_3 + OA_5}{2} = \theta,\ \frac{OA_2 + OA_6}{2} = \chi,\ \frac{OA_1 + OA_7}{2} = \lambda.$$

Obtain terms by continuous multiplication from the progression

$$1,\ x - \delta,\ x - \gamma,\ x - \epsilon,\ x - \beta,\ x - \zeta,\ x - \alpha,\ x - \eta,\ \&c.,$$

and obtain intermediate terms by multiplying the results respectively by

$$1,\ x - \theta,\ x - \chi,\ x - \lambda,\ \&c.,$$

the whole series being

$$1,\ x - \delta,\ x^2 - (\delta + \theta)x + \delta\theta,\ x^3 - (\delta + 2\theta)x^2 + (\gamma\epsilon + 2\delta\theta)x - \gamma\delta\epsilon,\ \&c.,$$

the terms of which are to be multiplied respectively by k, l, m, n, o, p, &c. Then the sum of the products, namely

$$k + (x - \delta) . l + \{x^2 - (\delta + \theta)x + \delta\theta\} . m + \&c.$$

will be the length of the ordinate PQ.

CASE II.

In the latter case let A_4B_4, A_5B_5, be the two middle ordinates, that is, put

$$\frac{A_4B_4 + A_5B_5}{2} = k, \quad b_4 = l, \quad \frac{c_3 + c_4}{2} = m, \quad d_3 = n, \quad \frac{e_2 + e_3}{2} = o, \quad f_2 = p, \quad \&c.$$

The co-efficients of the alternate terms are obtained by the continuous multiplication of the terms of the progression,

$$1, (x - OA_4)(x - OA_5), (x - OA_3)(x - OA_6), (x - OA_2)(x - OA_7),$$
$$(x - OA_1)(x - OA_8), \&c.,$$

and those of the remaining terms are obtained by multiplying the above co-efficients by the terms of the progression,

$$x - \frac{OA_4 + OA_5}{2}, \; x - \frac{OA_3 + OA_6}{2}, \; x - \frac{OA_2 + OA_7}{2}, \; x - \frac{OA_1 + OA_8}{2}.$$

Then

$$k + \left(x - \frac{OA_4 + OA_5}{2}\right) . l + \{x^2 - (OA_4 + OA_5) . x + OA_4 \times OA_5\} . m + \&c.,$$

will be the ordinate PQ;

$$\text{or,} \quad PQ = k + \left(x - \frac{1}{2}OA_4 - \frac{1}{2}OA_5\right) . l + (x - OA_4)(x - OA_5) . m$$
$$+ (x - OA_4)(x - OA_5)\left(x - \frac{1}{2}OA_5 - \frac{1}{2}OA_6\right) . n, \; \&c.$$

Thus putting $x - \dfrac{OA_4 + OA_5}{2} = \pi, \quad (x - OA_4)(x - OA_5) = \rho,$

$$\rho . \left(x - \frac{OA_3 + OA_6}{2}\right) = \sigma, \quad \rho . (x - OA_3)(x - OA_6) = \tau,$$

$$\tau . \left(x - \frac{OA_2 + OA_7}{2}\right) = v, \quad \tau . (x - OA_2)(x - OA_7) = \phi,$$

$$\phi . \left(x - \frac{OA_1 + OA_8}{2}\right) = \chi, \quad \phi . (x - OA_1)(x - OA_8) = \psi.$$

the equation to the curve will be

$$k + \pi . l + \rho . m + \sigma . n + \tau . o + v . p + \phi . q + \chi . r + \psi . s = PQ.$$

Prop. V.

Certain terms out of a sequence of values being given, arranged at known intervals, it is required to find any intermediate term as closely as possible.

On a fixed straight line erect at a constant angle the given terms arranged at the given intervals; and let a parabolic curve be drawn through their extremities by means of the preceding propositions. This curve will pass through the extremities of all the intermediate terms.

Prop. VI.

To find the approximate area of any curve a number of whose ordinates can be ascertained.

Let a parabolic curve be drawn through the extremities of the ordinates by means of the preceding propositions. This will form the boundary of a figure whose area can always be ascertained, and its area will be approximately equal to the area required.

SCHOLIUM.

These propositions are useful for the construction of tables by the interpolation of series, as also for the solution of problems which depend on finding the areas of curves, especially if the intervals between the ordinates are small and equal to one another; and rules applicable to any given number of ordinates can be derived and recorded for reference. For example: If there are four ordinates at equal intervals, let A be the sum of the first and fourth, B the sum of the second and third, and R the interval between the first and fourth; then the central ordinate will be $\frac{9B - A}{16}$, and the area between the first and fourth ordinates will be $\frac{A + 3B}{8}$ R.

Note also that when the ordinates stand at equal distances from one another, the sums of ordinates which are equally distant from the central ordinate, along with twice the central ordinate, supply data for a new curve the area of which is determined by means of a smaller number of ordinates and is equal to the area of the original curve. Moreover, if the sum of the first and second ordinates, the sum of the third and fourth, the sum of the fifth and sixth, and so on in succession are taken as new ordinates; or if the sum of the first three ordinates, the sum of the next three, and the sum of the succeeding three are taken; or if the sums of the ordinates are taken four at a time, or five at a time, the area of the new curve will be equal to that of the original curve. And in this way, when a number of ordinates are given of a curve whose area is required, the calculation of the area is reduced to that of the area of another curve by means of a smaller number of ordinates.

Through a given number of points not only parabolic curves but an infinity of other curves of different kinds can be drawn.

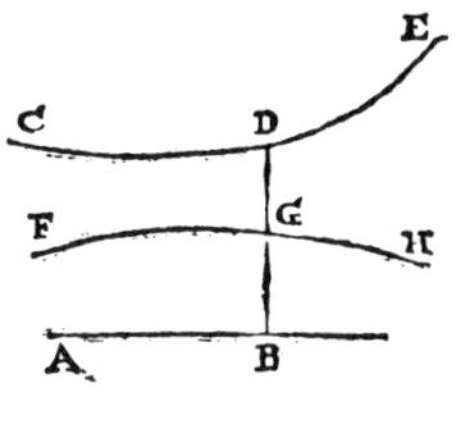

Let CDE, FGH, be two curves having a common abscissa AB, and ordinates BD, BG, lying in the same straight line ; and let the relation between the ordinates be defined by any equation whatever. Let any number of points be given through which the curve CDE is required to pass, and by that equation an equal number of points will be given through which the curve FGH will pass. By means of the foregoing propositions let a parabolic curve FGH be described passing through those points, and by the same equation a curve CDE will be given which will pass through all the points first given.
